# Puzzler

# GIANT BOOK
## OF CLASSIC
# PUZZLES

THIS IS A CARLTON BOOK

Puzzle content and layout design © Puzzler Media Ltd 2009
www.puzzler.com

This edition published in 2009 by Carlton Books Ltd
A Division of the Carlton Publishing Group
20 Mortimer Street, London, W1T 3JW

A CIP catalogue for this book is available from the British Library.

ISBN 978-1-84732-256-2

Printed in the UK by CPI Mackays, Chatham, ME5 8TD

The puzzles in this book previously appeared in *Puzzler Classic Puzzles* and
*Puzzler Classic Puzzles 2*

# Puzzler

# GIANT BOOK
## OF CLASSIC
## PUZZLES

**Over 450 mixed puzzles from the UK's
leading puzzle publisher**

CARLTON
BOOKS

# ROUNDABOUT

Solutions to Radial clues (1 to 24) either start from the outer edge of the circle and read inwards, or start from the inner ring and read outwards to the edge (so they are all five-letter words). Solutions to Circular clues read in either a clockwise or an anticlockwise direction around the circle.

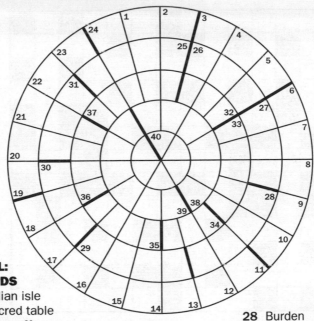

## RADIAL:
### INWARDS
6 Italian isle
9 Sacred table
10 Show-off
11 One who stares
17 Perspiration
19 Clever
20 Rush
21 Mountain ridge

### OUTWARDS
1 Three of a kind (in cards)
2 Trivial
3 Irritating
4 Country of Asia
5 Inappropriate
7 Gaelic nationality
8 Hunting dog (archaic)
12 Stage whisper
13 Trembling poplar

14 Separate
15 Horrify
16 Savour
18 Stand a round
22 Consumer
23 Dog-___, well-worn
24 Baby carriages

## CIRCULAR:
### CLOCKWISE
6 Inexpensive
11 Mildest
19 Fragment of pottery
24 Cunning
26 Sleep (colloq)
27 Fire remains

28 Burden
33 Early Scotsmen
34 Fastener
35 Church recess
36 Comfort
37 Characteristic
39 Ancient Greek city state
40 Buccaneer

### ANTICLOCKWISE
5 Scottish river
25 Domesticated
29 Vetch
30 Ruminant's stomach
31 Period of time
32 Commercials
38 Employee

# MISSING LINKS

The answer to each clue is a word which has a link with each of the three words listed. This word may come at the end (eg Head linked with Beach, Big and Hammer), at the beginning (eg Black linked with Beauty, Board and Jack) or a mixture of the two (eg Stone linked with Hail, Lime and Wall).

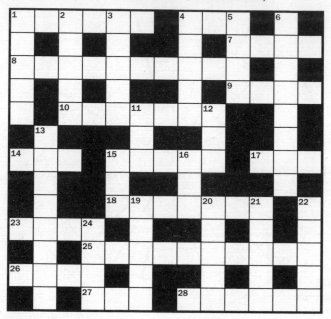

## ACROSS

- **1** Basket, Lunch, Table (6)
- **4** Head, Inspection, Sand (3)
- **7** Cue, Mobile, Pilot (4)
- **8** Money, Police, Racket (10)
- **9** Cobra, Penguin, Prawn (4)
- **10** Ant, Foot, Toy (7)
- **14** Master, Ring, Word (3)
- **15** Bank, Count, Whale (5)
- **17** Drip, Run, Spell (3)
- **18** Camera, Coffee, Replay (7)
- **23** Health, Junk, Processor (4)
- **25** Official, Prior, Ring (10)
- **26** Bamboo, Raspberry, Sugar (4)
- **27** Domestic, Name, Shop (3)
- **28** Dryer, Up, Woman (6)

## DOWN

- **1** Hanger, Rice, Round (5)
- **2** Country, Examine, Section (5)
- **3** Home, Man, World (5)
- **4** Fund, Star, Winner (5)
- **5** Petrol, Think, Top (4)
- **6** High, Issue, Lamp (8)
- **11** Lucky, Sherbet, Stick (3)
- **12** Baba, Punch, Truffle (3)
- **13** Column, Gain, Touch (8)
- **15** Jump, Lift, Slope (3)
- **16** Desert, Poison, Race (3)
- **19** Hen, Owl, Stag (5)
- **20** Indoor, Political, Stage (5)
- **21** Back, Eye, False (5)
- **22** Biscuit, Mark, Running (5)
- **24** Down, End, Skin (4)

# SKELETON CROSSWORD

Have double the fun with this puzzle: you've got to fill in the answers and the black squares! We've given you the bare bones to start and it will help you to know that the black squares in the finished grid form a symmetrical pattern, so that every black square has at least one other corresponding black square.

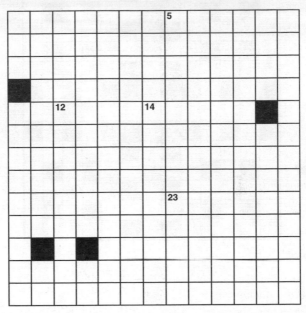

## ACROSS

1 Made uneven
8 Smaller quantity
9 Increase
10 List of options
13 Bind up (an injury)
16 Thick mass or tuft
17 Evocative of a past style
18 Dark area
19 Bid in advance
20 Labourer
21 Polished
24 Bunch of flowers
27 Anxiety, disturbance
28 Corner
29 Burning slightly

## DOWN

2 Owned by us
3 Rubberneck
4 Number in a rowing team
5 Minor actor
6 Flawed
7 Fictitious name
11 Go with
12 Colouring spread over a surface
13 Rider's heel spikes
14 Jewish religious leader
15 Caper
22 Reasoned judgment
23 Supply food
25 Skin irritation
26 Godsend

# DILEMMA

Two straightforward crosswords – but their clues have been mixed up. You have to decide which clue belongs to which grid, but two words have been entered to give you a start.

## ACROSS

1 Play a guitar
5 Barred enclosures
8 Group of singers
9 Greek epic written by Homer
10 Diminiash
11 Leg joint
12 Hard outer-covering
15 Canoe
18 Young relations
19 Improbable comedy
22 Perspire
25 Claude ___, French impressionist painter
26 Film award
27 Heavenly messenger
28 Northern city
29 Passenger ship
30 Fashion

1 Annoyed
5 Belt
8 White heron
9 Pit worker
10 Enthusiastic
11 Savoury jelly
12 Inexpensive
15 Door fastener
18 Spiral slide (6-7)
19 Love, worship
22 Salad plant
25 Showery month
26 Goddess of hunting
27 Wonderland girl
28 Bury
29 Coarse string
30 Part of a flower

**DOWN**

1 Child's magazine
2 Lift up
3 Fight
4 Kind, merciful
5 Strong metal
6 Meat juice
7 Dehydrate
13 Biblical king
14 Holiday ship
16 Give permission
17 Board-game
19 Distant, supercilious
20 Quantities of paper
21 Ahead of time
22 Hold tightly
23 Bird of prey
24 Incantation

1 ___ roll, cylindrical sponge
2 Sixteenth of a pound
3 Bravery award
4 Crushed with grief (6-7)
5 Fissure
6 Correct
7 Smooth, glossy
13 'Laughing' animal
14 Loft
16 Tree of the birch family
17 Centre of an amphitheatre
19 Becomes less colourful
20 Happen
21 Electronic communication (1-4)
22 Begin
23 Proclamation
24 Covered with slabs of baked clay

|   |   |   |   |   |   |   |   |
|---|---|---|---|---|---|---|---|
| ¹ |  | ² |  | ³ | ⁴ | ⁵ | ⁶ | ⁷ |

27 A N G E L

# PIECEWORD

With the help of the Across clues only, can you fit the 35 pieces into their correct positions in the empty grid (which, when completed, will exhibit a symmetrical pattern)?

**ACROSS**

1 Mock; secret hoard

2 Wicked; of the moon; Sicily's volcano

3 False; tranquillity

4 Pivot; colossus; horse's pace

5 On the flat; male fowl

6 Egg-shaped; come up

7 Turncoat

8 Slogan; lover's meeting

9 Compassion

10 Plot; shrewd

11 Foot digit; loan; chest bone

12 Canopy; dog's home

13 Mourning poem

14 Put off; noxious

15 Receive eagerly

16 Abrupt; express gratitude

17 Governor; fantasy

18 Train track; proportion;

___ of Dogs, London area

19 Complain; public

20 Put on record; steep in vinegar; negotiation

21 Go in; blunder

| | | | | | | | | |
|---|---|---|---|---|---|---|---|---|
| T | | | A | N | K | L | E | G |
| Y | S | T | M | | E | I | | R |
| | | R | S | L | E | B | R | A |

| A | C | H | L | E | A | C | | E |
|---|---|---|---|---|---|---|---|---|
| R | | E | E | | S | E | R | |
| E | A | C | N | T | E | | E | M |

| A | S | T | Y | | E | A | I | T |
|---|---|---|---|---|---|---|---|---|
| C | E | | | F | E | D | | O |
| K | E | N | C | E | | E | A | R |

| S | | T | S | E | | O | R | |
|---|---|---|---|---|---|---|---|---|
| E | V | E | U | L | E | | T | R |
| T | E | | L | | R | T | | A |

| T | E | R | | | E | F | | C |
|---|---|---|---|---|---|---|---|---|
| A | | R | T | I | D | U | | A |
| R | A | I | E | | | S | | P |

| T | | N | T | | O | | B | |
|---|---|---|---|---|---|---|---|---|
| E | A | L | O | U | S | V | A | N |
| R | | Y | R | | E | | T | |

| R | O | T | U | T | E | N | | T |
|---|---|---|---|---|---|---|---|---|
| N | | L | R | I | B | A | P | O |
| I | S | E | N | E | L | | A | R |

| E | M | E | P | | S | | T | H |
|---|---|---|---|---|---|---|---|---|
| | A | D | E | V | I | R | E | A |
| I | N | G | D | | B | O | | I |

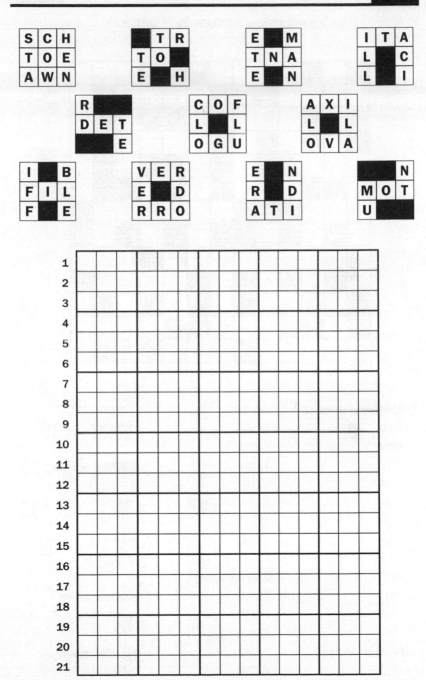

# JIG-WORD

No clues – just pattern and answers – but can you fit them in?

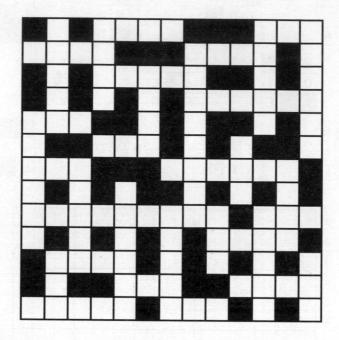

**3-letter words**
AIM
CAN
CRY
MUM
NOD
NOW
OAR
RED
SET
TOM
TWO

**4-letter words**
AREA

DAIS
DOGE
EARN
FARM
LATE
PLAN
TARN
VERA

**5-letter words**
CREAK
DREAR
IDIOM
IMAGE
INFER

ONION
TEMPO

**6-letter words**
ENFOLD
INFANT
KARATE
NONAGE
RANDOM

**8-letter word**
PRETENCE

**9-letter word**
GRENADIER

# SUM-UP

Using the totals given, can you calculate the price of each tin of peas, bag of sweets, box of cornflakes and bottle of milk?

# 4-SQUARE

Solve these four clues and then rearrange the solutions into a sixteen-letter phrase, for which a clue is given. The two diagonals also make four-letter words.

DIPLOMACY

FEMALE HORSE

SWORD HANDLE

BELONGING TO ME

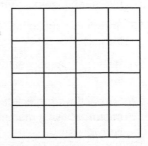

Clue: Maths on the brain? (6,10)

# CONTINUITY

No black squares – heavy bars mark the ends of words.

## ACROSS

1 Legendary creature also known as the Yeti (10,7)

2 Present; follow closely; slate; vein of metal

3 Infirmary; calf meat; crowded

4 Everlasting; educational talk; spinning toy

5 Preferably; Kentish kiln; football teams

6 Die; peculiar; small imperial weight; metal container

7 Churchman; reply; recount

8 Item of photographic equipment; upright; undisclosed fact

9 Affix; prophet; lubricate; apportion

10 Javelin; irritate; balms

11 Individual; East Midlands county town; prickling sensation

12 Immeasurable; thick mist; cereal plant

13 Say more; garden barrier; rebelling; upper limb

14 Pleasantly; gossip; punitive

15 Scrutinise; make into law; too; Ireland

16 Weird; ___heel, weak spot; firearm

17 Showy flower; quick look; nocturnal flying mammal; vital body organ

## DOWN

1 Stuck to; largest inland salt lake (7,3)

2 Car's trunk; chopper; footnotes

3 Beginning; cosseted; farm vehicle

4 Chart; Cologne's river; young girl; Aladdin's spirit friend

5 Journey plan; duty list; lascivious look

6 Mesh; stadium; soundness of mind; short sleep

7 Having nothing to do (2,1,5,3); threaten

8 Love-song; bird on a farthing; aural pain

9 Exists; antlered animal; planet's path; gratuity

10 Voter; modestly shy; ink smudge; white vestment

11 Condition; up to which time; however; ___ Fitzgerald, singer

12 Nothing; forearm bone; postbox aperture; conifer; solidify

13 Aged; leisure activity; Victoria Beckham's Spice name

14 Tiny; always; ___ film, food wrap; farm birds

15 Monaco's capital (5,5); crushed ice dessert

16 Illegal fire-raising; consumed; merely; less common

17 ___ and tatties, Scottish vegetable dish; after deductions; appear; period before Easter

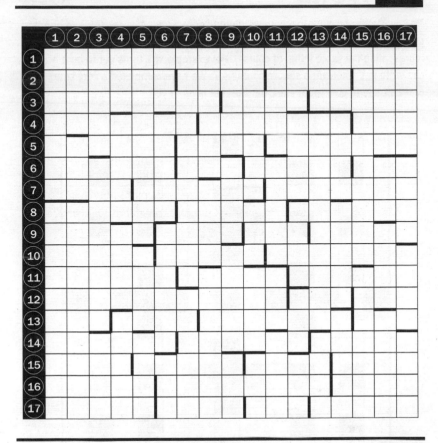

# RIDDLE ME REE

My first is in BATH but not in LOCK-UP,

My second's in HOT CHOCOLATE never in CUP,

My third's in both DOZY and DUVET,

My fourth's in HIT THE though not in HAY,

My fifth's in UNWIND and also PILLOW,

My sixth is in DREAMS but not RADIO,

My seventh's in EXTINGUISH but not seen in LIGHTS,

My whole is the hour that we retire at nights.

# KEYWORD

This puzzle has no clues in the conventional sense. Instead, every different number printed in the main grid represents a different letter (with the same number always representing the same letter, of course). For example, if 7 turns out to be a 'V', you can write in V wherever a square contains 7. We have completed a very small part of the puzzle to give you a start, but the rest is up to you.

| 18 | 11 | 1 | 8 | 15 | 4 T | ■ | 24 | 8 | 14 | 13 | 23 | 1 |
|----|----|----|----|----|----|----|----|----|----|----|----|----|
| 2 | ■ | 21 | ■ | 17 | 8 A | 22 | 2 | 3 | ■ | 23 | ■ | 9 |
| 25 | 8 | 10 | 4 | 23 | 14 R | ■ | 4 | 21 | 1 | 26 | 23 | 4 |
| 2 | ■ | 2 | ■ | 7 | ■ | ■ | 13 | ■ | 17 | ■ | ■ | 6 |
| 10 | 8 | 3 | 6 | 2 | 14 | ■ | 4 | 17 | 21 | 2 | 12 | 2 |
| 4 | 14 | 11 | ■ | 18 | 2 | 26 | 23 | 4 | ■ | 14 | 8 | 13 |
| ■ | 15 | ■ | ■ | ■ | 12 | ■ | 19 | ■ | ■ | ■ | 3 | ■ |
| 16 | 23 | 8 | ■ | 1 | 2 | 5 | 9 | 15 | ■ | 15 | 9 | 16 |
| 9 | 1 | 14 | 2 | 8 | 3 | ■ | 2 | 8 | 15 | 21 | 2 | 14 |
| 3 | ■ | 16 | ■ | 4 | ■ | ■ | 6 | ■ | 13 | ■ | ■ | 2 |
| 13 | 1 | 23 | 6 | 21 | 10 | ■ | 15 | 26 | 23 | 1 | 13 | 2 |
| 2 | ■ | 9 | ■ | 12 | 23 | 7 | 2 | 3 | ■ | 2 | ■ | 22 |
| 18 | 8 | 14 | 20 | 2 | 1 | ■ | 13 | 2 | 1 | 4 | 3 | 11 |

A B C D E F G H I J K L M

N O P Q R S T U V W X Y Z

(The small grid is provided for ease of reference only)

| 1 | 2 | 3 | 4 | 5 | 6 | 7 | 8 | 9 | 10 | 11 | 12 | 13 |
|----|----|----|----|----|----|----|----|----|----|----|----|----|
| 14 | 15 | 16 | 17 | 18 | 19 | 20 | 21 | 22 | 23 | 24 | 25 | 26 |

# CROSSWORD

## ACROSS

1 Ox-like (6)
5 Unpleasantly sticky (6)
9 Since (3)
11 Corrupter (7)
12 Collide with (3,4)
13 Well ventilated (4)
15 Large piece of cotton used as bed clothing (5)
16 Saunter (4)
17 Wrestling hold (4)
19 Painting implement (5)
20 Off-white gemstone (4)
24 Thing which is said to be the lowest form of wit (7)
25 Experienced person (3,4)
26 ___ up, confess (3)
27 Detection device (6)
28 Number in a football team (6)

## DOWN

2 Edict (5)
3 Small measurement of length (4)
4 Minor quake (5,6)
5 Pivotal person or thing (11)
6 Female relative (4)
7 Craziness (5)
8 Found (9)
10 Stone deposited by an avalanche (9)
14 Tibetan ox (3)
16 Romance (3)
18 Slice (5)
21 Tableware item (5)
22 Pierces, stabs (4)
23 Blade's sharpened side (4)

# STORY CROSSWORD

Transfer the words which complete the story to the grid and then put the circled letters in the right order to discover the name of the famous person therein described.

He was ___ (16A) in Grand Chute, Wisconsin, in 1908 and was ___ (13D) at Marquette University. He worked as a lawyer after graduating, then became a circuit-court judge in 1939. When America was drawn into World War II, he joined the US ___ (7A) Corps and served in the Pacific. He reached the ___ (9A) of captain.

In 1946 he was elected to the US Senate as a member of the Republican party. This was an era in which rumours were beginning to circulate about the way ___ (1A) infiltrators were becoming ___ (21A) in public life. An investigation was launched into these allegations and a number of high-profile trials were held.

Four years later, in 1950, he decided to ___ (4D) out about his _ _ (5D) that there were communists working in the Department of State. The allegations ___ (8A) him a great deal of public attention and he continued to accuse high-ranking figures of communist sympathies, though his claims were never substantiated.

In 1953 he was appointed chairman of a Senate ___ (1D) which was given the task of conducting investigations into un-American activities. His determination to root out communists at ___ (21D) cost ___ (23A) many of his colleagues and ___ (3D) the public. He conducted extremely thorough enquiries into the activities of ___ (18A) of his suspects and made ___ (2D) and more accusations. He even ___ (11D) the possibility that President Eisenhower might be involved.

In 1954 he accused the Secretary of the Army of concealing foreign espionage activities. The allegation brought about a backlash that he had not ___ (14D). The Secretary claimed that members of his committee ___ (6D) threatened army officials with investigation if they would not give preferential treatment to a committee consultant who had ___ (20D) been drafted.

He denied ___ (12A) charge, but an inquiry into his own activities was ___ (17A) up. It did not ___ (10A) likely that his political career could survive such a blow, especially as the press gave the matter wide publicity. He would not allow himself to ___ (19D) on the likely outcome of the case, but kept insisting on his innocence. In the end he was cleared of the charges, but the Senate ruled that he had ___ (19A) considerable harm to a number of senators in his investigations. He was allowed to ___ (22A) to the Senate, but his influence was considerably reduced.

He ___ (15A) in office in 1957.

# BOXWISE

Put these three-letter groups into the twelve numbered boxes to produce twelve six-letter words, each of which starts in one box and finishes in another as indicated by an arrow. For instance, 2 and 5 make a six-letter word, but not 5 and 9. One group has been filled in to start you off.

BAL ~~CHO~~ DER GEN

KEN LAD PON SEN

SIL TRY VER WEA

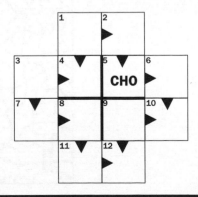

# TINKER, TAILOR ...

To discover who this person is unscramble the words in the verse, which hints at what the person does. Write these words into the boxes below, reading across, and, if you've placed them in the correct order, the arrowed column will spell out the occupation.

This CANDER can PALE and POTURIEET,

So gracefully whether LOOS or in a duet.

SQUAREBEA, CHATTEREN whatever POISONIT she is in,

Her MORNPERFACE leaves her UNICADEE in a spin.

OCCUPATION: _____

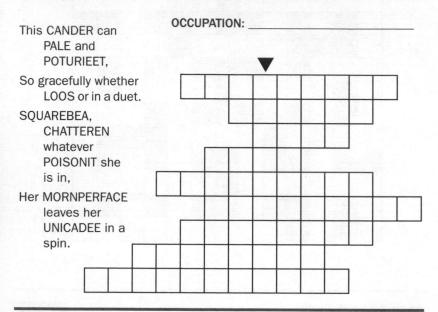

# SILHOUETTE

Shade in every fragment containing a dot – and what have you got?

# WORDSEARCH

The 45 words from the works of William Shakespeare have all been hidden in the diagram. They have been printed across (backwards or forwards), or up or down, or diagonally, but always in a straight line without letters being skipped. You can use the letters in the diagram more than once. You will probably find it helpful to mark the words in the diagram and cross them off the list as you find them.

```
O N W L V N E D A E R H T G T F
P O L L U S I O N W O B R N X E
R T U E G F P S A X I E E D S I
E H I E R A E L W B E D E I T H
R I G R S U L T B I A I G S A T
A N E H R E T L A C N N L E N R
U G S U Y I E F I B I D C D D E
Q G T E G B T L A M A N G G E T
S I D C A N D L E W A S T E R A
M F C B T T O E P T F U H N B W
U T B O J N S T R A R R F E Y M
R L A Z T E H O P E N P U R N G
E Z L R U L P C I S L D R S E T
E D E R X A W S E E A B E I H Y
J U T T Y K O E N E K W M R M F
D E Z A R C E R A C K I D U L Y
E Z I O P A R I T O R P L B R Y
F A D G E J E U R G N O C G H D
```

| | | | |
|---|---|---|---|
| BALE | FADGE | NOTHING-GIFT | TANE |
| BATEFUL | FRUSH | PANDERLY | THREADEN |
| BIBBLE-BABBLE | GALLIMAUFREY | PARITOR | TIRRIT |
| CADENT | GEST | PASH | TOAZE |
| CANDLE- | GLIKE | POIZE | TRUE-SEEMING |
| WASTER | GREE | POLLUSION | WAFTURE |
| CARE-CRAZED | HOX | PORTANCE | WALL-EYED |
| CONGRUE | JACK-A-LENT | PRIMY | WASP-TONGUE |
| COSIER | JUTTY | SHENT | WATER-THIEF |
| DISEDGE | KEECH | SQUARER | WAX-RED |
| DRUMBLE | LEESE | STANDER-BY | |
| ESCOT | MURE | SWINDGE | |

Just like a Jig-word – but instead of letters, numbers.

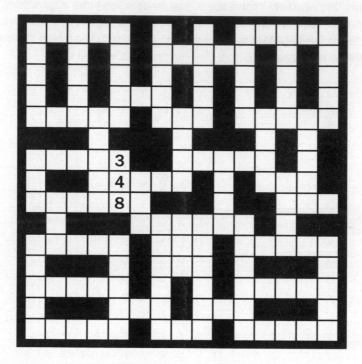

| 3-figure | 4-figure | | |
|---|---|---|---|
| 114 | 1039 | 23099 | 70913 |
| 163 | 2430 | 23136 | 83146 |
| 246 | 3926 | 23368 | 87111 |
| 348 | 6911 | 25007 | 91060 |
| 407 | | 34261 | 96203 |
| 410 | | 39130 | |
| 508 | **5-figure** | 43162 | |
| 511 | 10150 | 43915 | **6-figure** |
| 607 | 10992 | 52289 | 216345 |
| 625 | 12074 | 52617 | 347288 |
| 745 | 13412 | 61134 | 513084 |
| 834 | 15918 | 61408 | 624397 |
| 863 | 17102 | 65052 | 711642 |
| 914 | 19066 | 65054 | |
| | | 70234 | |

# BRACER

The first part of each clue gives a six-letter answer, five of whose letters make up the five-letter answers to the second part and four of which make up the four-letter answer to the third part. The unused letter from the first answer is entered into column A, and that from the second answer into column B. When completed, the two columns spell out two games.

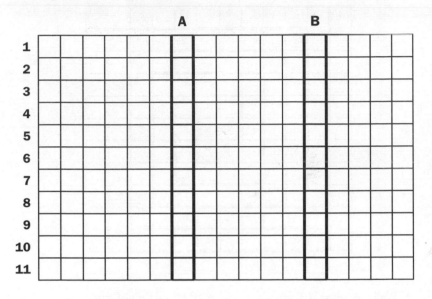

1 Gnawing mammal; male bee; swelling or bulge

2 Spoil, harm; ___donna, singer; prudish

3 Cot; apparent; authentic

4 Pace; take exam again; remainder

5 Pilfered; pebble; foot digits

6 Spin; hearth; rip

7 Totter, shuffle; muddle; go in front

8 Tooth decay; concerns; motor vehicles

9 Cloak; alloy; deceased

10 Close-fitting necklace; task; Sonny's former singing partner

11 ___ up, nervously tense; pig's noise; garden basket

# SPIRAL

Every answer (except the first) uses the last letter of the preceding answer as its initial letter, the chain thus formed following a spiral path to the centre of the grid. The diagonals spell two materials.

**START**

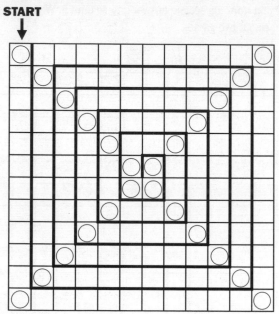

- Well-mannered (9)
- Ill-health (8)
- Indian Ocean islands (10)
- Natural sweetener (5)
- Out of work, surplus (9)
- Canadian city (7)
- Fruit and colour (6)
- Physical training (8)
- European country (7)
- Samson's treacherous mistress (7)
- After-school study (8)
- Fate (6)
- Inn (6)

- Pest, irritation (8)
- Excitable, fiery (9)
- Tree with poisonous pods (8)
- Supervisor (7)
- WW2 desert leader of German army (6)
- CS ___, author of the *Narnia* books (5)
- Rebuff, slight (4)
- Infuse tea (4)
- Royal Prince (7)
- Flying insect (4)
- Lobby (4)
- Cooking fat (4)
- Colouring (3)

# CROSSWORD

## ACROSS

1 Cajun dish (5)

4 Food tin (3)

6 Pale, tired (6,3)

7 Prosperous (4-2-2)

9 Tequila cocktail (9)

10 Stole (4)

12 Succour (4)

14 Confuse, mystify (8)

17 Lazy (8)

19 Pitch black (4)

21 Stick together (4)

23 Middle of a large centre of population (5,4)

25 Fire-raiser (8)

27 List of all stock (9)

28 No goals (3)

29 From what source? (5)

## DOWN

1 Academic vestment (4)

2 Therapist (7)

3 On the other side of the page (8)

4 Double file of pupils (9)

5 Protected area of countryside (8,4)

8 Soot particles (5)

11 Style of music associated with Pavarotti (5)

13 Scottish fjord (5)

15 Malignant spirit (5)

16 Complex human society (12)

18 Blue-green gemstone (5)

20 Old name for scrofula (5,4)

22 Up to the minute (5,3)

24 Available at the supermarket (2-5)

26 Computing term for memory size (4)

# JIG-WORD

No clues – just pattern and answers – but can you fit them in?

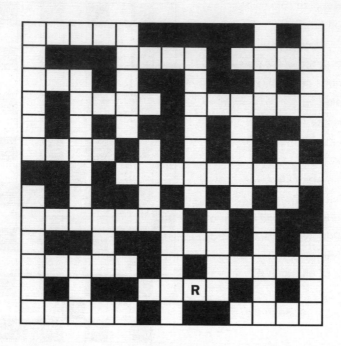

**3-letter words**
AGO
ASH
GEL
RUG
THE

**4-letter words**
DARE
HERE
ISLE
METE
OGLE
OOZE

SEER
SENT
TAIL
VOTE

**5-letter words**
ASKEW
CRUDE
EAGER
EVADE
FIEND
RAGED
TALON
THAWS
WORLD

**6-letter words**
ARREST
ASPECT
LIFTED

**7-letter words**
ENLARGE
GORILLA
SHATTER

**9-letter word**
LARGENESS

# DROP-OUT

In the top picture the girl is selecting an apron. In the bottom, she has made her purchase. Which apron did she buy?

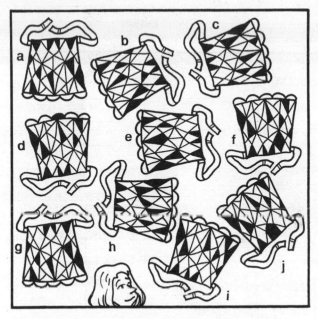

# TWO-TIMER

Two sets of clues to the same answers. Cryptic clues below and straight clues beneath the grid.

## ACROSS

1 Finest journey on horseback? (8)

5 Tax man? (4)

9 Light twinkler? (7)

10 Harshly criticise the Spanish team (5)

11 Amphibian found in leftovers (3)

12 Rubbish bride removed before Saturday (6)

15 Said I otherwise had included dolt (5)

17 Solo performance in the city (4)

19 Blush in colourful study (6)

22 In the way a learner set up office (6)

24 Something boring to do when sleepy? (4)

26 Ride round (5)

27 Comment about smear (6)

30 Clearing some of the meadow (3)

32 A doctor in the British Isles initially had a deer (5)

33 Story about equality Abel misconstrued (7)

34 Tax ring (4)

35 Broken platters make a mess! (8)

## DOWN

1 Only one per person but several people can make it (4)

2 Pen the French type (5)

3 Revolutionary palindrome (5)

4 Rude development on ship leads to imprisonment (6)

6 Include studies first (7)

7 Sign of person revealing info? (4-4)

8 On top I arranged selection (6)

13 Shoot pal (3)

14 First person said to be proprietor of island (4)

16 Criticism about missile (8)

18 Trade route (4)

20 Point mistakenly claimed (7)

21 Its closure prevents one seeing (6)

23 Spain out? Try Bath (3)

25 Be quiet – put on a cover presently! (4,2)

28 Among the calamari, a girl appeared (5)

29 Disprove engineer's objection (5)

31 One who lives for drink? (4)

## ACROSS

1 Sit across (8)
5 Caledonian (4)
9 Poetic word for the sun (7)
10 Jury (5)
11 Newt (3)
12 Wreckage (6)
15 Fool (5)
17 Norwegian capital (4)
19 Flush (6)
22 Place in an official seat (6)
24 Gape (4)
26 Bike (5)
27 Observation (6)
30 Pasture (3)
32 Film about a baby deer (5)
33 Biblical moral tale (7)
34 Road levy (4)
35 Smear with blobs (8)

## DOWN

1 Torso (4)
2 Fashion (5)
3 Helicopter's blade (5)
4 Constraint (6)
6 Comprise (7)
7 Sneak (4-4)
8 Choice (6)
13 Partly opened flower (3)
14 Hebridean isle (4)
16 Uncomplimentary remark (8)
18 Bar (4)
20 In tens (7)
21 Optical cover (6)
23 Health resort (3)
25 Settle completely (4,2)
28 Black ___, prison van (5)
29 Refute (5)
31 Ale (4)

# CRYPTIC CROSSWORD

## ACROSS

**1** Striking worker? (10)
**6** Sour drop that's sweet (4)
**9** Remove a surface with difficulty immediately (3,4)
**10** Where do fashionable patients go? (7)
**12** Exploit opportunity to gain point on court (4,9)
**14** How about a right-left combination in Essex? (6)
**15** Like finest, outstanding, incombustible material (8)
**17** Holy fish? (8)
**19** Roughly score about 100, but not in this game? (6)
**22** S-sea (8,5)
**24** Twelfth man's shyness (7)
**25** Bird spotted account (7)
**26** Fighting military initially who are ardent (4)
**27** Advance settlement (10)

## DOWN

**1** Exclude new outbuilding (4)
**2** Judge had rarebit ordered (7)
**3** Construct hastily despite strike at the same time (5,8)
**4** Done with the hands by the book? (6)
**5** Tending to take from this hive? (8)
**7** Scoundrel to rave over fruit (7)
**8** I send spray from chemist's shop (10)
**11** Fly-past? (6,4,3)
**13** Tom's company in a painful squeeze (10)
**16** Listen again to words of approval (4,4)
**18** Naval boxing weight? (7)
**20** Imprison criminal with penalty (7)
**21** Talk of pigs so violent (6)
**23** Bachelor had many a black mark (4)

# SKELETON CROSSWORD

Have double the fun with this puzzle: you've got to fill in the answers and the black squares! We've given you the bare bones to start and it will help you to know that the black squares in the finished grid form a symmetrical pattern, so that every black square has at least one other corresponding black square.

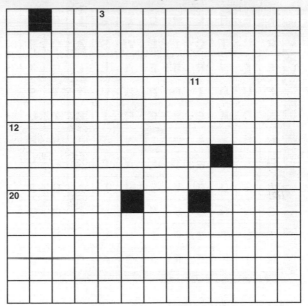

**ACROSS**

8 Foxglove
9 Notable age
10 Eighth of a mile
11 Noticeable
12 Sporting trophy
14 Idiot
17 Yearning for
19 ___ Pope, *Bad Girls'* Frances Myers
21 Manny ___, *Never Mind the Quality, Feel the Width* character
23 Exploding gently
26 ___ *Pity She's a Whore*, play by John Ford
27 Thrilled

**DOWN**

1 Stylish building
2 Borodin's prince
3 ___ Preminger, film director
4 Large wide bottle used for holding liquor
5 Norway's capital
6 Respect
7 Wheezes
13 Foresee
14 Busy buzzer!
15 Derogatory name for an old woman
16 Tattered, worn-out
18 Pierce with a pointed stake
20 Selina ___, 80s TV presenter
22 Bare
24 Jump up and down to punk music
25 Greek letter or small amount

# PATHFINDER

Starting from the bold centre letter, move up or down or sideways (but NOT diagonally) using all the letters to find the path through fourteen things or people to be seen on a football pitch.

| E | E | R | E | R | C | L | E | L | P | O |
|---|---|---|---|---|---|---|---|---|---|---|
| R | C | T | C | I | E | W | S | A | O | S |
| E | E | N | R | E | E | A | L | L | G | T |
| F | U | O | T | P | P | B | U | T | I | S |
| E | C | K | E | E | E | R | T | E | T | U |
| R | H | L | A | O | **G** | N | E | P | S | B |
| R | L | I | N | T | L | A | F | R | E | N |
| A | S | O | E | Y | E | M | L | A | G | R |
| B | S | R | C | S | N | I | D | F | C | O |
| T | S | T | O | P | I | L | L | I | R | E |
| R | I | K | E | R | G | O | A | E | L | D |

# DOT-TO-DOT

Join the dots in numerical order to reveal the hidden picture.

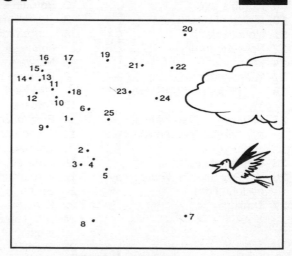

32 |

# PURPLE PASSAGE

In a Purple Passage, the grid of letters consists of an entertaining short story, reading across the rows from left to right and from top to bottom. However, some letters have been missed out. Not only that, but there are no spaces between words and no punctuation. Can you fill in the missing letters and work out where the word-breaks are to reveal the story?

```
[ ] I S C O [ ] E R I N [ ] H E [ ] A D N O C

H [ ] E S [ ] J O B A [ ] T E D H I S [ ] O U

[ ] E T R A [ ] W I T H A [ ] H O T [ ] R A P

H O [ ] S T I [ ] T O [ ] T H E N E [ ] T D A Y

[ ] H E P I [ ] T [ ] R E O F [ ] H E E S [ ]

H A D G [ ] N E A N [ ] I N I T [ ] P L A [ ]

E W A S A [ ] I C T U R [ ] O F A M O U S [ ]
```

# SO COMPLETE

ADRIAN, FRANCIS, BETHANY, MELINDA, NANETTE, TREVOR, PHILIP, EFFIE and MONICA were discussing their favourite TV sitcoms. Use the letters of their names once each to reveal the titles.

```
K E _ _ _ N G   U P   A _ P _ _ _ _ _ _ E S

O _ E   _ _ O _   _ _   _ _ _   G _ _ _ E

S T _ P _ O _   _ _ _   S _ _

V _ _ _ _   O _   D _ _ _ E _

_ _ _ T   O _   _ _ _   S U _ _ _ _   W _ _ E

R _ S _ _ G   _ _ M P
```

# CROSSWORD

## ACROSS

1 Dry run (8)
6 Control in an unfair way (9)
7 Of advanced years (3)
8 Cantankerous (5)
9 Alp (8)
12 Kiln for drying hops (4)
13 Mark for life (4)
16 Coastal swamp (4,5)
18 Person watching a game (9)
19 Taverns (4)
20 Pinnacle (4)
23 Drug which causes sleep or relieves pain (8)
26 Hard, leavened, ring-shaped roll (5)
27 Part of a bridle (3)
28 Make entire (9)
29 Time of need (5,3)

## DOWN

1 Decorative woollen tassel (6)
2 Unremitting (9)
3 Cantering (8)
4 ___ bun, sticky cake (7)
5 Uniquely (4)
10 Someone living closer to the Arctic (10)
11 Crime of having an illegal drug about one's person (10)
14 Unit of fineness of gold (5)
15 Concord (5)
17 Sleep late (3,2)
21 Reconstructed wood made from cuttings (9)
22 Vandal (8)
24 Boating event (7)
25 Unflinching (6)
26 Money paid to the courts as security (4)

# BACKWARDS

For this puzzle, we've filled in the answers, but there are letters in the grid, where the black squares should be. You need to black out the unwanted letters to make a symmetrical grid to match the clues, which are listed in random order.

| S | O | B | U | S | I | N | A | P | I | G |
|---|---|---|---|---|---|---|---|---|---|---|
| E | R | I | M | P | R | O | V | E | M | U |
| E | B | B | R | A | I | D | E | W | A | N |
| D | R | E | A | T | D | O | N | E | B | B |
| P | A | L | Y | L | E | A | D | A | S | P |
| A | D | O | L | E | S | C | E | N | C | E |
| N | A | G | A | I | C | E | N | D | O | T |
| T | W | O | L | D | E | L | E | I | N | E |
| O | L | D | E | A | N | T | W | A | D | D |
| R | E | R | A | U | C | O | U | S | P | A |
| B | A | Y | A | K | E | Y | A | K | I | D |

## ACROSS

— Small insect
— Friend
— Get better
— Young goat
— Drink cooler
— Pale
— Weep, cry
— Teenage years
— Ancient
— Poisonous snake
— Give assistance
— Farm animal
— Combine numbers
— Meadow
— Harsh, hoarse
— Harass
— Commit an act of wickedness
— Unlocking device
— Small spot
— Flow back
— Leaf used in cooking

## DOWN

— Bulky piece of wood
— Sign of agreement
— Parent
— Baby's clothes protector
— Multi-coloured shimmer
— Also
— Firearm
— Greek god of pastures
— Health resort
— Flee, hide
— Lacking moisture
— Catch sight of
— Plaything
— Boring tool
— Church seat
— Short-winged bird
— Domesticated animal
— Hawaiian garland
— Sphere
— Enquire
— High card

# JOLLY MIXTURES

In this puzzle, each clue is simply an anagram of the answer – but watch out!
There might be more than one possible solution to each clue. For instance, the
clue 'TALE' might lead to the answer 'LATE' or 'TEAL'. You'll have to look at how the
answers fit into the grid to find out which alternative is correct.

## ACROSS

| | | | | |
|---|---|---|---|---|
| 1 | LEAP | 21 | MEAD |
| 5 | CHAR | 22 | POLEMIC |
| 8 | ALOFT | 23 | SHAM |
| 10 | HOOTS | 25 | TERN |
| 11 | LONER | 28 | RON |
| 12 | ORB | 30 | LIVED |
| 14 | MARE | 32 | RINGO |
| 17 | BALE | 33 | SONAR |
| 19 | LEADING | 34 | PROD |
| 20 | ARTS | 35 | SUED |

## DOWN

| | | | | |
|---|---|---|---|---|
| 2 | ALOOF | 16 | CHARM |
| 3 | FAT | 17 | DREAD |
| 4 | LOOP | 18 | MELON |
| 5 | TEA | 23 | DOME |
| 6 | COBRA | 24 | VERSE |
| 7 | RATS | 26 | DOREE |
| 9 | FUEL | 27 | GNAT |
| 12 | LAMINAR | 29 | STOA |
| 13 | INBREED | 31 | ALP |
| 15 | RETAX | 32 | GUN |

# DOUBLE CROSS

When the letters of the answers from the upper grid are transferred to the lower grid, they give a quotation. Reading down column 'A' will give the name of its author.

|   | A | B | C | D | E | F | G | H | J | K |
|---|---|---|---|---|---|---|---|---|---|---|
| 1 |  |  |  |  |  |  |  |  |  | ■ |
| 2 |  |  |  |  |  | ■ |  |  |  |  |
| 3 |  |  |  |  |  |  | ■ |  |  |  |
| 4 |  |  |  |  |  | ■ |  |  |  |  |
| 5 |  |  |  |  |  |  |  |  |  | ■ |
| 6 |  |  |  |  |  | ■ |  |  |  |  |
| 7 |  |  |  |  |  |  | ■ |  |  |  |
| 8 |  |  |  |  |  | ■ |  |  |  |  |
| 9 |  |  |  |  |  |  |  |  | ■ |  |

1 Cellar
2 In front; worry
3 Wages; pigpen
4 Deduce; widespread
5 Torpid
6 Hunting dog; impolite
7 Result; offer
8 Trivial; employment
9 Contemplate

| 5D | 7A | 8A | 3B | 4B |  | 5A | 7E | 9C | 4K |  | 5H | 3A |  |  |
|----|----|----|----|----|----|----|----|----|----|----|----|----|----|----|
| 4E | 9H | 8G | 1B | 3E | 2E | 7J | 6D | 5G |  | 4C | 6B | 8E |  | 4H | 3J |
| 7H | 6G | 8B | 9G | 2B | 5C | 4D | 1G | 3H |  | 6H | 7B |  | 7F | 6A | 1D |
| 6J | 2A | 3F |  | 3D | 9B | 6E |  | 1E | 5E | 8K | 9A | 7C |  |  |  |
| 2K | 7D | 1F |  | 1A | 6C | 2H | 7K | 5B | 8C | 9E |  |  |  |  |  |
| 8H | 2G |  | 3C | 9D | 4J | 2C |  | 6K | 9F | 1C | 4A | 2J | 5F |  |  |
| 1H | 8D |  | 5J | 2D | 4G | 8J | 3K |  |  |  |  |  |  |  |  |

# ROUND TOUR

A fantastic puzzle in which each square counts at least twice – some count three or four times! The answer-words form two continuous chains, each of them starting at the top left-hand corner and following the directions of the arrows to and fro along alternate rows, and down and up along alternate columns. Moreover, the last letter of one word is the first letter of the next one. For example, the three consecutive words GINGER, RED and DAVID would appear in the completed puzzle as GINGEREDAVID, so be careful – it's not an easy puzzle!

## TO AND FRO

- Urgent ironing (8)
- Queen glows about scowls (7)
- Divides stocks (6)
- Captain's jumper? (7)
- Enlarge bore of 500 sheets (4)
- Tim nets new gloves (7)
- Starts care onboard (6)
- Mark musical composition (5)
- Mire muddied Arabian ruler (4)
- Relax area of responsibility (5)
- Lawrence has a leaf infusion (3)
- Horrify a quiet pal (5)
- Thin incline (4)
- Salamander is new team leader (4)
- Rests twisted lock of hair (5)
- Second beer transaction (4)
- Previously disturbed rest (4)
- Dragged along to marry (5)
- Russian country house in Vologda chalet park (5)
- A gale entangled seaweeds (5)
- Finish last point (3)
- Far down river softly (4)
- Father in agony (4)
- More agreeable northern ice queen (5)
- Split hire charge (4)
- Follow scut (4)
- Miss Stansfield is in Los Angeles (4)

- Concerning a fight (5)
- Reportedly goes round seabirds (5)
- Slumbered or pole vaulted, we hear (5)
- Chinese groups attempt adverts, it's reported (6)
- Love as returned Portuguese saint (3)
- Circle ancient city belonging to us (3)
- Rummage for part of plant (4)
- Plaything to youth leader (3)
- Affirmative you old son! (3)
- Dry tasting moment (3)
- Visitor to telephone Her Majesty (6)
- Italian capital has old ladies' man (5)

## DOWN AND UP

- Allow me trip rearrangement (6)
- Hill to right (3)
- Peruse about advert (4)
- Performs new odes (4)
- Sews in repaired tendons (6)
- Expensive marinade (5)
- Get ready re paper reshuffle (7)
- Upright Crete construction (5)
- Time right morning transport (4)
- Debatable doctor has nil time (4)
- Thanks one from Bangkok (3)
- Aide altered concept (4)

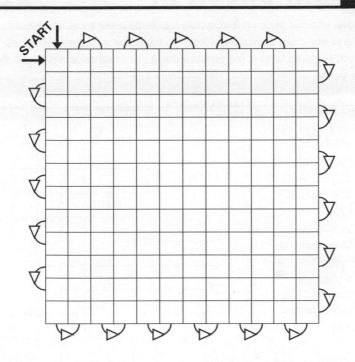

- Point at objective (3)
- Fail to meet girl (4)
- Economise on politician après ski (5)
- Organise blueprint (4)
- Bite Ulster political leader (3)
- Purr about eastern cleaner (5)
- Eric left weird antiquity (5)
- About soft peaked hat (3)
- Step around tame animals (4)
- Pole in evil act (3)
- Mesh after tax (3)
- Team leader spots rubbish (5)
- Greet icy shower (4)
- Look, fifty left lounge (4)
- See Saints defeat (4)
- Pass new baths (4)
- Sounds like unhurried blackthorn fruit (4)
- Hesitation before good work unit (3)
- Look briefly at ricochet (6)
- The Spanish go after eastern slippery customer (3)
- The French ant inclined (5)
- Coat cooked Mexican pancake ... (4)
- ... or bowled ball (3)
- Plead for British capital, for example (3)
- Inform about turf (5)
- Displays how onboard ship (5)
- Dispatched, it's said, for perfume (5)
- Thanks Danish leader a little bit (3)
- Female deer do point (3)
- Observes votes in favour, we hear (4)
- Solidify group (3)
- Sounds like 20cwt cask (3)
- Inside mine were more up-to-date (5)
- Seldom found undercooked (4)

# TINKER, TAILOR ...

To discover who this person is unscramble the words in the verse, which hints at what the person does. Write these words into the boxes below, reading across, and, if you've placed them in the correct order, the arrowed column will spell out the occupation.

He's the RGDNAE PREXTE you will need to call

When your KOA, MEL or CEHBE WRGOS a little too LALT.

He'll TUC the HSRNCBEA with a powerful INACHAWS,

So your outdoor retreat is TANE and tidy once more.

OCCUPATION: _____

# 4-SQUARE

Solve these four clues and then rearrange the solutions into a sixteen-letter phrase, for which a clue is given. The two diagonals also make four-letter words.

ROMAN CATHOLIC CHURCH SERVICE

CLOAK

CUTLERY ITEM

WEED

Clue: An indication of admiration (2,1,4,2,7)

# TRIO

Can you spot the three identical vases?

# TAKE FIVE

The three answers in this mini-crossword read the same across and down. We've given you clues to the three words, but NOT in the right order. See how quickly you can solve it.

**1** Constellation containing seven bright stars

**2** Stretched tight, strained

**3** Freshwater fish of the salmon genus

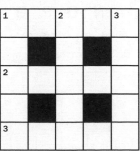

This puzzle has no clues in the conventional sense. Instead, every different number printed in the main grid represents a different letter (with the same number always representing the same letter, of course). For example, if 7 turns out to be a 'V', you can write in V wherever a square contains 7. We have completed a very small part of the puzzle to give you a start, but the rest is up to you.

| 23 | 24 | 9 | 1 | 4 | | 24 | | 7 | 10 | 19 | 21 | 24 |
|----|----|----|----|----|----|----|----|----|----|----|----|----|
| 6 | | 10 | | 13 | 3 | 2 | 3 | 24 | | 2 | | 17 |
| 1 | 10 | 6 | 24 | 10 | | 1 | | 1 | 25 | 3 | 26 | 24 |
| 17 | | 4 | | 24 | 22 | 19 | 13 | 24 | | 23 | | 18 |
| | 4 | 16 | 6 | 24 | 5 | 22 | | 4 | 14 | 24 | 22 | 22 |
| 15 | | 6 | | | 1 | | 24 | | 19 | | | 5 |
| 5 | 12 | 24 | 20 | 6 | 24 | | 11 | 24 | 25 | 24 | 22 | 4 |
| 10 | | | 24 | | 2 | | 24 | | | 2 | | 4 |
| 9 | 24 | 4 | 24 | 1 | | 4 | 26 | 5 | 20 | 1 | 17 | |
| 22 | | 14 | | 14 | 24 | 5 | 1 | 4 | | 10 | | 19 |
| 3 | 15 | 5 | 18 | 19 | | 12 | | 13 P | 22 | 6 | 26 | 8 |
| 20 | | 8 | | 10 | 24 | 24 | 12 | 24 E | | 23 | | 5 |
| 18 | 22 | 24 | 5 | 20 | | 10 | | 20 N | 24 | 24 | 23 | 17 |

## A B C D E F G H I J K L M
## N O P Q R S T U V W X Y Z

(The small grid is provided for ease of reference only)

| 1 | 2 | 3 | 4 | 5 | 6 | 7 | 8 | 9 | 10 | 11 | 12 | 13 |
|----|----|----|----|----|----|----|----|----|----|----|----|----|
| 14 | 15 | 16 | 17 | 18 | 19 | 20 | 21 | 22 | 23 | 24 | 25 | 26 |

# CROSSWORD

**ACROSS**

1 Aits (5)
4 Supremely regal (8)
11 Imbue, instil (9)
12 Garden shelter (5)
13 Dusted with sugar (4)
14 Cowled (6)
16 Piste runner (3)
18 Give money to (3)
19 Pie, tart etc (6)
22 Crumbly earthy mixture used as a fertiliser (4)
24 Japanese art of swordsmanship (5)
26 Winter garment (9)
27 Art of witty replies (8)
28 Quick, nimble (5)

**DOWN**

2 Impressive (7)
3 Towards the rising of the sun (4)
5 Alter for the good (5)
6 Incorporate (6)
7 Raw fibres of hemp and flax (3)
8 Personal warmth (10)
9 Card game where the loser undresses (5,5)
10 Board-game with counters (4)
15 ___ for, select (3)
16 Block up (4,3)
17 Commotion (6)
20 Uninterrupted transition from one piece of music or film to another (5)
21 Sea hazard often made of coral (4)
23 Pack (4)
25 Pinch, squeeze sharply (3)

# MISSING LINKS

The answer to each clue is a word which has a link with each of the three words listed. This word may come at the end (eg Head linked with Beach, Big and Hammer), at the beginning (eg Black linked with Beauty, Board and Jack) or a mixture of the two (eg Stone linked with Hail, Lime and Wall).

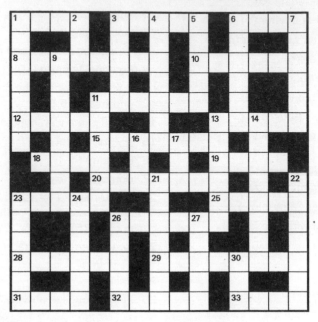

## ACROSS

1 Band, Brighton, Cake (4)
3 Boy, Cruiser, Log (5)
6 Bottoms, Rope, Tent (4)
8 Falls, Plum, Queen (8)
10 Court, Elbow, Table (6)
11 Corn, Snow, Soap (6)
12 Grass, Highway, Powers (5)
13 Finish, Stitch, Wood (5)
15 Coffee, Dislike, Success (7)
18 Farm, Poker, Press (4)
19 Drop, Rain, Test (4)
20 Nelson, Rear, Red (7)
23 Birthday, Garden, Labour (5)
25 Box, Break, Liquid (5)
26 Murder, Sheepdog, Time (6)
28 Begging, Box, Love (6)
29 Compound, Rate, Vested (8)
31 Ice, Stock, Sugar (4)
32 Dresser, Rarebit, Terrier (5)
33 Chicken, High, Netting (4)

## DOWN

1 Arms, Gear, Order (7)
2 Bag, Football, Tool (3)
3 Christmas, Service, Singing (5)
4 Bath, Electric, Wet (7)
5 Bank, Compare, Medical (5)
6 Republic, Skin, Split (6)
7 Driving, Object, Piano (6)
9 Chip, Personal, Programme (8)
11 Girl, Good, Man (6)
13 Choir, Market, Orchestra (6)
14 Bermuda, Equilateral, Eternal (8)
16 Lump, Round, Total (3)
17 Force, Mail, Pocket (3)
21 Letter, Reaction, Response (7)
22 Blower, Penny, Wolf (7)
23 Eye, Library, Servant (6)
24 Dove, Mock, Turn (6)
26 Away, Back, Over (5)
27 Key, Night, On (5)
30 Deal, Materials, Recruits (3)

Starting from the bold centre letter, move up or down or sideways (but NOT diagonally) to find the path through sixteen wild animals.

| M | I | H | C | R | E | C | P | I | A | U |
|---|---|---|---|---|---|---|---|---|---|---|
| P | A | N | S | O | N | O | P | H | R | G |
| L | L | Z | E | E | I | H | O | P | J | A |
| A | I | R | O | G | S | R | T | O | E | P |
| P | C | U | N | E | U | M | A | E | L | O |
| O | R | P | I | T | **L** | P | A | T | N | A |
| L | L | Y | G | I | E | O | R | L | L | E |
| A | A | B | E | R | I | L | D | E | Z | A |
| W | R | O | R | K | O | F | E | E | T | G |
| V | E | O | A | A | N | F | A | L | N | A |
| A | E | B | G | N | G | I | R | E | P | H |

# BRUSHWORK | 44

This artist prefers painting some objects to others. Which five objects in these six paintings turn up more often than the others – and where?

bian

# SKELETON CROSSWORD 45

Have double the fun with this puzzle: you've got to fill in the answers and the black squares! We've given you the bare bones to start and it will help you to know that the black squares in the finished grid form a symmetrical pattern, so that every black square has at least one other corresponding black square.

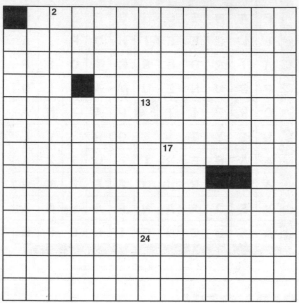

## ACROSS

1 Boundless
5 The ___, Jackie Collins novel
10 Breathing noisily
11 Terry Wogan's nationality
12 Alternative
13 Flower cluster resembling a bunch of grapes
15 Dana ___, Gillian Anderson's rôle in The X-Files
17 The Army Game character
19 André ___, American tennis player who won Wimbledon in 1992
20 ___ Barkin, actress in Fear and Loathing in Las Vegas
23 Catwalk worker!
24 ___ out, equipping
25 1746-1828 Spanish painter
26 Lost the grip on braking

## DOWN

2 Organ used to eat and speak
3 With ease
4 Dorothy L ___, English novelist
6 Pared
7 Roald ___, The Witches author
8 Support (a cause)
9 Unhappy
14 ___ Mutant Ninja Turtles, avenging reptiles
16 Impious
18 Western US pioneer known as 'Wild Bill'
21 River in France
22 Offensively self-satisfied

# BLACK OUT

Can you see which two artefacts are shown in silhouette at the top?

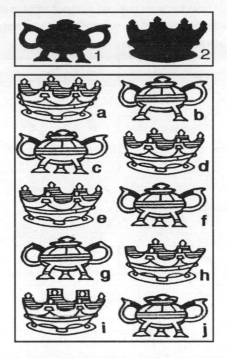

# SILHOUETTE

Shade in every fragment containing a dot – and what have you got?

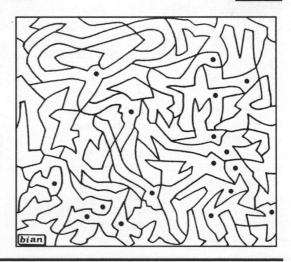

bian

# ROUNDABOUT

Solutions to Radial clues (1 to 24) either start from the outer edge of the circle and read inwards, or start from the inner ring and read outwards to the edge (so they are all five-letter words). Solutions to Circular clues read in either a clockwise or an anticlockwise direction around the circle.

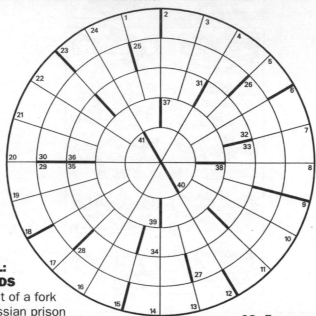

## RADIAL:
### INWARDS

1 Part of a fork
2 Russian prison
5 Dutch cheese
8 Pam ___, poetess
11 Hebrew prophet
14 Cold meal
15 Bakery product
16 Concur
17 Call out
18 Beg, sponge off
19 Picture
22 Tree of Lebanon
23 Detection device
24 Lengthwise

### OUTWARDS

3 Roof end
4 Snake
6 Allow in
7 Confuse
9 Paris river

10 Flower part
12 Tediously
13 Male honey-bee
20 Product obtained
   from tree sap
21 Prepared

## CIRCULAR:
### CLOCKWISE

6 Beverage
9 Tree
12 Affirmative
25 Regulation
26 Greasy
30 Perfect
33 Droplet
36 Sorrowful
37 Total

38 Ever, poetically
39 Greek sea

### ANTICLOCKWISE

1 Standard
5 ___ Rusedski,
   tennis player
17 Taxi
22 Non-believer in
   goodness
27 Money borrowed
28 Female relative
29 Chinese ex-leader
31 Gore
32 Wet earth
34 ___ Lane,
   Superman's girl
35 Worship
40 Droop
41 Ruby colour

# WORDSEARCH

The 40 legal terms have all been hidden in the diagram. They have been printed across (backwards or forwards), or up or down, or diagonally, but always in a straight line without letters being skipped. You can use the letters in the diagram more than once. You will probably find it helpful to mark the words in the diagram and cross them off the list as you find them.

```
V H A Y S Q T A F L Y A B U Z T
S E L F L U D O I I N E I L E R
A K R I F V P C R E O T A S E E
V P B D O I I R O T M T T G N B
H E P C I D D P O Y I A R R J M
L T A E O C B A R C T U X U G A
D T A C A U T A V E S O C A O H
E C W O S L I P M I E A V R C C
T N E M T C I D N I T E E N I W
W Y T L I U G E H Y L Q E B R C
I R F D E E B F U Z S B L I A I
T U U K C D B A R R I S T E R H
N J T A N I W M E T U T A T S F
E P E V E C C A L U M N Y I C E
S G R L D T N T L R J X D B A A
S O U I I T R I B U N A L I S L
C R W P V M H O L L I W Y L E T
S I L K E Y Q N F B T R I A L Y
```

| | | | |
|---|---|---|---|
| ADVOCATE | CODICIL | JUDICIARY | SUBPOENA |
| AFFIDAVIT | COURT | JURY | TESTATE |
| ALIBI | DEFAMATION | LAW | TESTIMONY |
| APPEAL | EDICT | LIBEL | TORT |
| BARRISTER | EVIDENCE | LIEN | TRIAL |
| BENCH | FEALTY | OATH | TRIBUNAL |
| CALUMNY | GAVEL | PRIVY | VERDICT |
| CASE | GUILT | RULE | WILL |
| CHAMBER | HABEASCORPUS | SILK | WITNESS |
| CIRCUIT | INDICTMENT | STATUTE | WRIT |

Just like a Jig-word – but instead of letters, numbers.

| 3-figure | 4-figure | 29161 | 86612 |
|---|---|---|---|
| 264 | 1284 | 30199 | 90839 |
| 286 | 2359 | 38008 | 92202 |
| 305 | 4850 | 43736 | 93126 |
| 362 | 8365 | 44233 | |
| 399 | | 48132 | |
| 468 | **5-figure** | 50104 | **6-figure** |
| 510 | 17904 | 51009 | 163982 |
| 516 | 18256 | 59216 | 293099 |
| 649 | 18891 | 60891 | 391136 |
| (713) | 20504 | 61200 | 425991 |
| 803 | 20609 | 63481 | 972141 |
| 917 | 21424 | 73033 | |
| 920 | 21837 | 80017 | |
| 981 | 28304 | 81011 | |

# CROSSWORD

## ACROSS

6 Docked (9)

7 Young snake-like fish (5)

8 Loud noise, racket (3)

9 Fashion (4)

10 Chinese religious statue (4)

12 Practice of being naked (8)

15 Half-yearly (8)

17 Throw away (7,2)

18 Lessen the severity of (8)

20 Brightness (of colours) (8)

23 Munch (4)

24 Piece of silicon in computers (4)

27 Be sickly (3)

28 Book containing recorded events of one year (5)

29 Animal money-box (5-4)

## DOWN

1 Running in a continuous current (9)

2 Arched (6)

3 Disdain (5)

4 Bookish (8)

5 Peculiarity (7)

11 Goods such as tools and household implements (11)

13 Matching sweater and cardigan (7)

14 Character on a musical stave (4)

16 Intact (7)

17 Female parents of animals (4)

19 Slim (5-4)

21 Way of thinking (8)

22 In bits and pieces (7)

25 Aerodrome shed (6)

26 Lecherous woodland being (5)

# STORY CROSSWORD

Transfer the words which complete the story to the grid and then put the circled letters in the right order to discover the name of the famous person therein described.

The ___ (5D) of a Lancashire cotton spinner who became a Labour MP, he was born in Stockport in 1909 and educated at Ealing County School in London. He ___ (17D) to play table tennis as a child, not realising that this would ___ (14D) him to international fame. His skill was so great, though, that by the ___ (10D) he was twenty, he was the world table-tennis champion.

He decided to take up tennis, a move which ___ (24A) many doors for him. He ___ (18A) hard at his ___ (22D) sport, modelling his techniques on those of the French player Henri Cochet. He was particularly ___ (22A) for the running forward ___ (3D) at which he excelled.

The ___ (13D) of his hard work was that he decided to ___ (19D) the Wimbledon tennis tournament in 1930. He beat the Italian ___ (11A) Umberto de Porpurgo in the third round. As a result of this performance, he was picked for the Davis ___ (15A) in Paris in 1933. He defeated Cochet and ___ (1D) won the trophy for the first time in twenty-one years.

In 1934 he beat the Australian Jack Crawford to win the Wimbledon singles title. His victory was to ___ (20A) members of the All-England Club and the Lawn Tennis Association who ___ (12D) not come to terms with the idea of ___ (2D) from a working-class background becoming a champion. Despite the opposition of these ___ (12A), he ___ (6D) on with his game, winning Wimbledon in both 1935 and 1936.

He won the United States title in 1933, 1934 and 1936, the Australian title in 1934 and the ___ (7A) title in 1935. He also won many doubles and mixed-doubles titles. His Davis Cup record was outstanding – in twenty ties he lost ___ (13A) seven out of fifty-two matches. He was never ___ (16D) than when he was playing tennis and his successes ___ (23A) him the ___ (21D) of the British public, who ___ (16A) him in high esteem.

In 1936 he turned professional. Two years ___ (4D) he became an American citizen, serving in the US Air Force during the Second World War. When the war was ___ (8A), he set up a sportswear company which achieved good ___ (3A) and became highly successful.

He was ___ (9A) to be heard on sports broadcasts and was a member of the BBC radio team at Wimbledon for forty years. In 1984, a statue of him was unveiled at Wimbledon. He died in 1995.

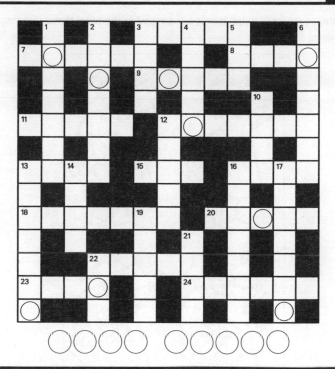

# TRILINES

Can you draw three straight lines from one edge to another, dividing the box into five parts with each section containing two different symbols?

# PICTURE THIS

Each picture contains a detail that is not present in the other three. Can you spot the four extra details?

# TAKE FIVE

The three answers in this mini-crossword read the same across and down. We've given you clues to the three words, but NOT in the right order. See how quickly you can solve it.

**1** Rage

**2** Opposite of south

**3** Particle of sand

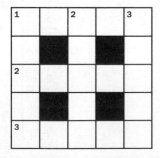

# WHAT'S MISSING?

Each picture is missing a detail that is present in the other seven. Can you spot all eight missing details?

# TWO-TIMER

Two sets of clues to the same answers. Cryptic clues below and straight clues beneath the grid.

## ACROSS

6 Like two similar strikers (4-7)

8 Some slowcoaches are depressed (3)

9 Very small portion of sweetmeat (3)

10 Bird indicating canine happiness (7)

12 I had one to replace the dolt (5)

13 Dead keen boy (5)

14 Make regular journeys to the fold (3)

16 Be amazed at the miracle (6)

17 More cunning toxophilite (6)

18 All right to include a tree (3)

20 In the raw fully naked, that's dreadful! (5)

22 Virtuous sort of support is psychological (5)

23 It's a big blow in the China Seas and West Pacific (7)

24 No odd goings-on in this boat! (3)

26 One champion (3)

27 Do take steps after a meal (6-5)

## DOWN

1 Form of worship (3)

2 Not sink moving aloft (5)

3 Light-coloured petals dispersed (6)

4 Bill to deliver bitter (5)

5 Some housewives getting stitch (3)

6 Literally exchange a brief conversation (4,3,4)

7 Release, hand over broken cane (11)

10 Print of timber chopped up (7)

11 Understand the door is locked (5,2)

14 In favour of support for the most part (3)

15 Kay moved the beast (3)

19 Stick broken head on again (6)

21 Being dishonest at length (5)

22 Ivory grinder? (5)

25 Kelvin and I quietly have short sleep (3)

26 One caught part of play (3)

## ACROSS

**6** Compatible (4-7)
**8** Moo (3)
**9** Tiny (3)
**10** Bird (7)
**12** Foolish person (5)
**13** Patron saint of Wales (5)
**14** Work steadily at (3)
**16** Marvel (6)
**17** Bowman (6)
**18** Acorn tree (3)
**20** Very bad (5)
**22** Ethical (5)
**23** Asian hurricane (7)
**24** Ararat boat (3)
**26** Top card (3)
**27** Social occasion (6-5)

## DOWN

**1** Church seat (3)
**2** Stay up in the air (5)
**3** Type of crayon (6)
**4** Pungent (5)
**5** Use a needle and thread (3)
**6** Verbatim (4,3,4)
**7** Liberation (11)
**10** Engraved design (7)
**11** Finally grasp (5,2)
**14** For (3)
**15** Ox (3)
**19** Hold fast (6)
**21** Prone (5)
**22** Tooth (5)
**25** Nap (3)
**26** Parliamentary law (3)

# SKELETON CROSSWORD

Have double the fun with this puzzle: you've got to fill in the answers and the black squares! We've given you the bare bones to start and it will help you to know that the black squares in the finished grid form a symmetrical pattern, so that every black square has at least one other corresponding black square.

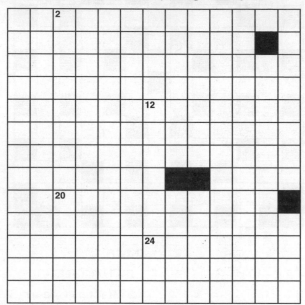

**ACROSS**

1 Overpriced
4 Skiing discipline
9 Smacked heavily
10 Bodily constriction between the ribs and hips
11 Work
12 Kitchen appliance which liquidises soups
14 Amateur
16 Lend a hand
19 Countersign
21 Be miserable
23 Jewelled coronet
24 Sweetener
25 Annually
26 Hoax

**DOWN**

1 Hooded robe
2 Acutely
3 Scenic ponds
5 Disobedient, uncontrolled
6 Estate owner in Scotland
7 Full development
8 Sun-dried brick
13 Smoothly
15 Letters for abroad
17 Entreat
18 Brief and abrupt
20 Histrionic scene
21 Proverbial centre
22 Additional tax

...

# JIG-WORD

No clues – just pattern and answers – but can you fit them in?

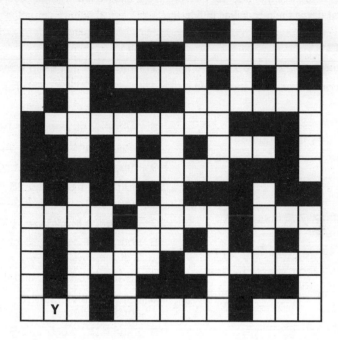

| 3-letter words | EASE | EVENT |
|---|---|---|
| ADO | HILL | TWINE |
| AIR | LOUD | |
| ALB | OKRA | **6-letter words** |
| EVE | OPAL | CURATE |
| EYE | PATE | ELICIT |
| ODD | PEST | ESCAPE |
| PET | PIER | GOBLET |
| PIE | POST | MANTLE |
| PIN | STUD | STROLL |
| RED | TERN | TARTAN |

| **4-letter words** | **5-letter words** | **8-letter word** |
|---|---|---|
| AJAR | APRON | REPARTEE |
| ALOE | ELATE | |

# DATELINE

A number jig with a difference: with clues to figure out (with the help of a calculator if you wish!) to discover the date in the shaded line – in this case, a significant day in the recognition of bravery.

## ACROSS

1 Three-sevenths of 602

3 Reverse 1 Across, then divide by 4

5 Divide 33 Across by 63, then multiply by 4 squared

7 Freezing-point Fahrenheit

8 Cube root of 7880599

9 Roman CCCLXI

11 Multiply 7 Across by 11, subtract 7

13 Five-seventeenths of 2771

14 Multiply 27 Across by 518

16 Square 33 Across, subtract 35319

21 Inches in 1¾ miles

22 Minutes in a leap years's February

25 Four packs of cards plus three aces

27 Add the square root of 1369 to the square root of 5329

28 Number of Sherlock Holmes's house in Baker Street

30 Add the digits of 1 Across, then multiply by the sum of the digits of 1 Down

31 Triple 18, subtract three

32 Multiply the lives of a cat by 100

33 Square the former age of majority

34 Five-twenty-thirds of 1357

## DOWN

1 Number of inches in 63 yards

2 Multiply 7451 by 5 Across

4 A dozen baker's dozens

5 Outbreak of World War Two

6 Year of Prince Charles's birth

9 Cube 4 Down, subtract 5314

10 Multiply 24 Down by 28 Across, then add 6401

12 Old pence in £21

15 Pounds in 2 tons, 15 cwt and 7 stone

17 Reverse 19 Down, add 4495

18 Diamond plus golden anniversaries

19 Square 36, subtract 55

20 Ounces in 2688 stones

23 19 Down minus 11 squared

24 Subtract the first three digits of 26 Down from 50 gross

26 Divide 22 Across by 7 Across

29 8 per cent of 3300

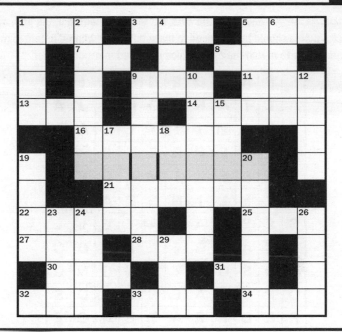

# MATCH UP

While putting the final touches to his work, the artist noticed that there were five discrepancies between his picture and the model. Can you spot them?

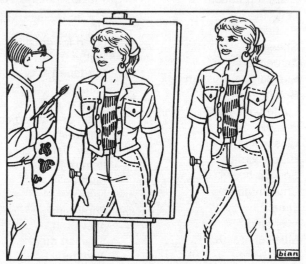

# BACKWARDS

For this puzzle, we've filled in the answers, but there are letters in the grid, where the black squares should be. You need to black out the unwanted letters to make a symmetrical grid to match the clues, which are listed in random order.

| S | P | A | D | D | E | N | D | A | I | L |
|---|---|---|---|---|---|---|---|---|---|---|
| A | L | T | A | R | A | O | U | I | J | A |
| T | O | O | M | I | T | T | E | D | A | D |
| A | L | L | E | P | R | E | T | E | W | E |
| Y | A | L | E | X | I | M | A | D | E | N |
| E | Y | E | L | I | N | E | R | A | A | I |
| S | E | E | K | A | K | A | T | E | L | L |
| E | R | A | N | G | E | L | E | A | D | O |
| N | O | S | O | R | T | I | N | G | N | U |
| O | P | E | R | A | E | N | E | E | D | S |
| R | E | D | E | B | A | T | E | R | O | E |

**ACROSS**

— Relate
— Yemeni port
— Wants
— Hair preparation
— Left out
— Bother
— Sheep
— Arguer
— Supplementary items
— Before
— Large passenger-carrying vessel
— Classifying
— US university
— Seance board
— Church table
— Time
— Everyone
— Musical drama
— Search

**DOWN**

— River barrier
— Short letter
— Moose
— Owing
— Seize
— Tier
— Linen for dressing wounds
— Skill
— Burdened
— Parasite
— Keen
— Open or wooded country
— Mineral
— Spicy dish
— Item of jewellery
— Born as
— Leak
— Coral reef
— Alleviated
— Spanish man
— Assisted

In this puzzle, each clue is simply an anagram of the answer – but watch out! There might be more than one possible solution to each clue. For instance, the clue 'TALE' might lead to the answer 'LATE' or 'TEAL'. You'll have to look at how the answers fit into the grid to find out which alternative is correct.

## ACROSS

| | | | | |
|---|---|---|---|---|
| **1** | TIME | **21** | CARE |
| **5** | GORE | **22** | CITADEL |
| **8** | STARE | **23** | RELY |
| **10** | ROMAN | **25** | VEER |
| **11** | TUBER | **28** | TEA |
| **12** | WEE | **30** | GROAN |
| **14** | TORT | **32** | SUPER |
| **17** | SATE | **33** | VOILE |
| **19** | ARTICLE | **34** | WOLF |
| **20** | PALE | **35** | MANE |

## DOWN

| | | | | |
|---|---|---|---|---|
| **2** | AMONG | **16** | TREAD |
| **3** | RAT | **17** | LEAST |
| **4** | WEST | **18** | EAGER |
| **5** | ROB | **23** | POLO |
| **6** | OUTER | **24** | LARGE |
| **7** | MUST | **26** | SERVE |
| **9** | WENT | **27** | FREE |
| **12** | VALENCE | **29** | RAID |
| **13** | RATTEEN | **31** | OWN |
| **15** | EARLY | **32** | APE |

# CRYPTIC CROSSWORD

## ACROSS

1 Accident-prone tourist? (7)
5 Fool partly a comedian (7)
9 Decline to go with hoarder, a council worker (6,9)
10 Value of notability for the most part (5)
11 It is complicated to work out in detail (9)
12 Again guaranteed to have restored confidence (9)
14 Nothing in fog that is damp (5)
15 Wait at start of tennis match (5)
16 Headmistress fully content despite it being nerve-racking (9)
18 Near to said tea garment that can be worn in bed (9)
21 Deserve an order (5)
22 Male star-studded dinner? (10,5)
23 Cricket match and feature of it in practice (4,3)
24 Beat fellow on the line (7)

## DOWN

1 Thus without us, boatman becomes bowler (7)
2 Devilishly hot areas? (8,7)
3 Has to step for great speed (9)
4 Dog gets up before explosive gathering (5)
5 No end of gin hesitantly carried by Dutchman (9)
6 Strange, Leo, it will remain motionless (3,2)
7 Having a new feature – or a quarrel (4,1,10)
8 It pours from hill fissure (7)
13 Rosalind's found on open land in Ireland (9)
14 Strong-smelling substance on lemon pie or other fruit (4,5)
15 Smooth over mine to make play area (7)
17 Chattel turned out to be old shoe fastening (7)
19 Wildcat spotted by guide leader in the row (5)
20 N-note replacement music (5)

# STAIRCASE

When these Biblical characters are correctly placed along the horizontal rows, the letters in the diagonal staircase will spell out another one.

ABEL    ABSALOM    EPHRAIM

ESTHER    ISAAC    ISRAEL    NOAH

# DOT-TO-DOT

Join the dots from 1 to 30 to reveal the hidden picture.

# CROSSWORD

## ACROSS

**4** Timber tree of the olive family (3)

**8** Dot at the end of a sentence (4,4)

**9** Regard as the same (6)

**10** Composure (6)

**11** Period between the beginning and end of a process (4,4)

**13** Netherlands cheese (4)

**15** Sulked, was miserable (5)

**16** Money owed (4)

**18** Bruise on the face (5,3)

**20** Satanic creatures (6)

**22** Writing-desk (6)

**23** Form a barrier round (8)

**24** Shell (peas) (3)

## DOWN

**1** Shouldered (6)

**2** Range of singing voice (4)

**3** Butt (4)

**4** Trick done with sheets (5-3,3)

**5** Heavenly messenger (6)

**6** Mated (of stags) (6)

**7** Flower support (4)

**12** Stuff your face (3)

**13** Go back, as of the tide (3)

**14** Take the ___, make fun of (6)

**15** Gather together (4,2)

**17** Ring for an arm or leg (6)

**19** Hulking rough-mannered fellow (4)

**20** Waterfowl (4)

**21** Former German currency (4)

# URN-INGS

Can you see which three of these urns are identical?

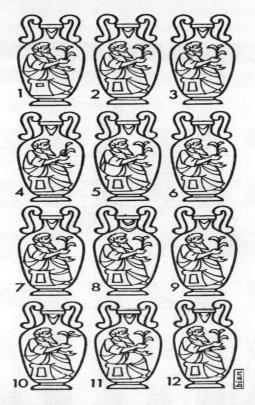

# 4-SQUARE

Solve these four clues and then rearrange the solutions into a sixteen-letter phrase, for which a clue is given. The two diagonals also make four-letter words.

BECOME WEARISOME

MIDDAY

CAUSE PAIN

JUMP INTO WATER

Clue: Silent-screen star (7,9)

# KEYWORD

This puzzle has no clues in the conventional sense. Instead, every different number printed in the main grid represents a different letter (with the same number always representing the same letter, of course). For example, if 7 turns out to be a 'V', you can write in V wherever a square contains 7. We have completed a very small part of the puzzle to give you a start, but the rest is up to you.

| 16 | 2 | 4 | 18 | 16 | 11 | 10 | | 6 | 11 | 19 | 4 | 10 |
|----|----|----|----|----|----|----|----|----|----|----|----|----|
| 25 | | 25 | | 19 | | 13 | | 2 | | 12 | | 1 |
| 5 | 10 | 17 | 18 | 24 | | 19 | 4 | 17 | 16 | 10 | 24 | 10 |
| 8 | | 18 | | 12 | | 7 | | 9 | | 5 | | |
| 23 | 25 | 17 | 8 | 10 | 15 | 2 | 11 | | 15 | 11 | 19 | 10 |
| 9 | | | | 26 | | 17 | | 4 | | 25 | | 5 |
| 10 | 12 | 25 | 7 | 10 | 7 | | 20 | 25 (A) | 17 (S) | 21 (P) | 10 | 5 |
| 10 | | 24 | | 7 | | 17 | | 21 | | | | 19 |
| 11 | 25 | 8 | 9 | | 8 | 23 | 18 | 8 | 16 | 9 | 10 | 5 |
| | | 18 | | 15 | | 25 | | 18 | | 10 | | 11 |
| 10 | 24 | 3 | 2 | 18 | 5 | 26 | | 17 | 10 | 18 | 22 | 10 |
| 11 | | 2 | | 24 | | 10 | | 14 | | 5 | | 17 |
| 1 | 24 | 10 | 25 | 7 | | 7 | 10 | 17 | 18 | 17 | 8 | 17 |

## A B C D E F G H I J K L M
## N O P Q R S T U V W X Y Z

(The small grid is provided for ease of reference only)

| 1 | 2 | 3 | 4 | 5 | 6 | 7 | 8 | 9 | 10 | 11 | 12 | 13 |
|----|----|----|----|----|----|----|----|----|----|----|----|----|
| 14 | 15 | 16 | 17 | 18 | 19 | 20 | 21 | 22 | 23 | 24 | 25 | 26 |

# ADD-A-LETTER

Insert or add a letter to these four-letter words to make five-letter words which fit the rhyming clues. The six added letters should spell out a word.

| | | |
|---|---|---|
| REAM | | Dairy product to top apple pie |
| GRAN | | Grumble, moan, gripe or sigh |
| LEAN | | Acquire knowledge, expand your brain |
| RISE | | Washing machine function, comes before 'drain' |
| SPIN | | Skeletal feature; the backbone |
| SATE | | Utter in a convincing tone |

# SMASHING

Four of the six shapes at the top can be found hidden in the picture. Can you work out which ones and where they are?

Every answer (except the first) uses the last letter of the preceding answer as its initial letter, the chain thus formed following a spiral path to the centre of the grid. The diagonals spell out the names of two ducks.

**START**

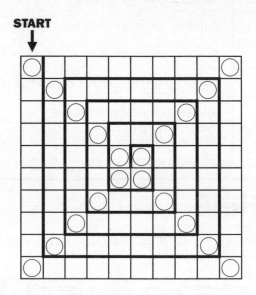

- Darling (7)
- Portable folding seat (9)
- Cavalier's opponent (9)
- Not easy (9)
- Meddle (6)
- Eraser (6)
- Scoundrel (6)
- Pedal (5)
- Mackintosh (8)
- Outburst (7)

- Scarf (7)
- Proportion (5)
- Past (4)
- Part of the eye (6)
- Unfriendly, detached (5)
- Excess flesh (4)
- People carrier (3)
- ___ Tuesday, pancake day (6)
- Slippery fish (4)
- Ocean (3)

# BOXWISE

Put these three-letter groups into the twelve numbered boxes to produce twelve six-letter words, each of which starts in one box and finishes in another as indicated by an arrow. For instance, 2 and 5 make a six-letter word, but not 5 and 9. One group has been filled in to start you off.

INT     NED     SON     NET

EAR     APP     SQU     PLA

EAL     END     TED     LES

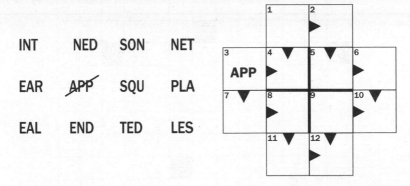

---

# FITBITS

This gang is celebrating a successful raid, but can you be successful in finding out which two of the four details on the left (which might be drawn at different angles from the orginals) belong to which two criminals?

# SKELETON CROSSWORD

Have double the fun with this puzzle: you've got to fill in the answers and the black squares! We've given you the bare bones to start and it will help you to know that the black squares in the finished grid form a symmetrical pattern, so that every black square has at least one other corresponding black square.

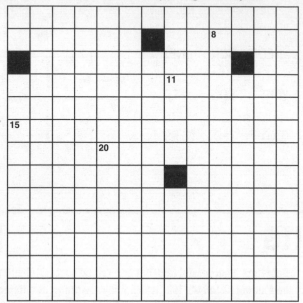

## ACROSS

- **2** Saying
- **7** Sound made by a cat
- **8** Lines
- **9** Product of a hen
- **10** Furnish (provisions)
- **11** Marking with print
- **13** Transgress
- **15** Great divide
- **18** Cerebral organ
- **20** Prefix meaning 'hearing'
- **21** Fussy
- **23** Spry
- **25** Possesses, owns
- **27** Drink from beans
- **29** Paying court to
- **31** ___ Mack, *The Sketch Show* comedian
- **32** Scandinavian god of thunder
- **33** Cuts (grass)
- **34** Written records of a meeting

## DOWN

- **1** Language related to Xhosa
- **2** Demonstrates
- **3** Does as told
- **4** Morayshire town
- **5** Intermediary
- **6** ___ Taylor, actress
- **10** World's deepest ocean
- **12** Oriental root said to have curative properties
- **14** Gandhi's country
- **16** Total
- **17** Spring month
- **18** Feather scarf
- **19** Muhammad ___, ex-boxer
- **22** Mutilate
- **24** Prepares (for stardom)
- **25** Troy's beauty
- **26** Brushed
- **28** Darts players' line
- **30** Common amphibian

# WORDSEARCH

The 42 composers have all been hidden in the diagram. They have been printed across (backwards or forwards), or up or down, or diagonally, but always in a straight line without letters being skipped. You can use the letters in the diagram more than once. You will probably find it helpful to mark the words in the diagram and cross them off the list as you find them.

```
A T I B T Z F K S L L E W O H N
R H N E C A I O M W A L T O N E
N O I R H I N G A C S A M T V V
O M L N A B Z N I W H S R E G O
L S L S I W I L L I A M S O N H
D O E T K J O P L I N T K R B T
H N B E O H R Y I O T I O B L E
R C M I V E S E W O F D T B I E
T A A N S Y K S N I V A R T S B
L R C B K U W I A K B U A C S S
E L A H Y J D A H I C E B G C I
M I E Z M D A L G H H U R A M T
M S P W O A A N U N J T R T E N
U Z I H O M N N A S E L A B N E
H T E O B D W I V C A R G M O M
B E N E D I C T N T E L L X T E
C O R E L L I A T O Q K E Z T L
N T B U S O N I M K V A E L I C
```

| | | | |
|---|---|---|---|
| ARNOLD | BUSONI | IVES | RACHMANINOV |
| BACH | CILEA | JANACEK | SCARLATTI |
| BARTOK | CLEMENTI | JOPLIN | STRAVINSKY |
| BEETHOVEN | CORELLI | LAMBERT | TCHAIKOVSKY |
| BELLINI | ELGAR | LISZT | THOMSON |
| BENEDICT | FINZI | MACDOWELL | VAUGHAN |
| BERNSTEIN | GERSHWIN | MASCAGNI | WILLIAMS |
| BLISS | HODDINOTT | MATHIAS | WAGNER |
| BOITO | HOWELLS | MENOTTI | WALTON |
| BRUCH | HUMMEL | MOZART | WILLIAMSON |
| BRUCKNER | IBERT | NONO | |

# STORY CROSSWORD

Transfer the words which complete the story to the grid and then put the circled letters in the right order to discover the name of the famous person therein described.

On January 4th, 1809, a boy was born in Coupvray to a ___ (1D) and his wife. Even as a toddler, he liked to ___ (1A) in his father's work and was often to be found in his tack workshop.

One day, while his father was out of the workshop for a few ___ (13D), talking to a passing ___ (19D), the knife the little boy was using cut his eye. There was no ___ (23A) help available, so a ___ (21D) woman treated him with a herbal ___ (12A). Although she managed to staunch the flow of blood, the thing his parents ___ (8A) happened: he lost the sight of the injured eye. His other eye developed an infection, and two years ___ (10A) he became completely blind.

In 1814, Coupvray was invaded by Russian soldiers. He ___ (3D) their taunts and ill-treatment as they mocked him for his ___ (17D) ways. It was not long before the soldiers had managed to ___ (24A) his self-confidence and he scarcely went out of the house.

A year later, a new priest came to Coupvray. He found the boy bright and ___ (2D), and offered to become his teacher. Realising his pupil's potential, the priest arranged for him to go to the National Institute for Blind Youth in ___ (18A) Paris. In February 1819,

he became a ___ (15D) at the school. The Institute's teachers __ _ (25A) by fear. Boys who were slow and ___ (16D) at their lessons were given the ___ (9A). He ___ (14A) the rules and worked hard, even though he found the mindless ___ (4D) of the lessons hard to bear.

In 1821, a demonstration was given at the Institute of a system of 'night writing' which used dots and dashes punched into paper. He immediately started work to improve this system, and soon came up with a series of embossed dots which would ___ (20A) blind people to read at a ___ (7D) pace. Although his idea was as yet ___ (11A), the Head of the Institute prematurely introduced it to his pupils in a move which was to ___ (6D) the Governors and lead to the Head's dismissal.

Later, when he in turn became a ___ (4A) at the Institute, he secretly taught the children his new reading system, seeing it as an ___ (5D) to their learning.

In 1835, he contracted tuberculosis. It could not be ___ (18D), and he died from it on January 6th, 1852. Although his invention did not achieve recognition in his own lifetime, his system of dots is now highly __ _ (22A) by blind people everywhere.

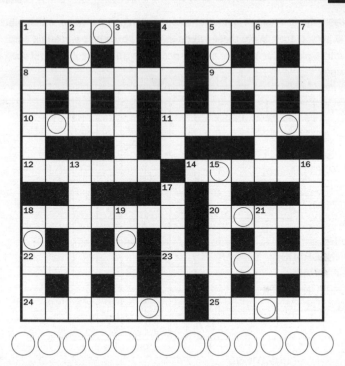

# FOURSOME

Can you see which four of these vases are exactly the same?

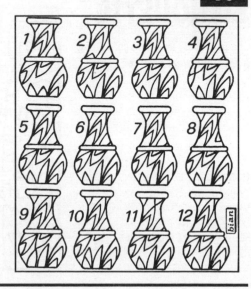

# TINKER, TAILOR ...

To discover who this person is unscramble the words in the verse, which hints at what the person does. Write these words into the boxes below, reading across, and, if you've placed them in the correct order, the arrowed column will spell out the occupation.

He KROWS with
SKOBO and
HAPPLSTEM, too,

STRIPENTER
GANNIMES so that
you

Can DARE and
TUNNEDRADS
what's DAIS

In SAGGELUNA EVILA
and dead.

OCCUPATION: _____

---

# SILHOUETTE

Shade in every fragment containing a dot - and what have you got?

## ACROSS

1 It tells how aircraft may fly (11)
7 River god of a cold region (5)
8 I'd pass him crashing towards the centre of the vessel (9)
10 Going off back to team leader in the circle (7)
11 Came the revolution, used this weapon? (7)
12 It is clear that the apprentice is in agony (5)
13 Arthur Negus initially left behind strange traces of forefathers (9)
16 The Marines and I would otherwise have a month in France (9)
18 Frenchman keen for a giant (5)
19 Feature about bridge partners not having arrived in it (7)
22 Knock sailor returning two Cockney items of headwear (3-1-3)
23 Was guilty, having been sent to prison (9)
24 Trouble navy on deck (5)
25 Unprotected with a team of attackers? (11)

## DOWN

1 Uncomfortable, unwell and relaxing (3,2,4)
2 Alien involved in forge (7)
3 Type of action taken by railway worker back on top (9)
4 A few on the island giving the truth (5)
5 Fashionable groups of workers perhaps (7)
6 Innocent one enters the body of the church (5)
7 Precipitate action of a pedestrian (11)
9 Explain how the barn is illuminated? (4,5,2)
14 Case for an explosive vehicle on the hill (9)
15 This rogue could become virtuous (9)
17 Mother's pet dog (7)
18 The name concocted for an inflammable gas (7)
20 Directed me to help out (5)
21 Giant bird on a pole (5)

# DILEMMA

Two straightforward crosswords – but their clues have been mixed up. You have to decide which clue belongs to which grid, but two words have been entered to give you a start.

## ACROSS

1 Root vegetable
5 Attack
9 Core
10 Untidy person
11 Natural gift
12 Bacon slice
15 Unconscious
17 Noise of disapproval
18 Upright
19 Pass away
20 Drink a small amount
22 High temperature
24 Hive dweller
26 Place of incarceration
27 Table attendant
28 Run after
30 Bird of the dove family
31 Bestowed, granted
32 Raised on one side
33 Buy back

1 Grasp
5 Old parish officer
9 Frequently
10 Troublesome creatures
11 Scowl
12 Walked unsteadily
15 Members of a boys' club
17 Nevertheless
18 Deciduous conifer
19 Devour
20 Become solid
22 Theme
24 Ancient
26 Drinking vessel
27 Benefactors
28 Scamp
30 Hair covering the forehead
31 Poem about the author's emotions
32 Turn
33 Ribbed

**DOWN**

| | | | |
|---|---|---|---|
| 1 | Secret | 1 | Pie topping |
| 2 | Tower | 2 | Disquiet |
| 3 | Chewy sweet | 3 | Cutting and shaping tool |
| 4 | Farm bird | 4 | Cancelled |
| 5 | Implore | 5 | Skill |
| 6 | Fabric stiffener | 6 | Join the army |
| 7 | Tree-lined road | 7 | Began to grow light |
| 8 | Continent | 8 | Most recent |
| 13 | Spooky | 13 | Carpenter's boring tool |
| 14 | Sag | 14 | Large black bird |
| 15 | Wood fastener | 15 | Biting |
| 16 | Northern sea duck | 16 | Piece of furniture |
| 20 | Ghost | 20 | Daze |
| 21 | Colourful bird | 21 | Christmas glitter |
| 22 | Search for food | 22 | Violent commotion |
| 23 | Compel | 23 | Gorge |
| 24 | Rebound | 24 | Alternatives |
| 25 | Talked in a boring way | 25 | Admire |
| 29 | Organ of sight | 29 | Cover |
| 30 | Household animal | 30 | Resinous tree |

Just like a jig-word – but instead of letters, numbers.

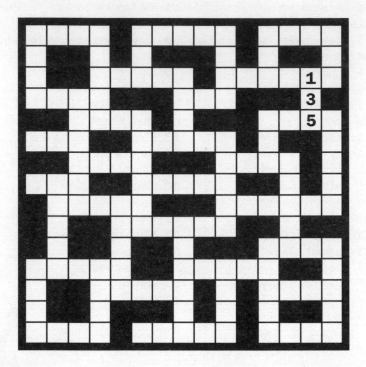

| 3-figures | 1701 | 5-figures | 81524 |
|---|---|---|---|
| (135) | 2198 | 11077 | 87174 |
| 214 | 2757 | 20617 | 90009 |
| 322 | 2881 | 29220 | 94685 |
| 402 | 3477 | 32220 | |
| 571 | 4567 | 34168 | **6-figures** |
| 782 | 5043 | 45678 | 187950 |
| 876 | 5871 | 45952 | 292424 |
| 986 | 6120 | 50613 | 403804 |
| | 7027 | 56789 | 551102 |
| **4-figures** | 7775 | 60408 | 626216 |
| 1211 | 8649 | 62127 | 701402 |
| 1234 | 9362 | 71142 | |
| 1357 | 9871 | 74748 | |

This puzzle has no clues in the conventional sense. Instead, every different number printed in the main grid represents a different letter (with the same number always representing the same letter, of course). For example, if 7 turns out to be a 'V', you can write in V wherever a square contains 7. We have completed a very small part of the puzzle to give you a start, but the rest is up to you.

| 8 | 10 | 24 | 9 | | 13 | 21 | 7 | 14 | 19 | 19 | 20 | 3 |
|---|---|---|---|---|---|---|---|---|---|---|---|---|
| 15 | | 10 | | 6 | | 15 | | 4 | | 3 | | 3 |
| 10 | 4 | 2 | 4 **N** | 9 **O** | 1 **W** | 4 | | 13 | 14 | 13 | 15 | 20 |
| 4 | | 3 | | 20 | | 24 | | 10 | | 3 | | 13 |
| 24 | 14 | 13 | 11 | 10 | 15 | 20 | 14 | 16 | 14 | 3 | 24 | |
| 14 | | | | 23 | | 3 | | 16 | | 21 | | 9 |
| 21 | 9 | 17 | 3 | 12 | 13 | | 22 | 3 | 23 | 18 | 25 | 7 |
| 3 | | 9 | | 10 | | 1 | | 7 | | | | 24 |
| | 14 | 4 | 12 | 9 | 5 | 14 | 21 | 15 | 12 | 14 | 0 | 4 |
| 14 | | 26 | | 10 | | 12 | | 19 | | 24 | | 15 |
| 19 | 15 | 7 | 2 | 13 | | 18 | 15 | 20 | 21 | 25 | 9 | 4 |
| 14 | | 3 | | 20 | | 14 | | 3 | | 20 | | 21 |
| 13 | 23 | 20 | 15 | 25 | 14 | 4 | 26 | | 26 | 20 | 10 | 3 |

A B C D E F G H I J K L M

N O P Q R S T U V W X Y Z

(The small grid is provided for ease of reference only)

| 1 | 2 | 3 | 4 | 5 | 6 | 7 | 8 | 9 | 10 | 11 | 12 | 13 |
|---|---|---|---|---|---|---|---|---|---|---|---|---|
| 14 | 15 | 16 | 17 | 18 | 19 | 20 | 21 | 22 | 23 | 24 | 25 | 26 |

# ADD-A-LETTER

Insert or add a letter to these four-letter words to make five-letter words which fit the rhyming clues. The six added letters should spell out a word.

| BEAT | | An animal – maybe fierce, strong and wild; |
|------|--|--------------------------------------------|
| BRED | | Uncovered, like your skin when the weather's mild; |
| FAKE | | Several, of corn, make your breakfast, perhaps; |
| SHUT | | A cheer, while the winner does his victory laps; |
| NOSE | | This is a rope that the hangman is using; |
| SAIL | | This one moves so slowly it could be snoozing! |

---

# VISIGRID

Can you see which one of the seven impressions was made by the roller?

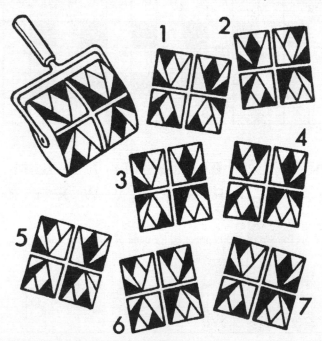

# CROSSWORD

**ACROSS**

1 Person unable to sleep (9)
9 Fatness (7)
10 Electrically charged atom (3)
11 Arrest (3,2)
12 Mothballed (2,3)
14 Sliding trough (5)
16 Stick (5)
18 Small dog's bark (3)
19 Hard drinker (3)
21 Person who settles up (5)
22 Egg-shaped (5)
23 Sound forming a syllable (5)
25 Constructed (5)
26 Part of the lower body (3)
27 Piece of journalism (7)
28 Person who inflicts great pain and suffering (9)

**DOWN**

1 Stupid behaviour or action (6)
2 Ridicule (4,2)
3 World of trade (11)
4 Dishonourably (7)
5 Study (3)
6 Have a good look around (11)
7 Calf-length skirt (4)
8 Printed characters (4)
13 Aquatic bird of the rail family (4)
15 Indication of saintliness (4)
17 Small dog of various breeds used to hunt in burrows (7)
19 Scent bag (6)
20 Mood (6)
23 Calf's meat (4)
24 Escorted by (4)
25 Risk money on the outcome of an event (3)

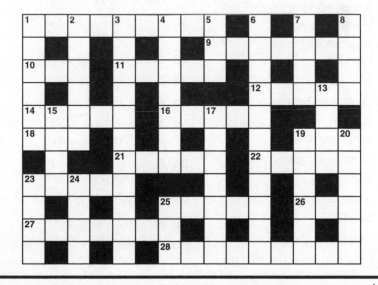

# TWO-TIMER

Two sets of clues to the same answers. Cryptic clues below and straight clues beneath the grid.

## ACROSS

1 Whimsical quin at play (6)

5 Variety of nectar to cause a hypnotic state (6)

9 Ghostly eastern lake (5)

10 Decreased at home (6)

11 Vandalised pig pen found in the forest (6)

12 Of interest to consumers? (6)

15 Invisible passage for translation has not been prepared (6)

17 Bird to sway to and fro endlessly (3)

18 We must make an effort to do this ourselves (5)

19 Be very eager to have a small cube (3)

20 Broadcast so it can be heard (3)

22 What we do for the rest of the night (5)

24 Retiring from the cast (3)

26 On time to help an actor (6)

27 Weaken the Italian appearing in another duet (6)

28 Stern guide (6)

30 Two names for the beast (6)

31 Overturned counter at African port (5)

32 Four-foot cycle (6)

33 Ploughed a mowed field (6)

## DOWN

1 Case of the shakes (6)

2 Extremely small bomb? (6)

3 Provoke with a sharp instrument (6)

4 I leave new diet for him (3)

5 Unite most of the rank (3)

6 Feel sorry for the salesman with ten others (6)

7 Secured from Daniel (6)

8 Part of a car is English in England (6)

13 He gives Spaniard an alternative (5)

14 Was a junior officer shortly to get praise? (5)

15 Awfully rude about the note that incited (5)

16 A number had a meal, it is reported (5)

20 Courage for a ghost (6)

21 Dull court room (6)

22 Round field of activity (6)

23 Talk wildly about one, one who robs in the main (6)

24 Extracted what had been absorbed (6)

25 Dye that's liable to run! (6)

29 Run into a sheep (3)

30 Crowded mass on first June morning (3)

## ACROSS

1 Fanciful (6)
5 Stupor (6)
9 Creepy (5)
10 Pressed (6)
11 Forest in NE London (6)
12 Eatable (6)
15 Not noticed (6)
17 Legendary bird (3)
18 Strive (5)
19 Perish (3)
20 Female pig (3)
22 Slumber (5)
24 Bashful (3)
26 Without delay (6)
27 Add water (6)
28 Steering device (6)
30 Dog-like animal (6)
31 Moroccan port (5)
32 Bicycle for two (6)
33 Grassland (6)

## DOWN

1 Tremble (6)
2 Molecular (6)
3 Stylus (6)
4 Spread grass for drying (3)
5 Dead-heat (3)
6 Regret (6)
7 Pinned down (6)
8 Motor (6)
13 Contributor (5)
14 Extol (5)
15 Exhorted (5)
16 Rowing crew (5)
20 Alcoholic drink (6)
21 Lacking animation (6)
22 Globe (6)
23 Sea-robber (6)
24 Drew into one's mouth (6)
25 Egg-yolk colour (6)
29 Tup (3)
30 Preserve (3)

There are eight differences between these two cartoons. Can you spot them?

# COG-ITATE

Can you work out which two weights will rise, and which two will fall when the man turns the lever as shown?

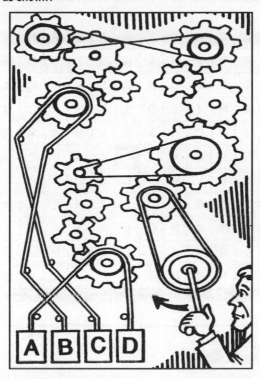

# TWO-BY-TWO

Each word in a clue can be preceded by the same two letters to spell out another word. For instance INTER, LATE and TENT can be preceded by PA to make PAINTER, PALATE and PATENT. Can you solve the three clues below, then spell out the three pairs of letters to make a six-letter word?

INK    RIFT    ROUGH

HEIST    ONE    TIRE

AIR    AMBER    URN

# PATHFINDER

Starting from the bold centre letter, move up or down or sideways (but NOT diagonally) using all the letters to find the path through fifteen rulers and leaders.

| A | C | R | P | T | N | E | D | E | R | P |
|---|---|---|---|---|---|---|---|---|---|---|
| P | R | E | U | S | N | G | I | S | C | H |
| T | O | M | O | R | G | E | N | E | R | A |
| A | N | I | V | O | I | E | R | R | O | N |
| I | R | C | E | R | O | V | E | A | M | R |
| N | E | O | R | E | **S** | A | H | L | C | O |
| C | V | Y | M | P | C | N | C | I | H | T |
| O | O | G | E | R | E | I | N | E | T | A |
| M | M | A | N | O | L | A | T | F | C | I |
| C | R | E | D | T | L | C | H | R | M | D |
| O | N | D | U | C | O | R | A | I | A | N |

# STAIRCASE

When these foodstuffs are correctly placed along the horizontal rows, the letters in the diagonal staircase will spell out another one.

BISCUIT    CHICKEN    CUSTARD    PANCAKE    RISSOLE    TAPIOCA    YOGHURT

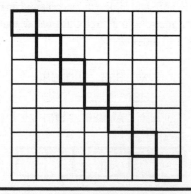

No clues – just pattern and answers – but can you fit them in?

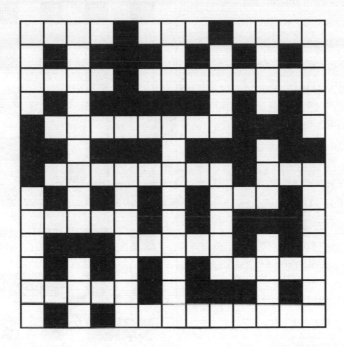

**3-letter words**
AFT
BYE
EAR
EBB
GOT
LET

**4-letter words**
COMA
COVE
FAWN
PATH

RUIN
VOTE
WREN

**5-letter words**
ARENA
EGRET
NIECE
OFFER
SHAPE
TRACE

**6-letter word**
FACTOR

**7-letter words**
MEASURE
ROOKERY

**8-letter words**
DORMOUSE
FORTIETH
NEGATIVE

**9-letter words**
EMERGENCY
EQUITABLE
METRONOME

# CROSSWORD

## ACROSS

1 Reduce in height (8)

6 Old armed soldier (9)

7 Great amount (3)

8 Secret political faction (5)

9 With no idea (8)

12 Nullify (4)

13 Male admirer (4)

16 Esteem for your own abilities (4-5)

18 Transport salesman (3,6)

19 Press (4)

20 Farmland unit (4)

23 Hypersensitive (8)

26 Moveable part of a helmet, that covers the face (5)

27 Garment often underwired (3)

28 Childminder (9)

29 Remote (8)

## DOWN

1 Appropriate (6)

2 Liable to change (9)

3 Squeezed together (8)

4 Quake (7)

5 Of the mouth (4)

10 Native of the warmer regions (10)

11 Inner division (10)

14 Sign up (5)

15 Sound of a bird (5)

17 Slow musical piece (5)

21 Recycled wood (9)

22 Domestic chimer (8)

24 Swell (7)

25 Striped (6)

26 Windmill blade (4)

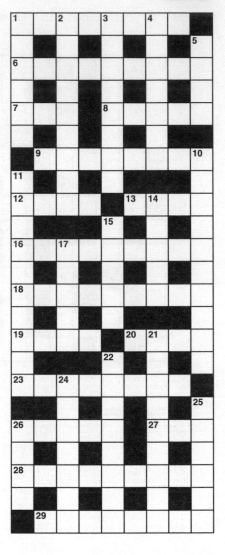

# CROSSWORD

## ACROSS

4 In the future (5)
9 Accomplish (7)
10 Throw out (of the premises) (5)
11 Affectionate name for grandma (3)
12 Ewe's mate (3)
13 Transient craze (3)
14 Reduce to ashes (7)
15 Large shop selling different kinds of goods (10,5)
19 Cough syrup (7)
20 Thick mat (3)
21 Plastic coat? (3)
22 View, look at (3)
23 Snap taken by a camera (5)
24 Reveal (secrets) (4,3)
25 Diaper (5)

## DOWN

1 Loathing (6)
2 Pretence (4)
3 Series of small holes (11)
4 Give the use of for a time (4)
5 Airtight receptacle for processed foods (3,3)
6 Thing you need to make a vehicle move backwards (7,4)
7 Title given by foreigners to the emperor of Japan (6)
8 Eye ailment (4)
16 Wing, in poetry (6)
17 Blunder (4,2)
18 Arouse (6)
19 Run with long strides (4)
20 Depend confidently (4)
21 Arguable (point) (4)

# LETTER SET

All the letters needed for the answers in each row and column are given – cross-referencing coupled with anagram skills will ensure the correct solution. To get started, locate the rarer letters first.

**ACROSS**

1 AEGHNPRT
2 AAEEORSS
3 AINNPTO
4 ADEGLNNS
5 EROTY
6 ABEHIRTV
7 AAEEPRT
8 EEEHLOST
9 AADESSSY

**DOWN**

1 AAEPSSTV
2 AEEIRRST
3 BEEENOST
4 ANORS
5 AEGGHOPRY
6 ELORT
7 AAAEISST
8 AEENNPTY
9 ADDEHHLN

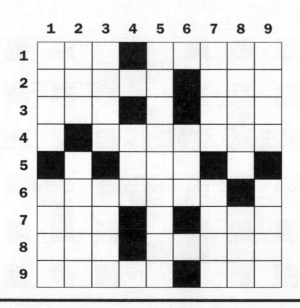

# ARROWORD

The arrows show the direction in which the answer to each clue should be placed.

| Cleopatra's killer | Uses a chair | | 20th Greek letter | | Play music for voluntary donations | | Permanent picture on the skin |
|---|---|---|---|---|---|---|---|
| | | | Salt Lake state — Drink cooler | | | | |
| Wife of Osiris in Egyptian myths | | | | | Jennifer Saunders' *Ab Fab* role | | Bypass, sidetrack |
| Admission vouchers | | | | | | | |
| | | | | First musical note | | | |
| Of Man or Dogs? | Available if needed (2,4) | | Type of industrial action (2-4) | Debt note (inits) | | | |
| | | | | 21st Greek letter | | Annoyed | |
| Dash, life | | Geometrical painting style (2,3) | | | | | |
| | | | | | Sir __ Hutton, cricketer | | East Anglian cathedral |
| Be quiet! | | Industrial northern French city | | | | | |
| | | | | Estuary fish | | | |
| (Put) in contact with (2,2) | | Character in *Peter Pan* | | | | | |

# GIANT CROSSWORD

## Across

1 Musical group (9)
6 Lessened the strength of (8)
10 Travel across snow (3)
11 Pester (5)
12 Sedimentations (8)
13 Malady (7)
15 Stripe of contrasting colour (4)
17 Cold ___, ignore (8)
19 Sense of concern or curiosity (8)
21 Circle (4)
23 Triumph (7)
24 Unlearned (8)
27 Analysed (8)
30 Shattered, boken into pieces (7)
33 Buzz (3)
34 Long period of time (3)
35 Insistence (8)
36 Render capable for a task (7)
37 Distinctly (7)
39 Bitter (4)
40 Reinstate (7)
44 Feel of a surface (7)
47 Jointed appendage (4)
48 Make an effort (7)
50 Precisely (7)
51 Chance upon (8)
52 Pitch (3)
53 Wrath (3)
54 Believe to be true (7)
58 Supply that can be drawn on (8)
60 Distribute loosely (8)
62 Imaginary water nymph (7)
63 Let have for a limited time (4)
65 Covering for a letter (8)
66 Frozen dessert (3-5)
68 Medicine (4)
70 Tugging along behind (7)
74 Entrance way alarm (8)
75 Unit of weight (5)
76 Possess (3)
77 Lately (8)
78 Immensity (9)

## Down

1 The tenth month of the year (7)
2 Series of linked objects (5)
3 Looked at (4)
4 Faucets (4)
5 The largest continent (4)
6 Broadest (6)
7 More or less (13)
8 Artist's tripod (5)
9 Damaged irreparably (9)
14 Extremely sharp or acute (7)
16 Fingers (6)
18 Kill by submerging in water (5)
20 Earth's nearest star (3)
22 Individual unit (4)
25 Embarrassed (7)
26 Mood (6)
28 Immediate (7)
29 At a previous point in time (7)
30 Pointed weapon (5)
31 Natives of Kuwait, eg (5)
32 Movement downward (7)
38 Alphabetic characters (7)
41 Building (7)
42 Leaves prepared for smoking (7)
43 Non-professional (7)
45 Set free (5)
46 North African country (5)
48 Promotion of some product (13)
49 Conservatives (6)
55 Strange (7)
56 Stripped of rind or skin (6)
57 Abel's brother (4)
58 Oddment (9)
59 Dish out (5)
61 Dress-making aid (3)
64 Grades, stages (7)
65 Utilise (6)
67 Arch (5)
69 Gamut (5)
71 Lengthy (4)
72 Not in action (4)
73 Caprine animal (4)

All the clues in capital letters are anagrams of the names of creatures – those clues not in capital letters lead to normal solutions.

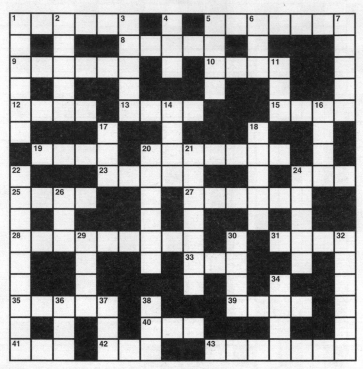

## Across

**1** ALRSUW (6)
**5** AELMPRY (7)
**8** AEHNY (5)
**9** Mollycoddle (6)
**10** HMOT (4)
**12** Slab of grass (4)
**13** APSW (4)
**15** AGOT (4)
**19** AEFL (4)
**20** ABCIORU (7)
**23** AALKO (5)
**24** Home for 40 Across (3)
**25** ENOX (4)
**27** CEGNTY (6)
**28** AADILLMOR (9)
**31** ABER (4)
**33** LOW (3)
**35** ADELN (5)
**39** AGNT (4)
**40** GIP (3)
**41** ART (3)
**42** EEW (3)
**43** ACELOPT (7)

## Down

**1** AIIPTW (6)
**2** ELMRU (5)
**3** EHRSW (5)
**4** Animal doctor (3)
**5** ABLM (4)
**6** Got together (3)
**7** Sailing vessel (5)
**11** GHO (3)
**14** AELS (4)
**16** Mother's sister (4)
**17** AKY (3)
**18** DHNOU (5)
**20** ACELTT (6)
**21** ACCNOOR (7)
**22** AABELOPRR (5,4)
**24** EERST (5)
**26** Forest tree (3)
**29** Prayer ending (4)
**30** GLSU (4)
**32** ABBIRT (6)
**34** AEHR (4)
**36** Appropriate (3)
**37** DEO (3)
**38** AEP (3)

# KEYWORD

This puzzle has no clues in the conventional sense. Instead, every different number printed in the main grid represents a different letter (with the same number always representing the same letter, of course). For example, if 7 turns out to be a 'V', you can write in V wherever a square contains 7. We have completed a very small part of the puzzle to give you a start, but the rest is up to you.

| 17 | 6 | 20 | 15 | | 9 | 17 | 2 | 14 | 20 | 18 | 1 | 19 |
|----|----|----|----|----|----|----|----|----|----|----|----|----|
| 18 | | 18 | | 11 | | 19 | | 13 | | 20 | | 5 |
| 12 | 19 | 4 | 5 | 18 | 21 | 19 | | 16 | 18 | 20 | 17 | 19 |
| 12 | | 5 | | 17 | | 17 | | 18 | | 19 | | 4 |
| 24 | 19 | 18 | 21 | 10 | 14 | 18 | 4 | 1 | 19 | 4 | 17 | |
| 6 | | | | 14 | | 22 | | 24 | | 7 | | 7 |
| 4 | 19 | 19 | 15 | 19 | 21 | | 26 | 9 | 22 | 25 | 19 | 4 |
| 19 | | 8 | | 4 R | | 23 | | 11 | | | | 18 |
| | 17 | 19 | 3 | 18 A | 7 | 19 | 13 | 18 | 4 | 6 | 18 | 13 |
| 2 | | 2 | | 21 D | | 12 | | 26 | | 11 | | 21 |
| 20 | 6 | 1 | 4 | 19 | | 24 | 19 | 20 | 6 | 12 | 18 | 21 |
| 19 | | 9 | | 4 | | 25 | | 19 | | 19 | | 18 |
| 16 | 9 | 4 | 19 | 17 | 1 | 4 | 25 | | 17 | 20 | 6 | 21 |

## A B C D E F G H I J K L M
## N O P Q R S T U V W X Y Z

(The small grid is provided for ease of reference only)

| 1 | 2 | 3 | 4 | 5 | 6 | 7 | 8 | 9 | 10 | 11 | 12 | 13 |
|----|----|----|----|----|----|----|----|----|----|----|----|----|
| 14 | 15 | 16 | 17 | 18 | 19 | 20 | 21 | 22 | 23 | 24 | 25 | 26 |

# WORK FORCE

Four of the eight photographs below this picture were taken at the scene. Can you see which four?

# PHOTO OPPORTUNITY

Which one of the nine photographs was taken by the photographer?

# ROUNDABOUT

Solutions to Radial clues (1 to 24) either start from the outer edge of the circle and read inwards, or start from the inner ring and read outwards to the edge (so they are all five-letter words). Solutions to Circular clues read in either a clockwise or an anticlockwise direction around the circle.

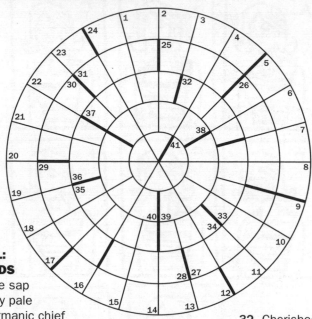

## RADIAL:
## INWARDS

1 Tree sap
2 Very pale
3 Germanic chief god
8 Spanish square
12 Javelin
15 Willow for baskets
18 Seashore
19 Sailor's cry
20 Right-hand page
24 Sewer

## OUTWARDS

4 Masticates
5 Intone
6 Goddess of the harvest
7 Stringed instrument
9 Sky blue
10 Viper

11 Larry ___, harmonica player
13 Uplift
14 Sum up (abbrev)
16 Come to a point
17 Savour
21 Water animal
22 Make a speech
23 Planet's path

## CIRCULAR:
## CLOCKWISE

9 Go astray
25 Boar's mate
26 Little ___, Dickens character
28 Special branch of the forces (initials)
31 Anger

32 Cherished
34 Hawaiian garland
36 Deed
37 Put to shame
40 Orient
41 Cardboard container

## ANTICLOCKWISE

4 Grassy expanse
8 Mail
16 Strong tying fibres
23 Row of houses
27 Lord of the realm
29 Cast a ballot
30 Golf peg
33 Two-way
35 Savoury jelly
38 Inheritor
39 Cutting tool

# MISSING LINKS

The answer to each clue is a word which has a link with each of the three words listed. This word may come at the end (eg Head linked with Beach, Big and Hammer), at the beginning (eg Black linked with Beauty, Board and Jack) or a mixture of the two (eg Stone linked with Hail, Lime and Wall).

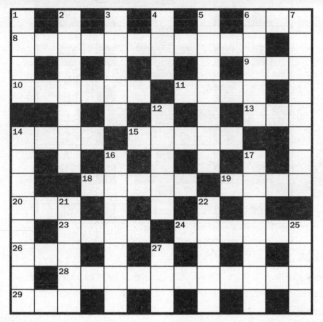

## ACROSS

6 Dial, Seeker, Trap (3)
8 Hostile, Natural, Working (11)
9 Bag, Time, Trade (3)
10 Action, Descendant, Route (6)
11 Circle, Conscious, Precious (4)
13 Belly, Luck, Plant (3)
14 Baby, Living, Russian (4)
15 Grand, Straw, Touch (5)
18 Field, Labour, Task (5)
19 Child, Nest, Puppy (4)
20 Art, Festival, Idol (3)
23 First, Fixed, Going (4)
24 Flag, Shop, Unit (6)
26 Lift, Lodge, Slope (3)
28 Lock, Oven, Winning (11)
29 Detector, Down, White (3)

## DOWN

1 Boy, Count, Hunter (4)
2 Control, Length, Responsibility (7)
3 Air, House, Wall (5)
4 Day, Liner, Off (3)
5 Director, Major, Strike (7)
6 Comic, Lighting, Search (5)
7 Attitude, Effect, Equity (8)
12 Football, Fork, Perfect (5)
14 Bomb, Instructions, Waste (8)
16 Drama, Jewellery, National (7)
17 Chamber, Privy, Town (7)
21 Asking, Cut, War (5)
22 Mail, Navy, Pardon (5)
25 Binder, Finger, Tone (4)
27 Drum, Essential, Lamp (3)

# DILEMMA

Two straightforward crosswords – but their clues have been mixed up. You have to decide which clue belongs to which pattern, but two words have been entered to give you a start.

## ACROSS

| | |
|---|---|
| **1** Hot drink | **1** Shrill cry of fear |
| **5** Barked sharply | **5** Entertained |
| **9** Bread-maker | **9** Tusk material |
| **10** Wine jug | **10** Brawl |
| **11** Task | **11** Weighing device |
| **12** Young angel | **12** Lumpy, rugged |
| **15** Front of a building | **15** Harmless |
| **17** That woman | **17** Knight's title |
| **18** Took things easy | **18** Sweetener |
| **19** Delve | **19** Resting place |
| **20** Constricting snake | **20** Rider Haggard novel |
| **22** Doze, slumber | **22** Artist's stand |
| **24** Drink daintily | **24** Explosive (inits) |
| **26** Person with a drug habit | **26** Be present (at) |
| **27** Rogue | **27** Permissiveness, licence |
| **28** Cutting implements | **28** Posted |
| **30** Popular fruit | **30** Unusual object |
| **31** Sorcery | **31** Church walkway |
| **32** Expanse of arid land | **32** Required |
| **33** Beat | **33** Cloth dealer |

## DOWN

1  Laundry stiffener
2  Roof timber
3  ___ Tower, Parisian landmark
4  Adam's partner
5  Word of agreement
6  Any immense number
7  Wan
8  Giving medicine to
13  Biblical king
14  River nymph
15  Ring-shaped roll
16  ___ Smith, TV cook
20  Gotham City superhero
21  Look up to
22  Make popular
23  Royal residence
24  Angry outburst
25  Member of a sporting side
29  Parent
30  Auction offer

1  Spiny plant
2  Agricultural worker
3  Counting device
4  Spring month
5  Metric land measure
6  Bowman
7  Ancient Egyptian sacred beetle
8  Evaded
13  Period of darkness
14  Constructed
15  High temperature
16  Huge man
20  Dismissed, fired
21  Moral philosophy
22  Plot, conspire
23  Run in tights
24  Be sparing
25  Dictator
29  Use a chair
30  Aged

# CROSSWORD

## ACROSS

1 Film based on the life of a famous person (6)
5 Infectious (of a tune) (6)
9 Single unit (3)
11 Space to stretch out (7)
12 Park wardens (7)
13 Having a non-gloss finish (4)
15 Put your foot down heavily (5)
16 Livery (4)
17 Agreeable (4)
19 Soft and fluffy, feathery (5)
20 Bathing beach or open-air swimming pool (4)
24 Dream-like (7)
25 Experienced performer (3,4)
26 World's second-largest bird (3)
27 Container that tips out its contents at the bottom (6)
28 Temporarily lose control and let fury take over (3,3)

## DOWN

2 Bullion bar (5)
3 High deck astern (4)
4 Financial supervisor (11)
5 Dignified, grand (11)
6 Very small (4)
7 Animal associated with laughing (5)
8 Tendency to fat (9)
10 Whitish (hair) (3,6)
14 End of the foot (3)
16 Solidify (3)
18 Rare object (5)
21 Very cross (5)
22 Pry (4)
23 Fringe (4)

# CROSSWORD

## ACROSS

1 Steak (1-4)
5 Blast of a horn (4)
6 Assessor (6)
7 Span (4)
8 Swelling on the toe (6)
9 Tablet you drop in the tub (4,4)
12 Flying craft (9)
15 Complain, pester (3)
16 TV studio sign (2,3)
17 Small seed (5)
18 Is able (3)
19 On each occasion (5,4)
21 Cannibal (3-5)
24 In a mess (6)
25 Cereal by-product (4)
26 Stick of coloured wax for drawing (6)
27 Single time (4)
28 Condition (5)

## DOWN

2 Great technical skill or brilliance (7)
3 Sustain (7)
4 Brief (7)
5 Unruffled (8)
9 Mental ability (10)
10 Instrument used to measure air pressure (4,5)
11 Compared with the last twelve months (4-2-4)
13 Descendants (7)
14 Revolutionary (9)
20 Abjure (8)
21 Nomad (7)
22 Entice (7)
23 Furthest, last (7)

# PIECEWORD

With the help of the Across clues only, can you fit the 35 pieces into their correct positions in the empty grid (which, when completed, will exhibit a symmetrical pattern)?

## ACROSS

1 South American country

2 Woodwind instrument; squeeze

3 Coffer; coil of yarn

4 Lawn scraper; hickory nut; immense

5 Animal den; Dutch cheese

6 Encounter; fragrance; lecherous look

7 Lukewarm

8 Edge along; golden treacle

9 Long hair curl

10 Savage; gangway

11 Act on stage

12 Insect grub; Indian corn

13 Emit rays

14 Verse; stiff

15 Muffler

16 Group of cattle; wigwam; unattached

17 Ninth Greek letter; lazy

18 German city; wash; highest male voice

19 Serpent; condition

20 Step; be aware of

21 Reject

---

Grid pieces:

Row 1 pieces:
- R E E / E _ V / L T O
- N _ V / E D A / A _ L
- B R U / B _ E / L A R

Row 2 pieces:
- _ M _ / R U P / U _ R
- I A / _ P R / K E I
- S L E / H _ T / I Z E

Row 3 pieces:
- T A T / _ S E / S S
- _ B O / T E _ / H E S
- T E / _ R I / F _ N

Row 4 pieces:
- E P E / _ S _ / L E A
- _ A _ / C R E / O _ Q
- R _ / E S S / N _ A

Row 5 pieces:
- E _ F / I D L / N _ A
- E P I / I _ L / N G L
- N _ N / G I D / _ C _

Row 6 pieces:
- E _ K / N S E / T _
- _ A I / R M _ / _ M A
- D _ R / _ S Y / E T

Row 7 pieces:
- D I A / U _ I / C A R
- A S T / M _ Y / E E R
- D _ T / O _ A / N _ C

Row 8 pieces:
- T E / _ P E / V A
- R _ / E P _ / _ R I
- E _ R / R H Y / _ O _

106 |

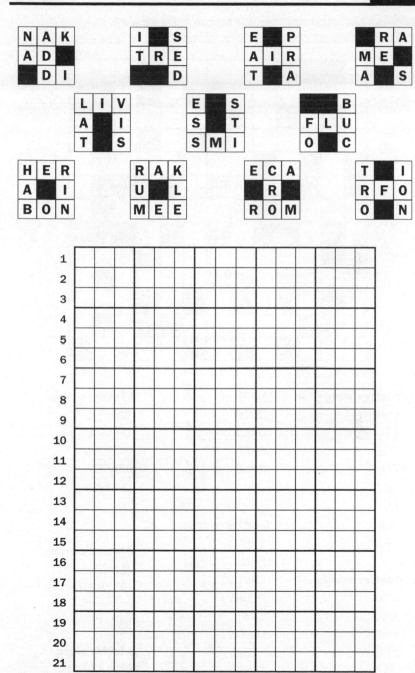

# JIG-WORD

No clues – just pattern and answers – but can you fit them in?

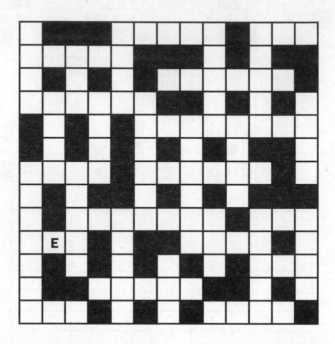

### 3-letter words
BAG
EEL
EGG
ELL
NIL
ROT
TEA
URN

### 4-letter words
ABLE
AFAR
ARCH
CREW
DASH
DAUB
DOOR
OMEN
RATE
ROSE

### 5-letter words
ARENA
BELIE
CABLE
DECRY
EASEL
LARGO
REGAL
TENSE

### 6-letter words
BALDER
DIATOM
REDDEN
TEASER
WARMLY

### 7-letter words
ADVERSE
BLENDER

### 8-letter word
ECTODERM

# SUM-UP

Using the totals given, can you calculate the price of each banana, orange, apple and pear?

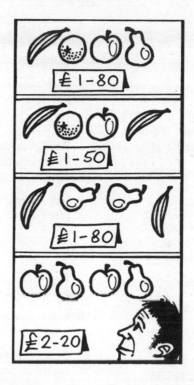

£1-80

£1-50

£1-80

£2-20

# 4-SQUARE

Solve these four clues and then rearrange the solutions into a sixteen-letter phrase, for which a clue is given. The two diagonals also make four-letter words.

PANS

A FEW

OTTER'S DEN

DONATED

Clue: Shift a footballer's target (4,3,9)

# CONTINUITY

No black squares – heavy bars mark the ends of words.

## ACROSS

1  1582 time change (9,8)

2  Take away; close; Egypt's river; kitchen stove

3  Eternal; ogre; supernatural being

4  Sell; parrot-fashion learning; reverence; deserter; stitch

5  Finished; peruse; dregs; duelling sword

6  Pebble; cure leather; tatter; attack

7  Fish eagle; hesitate; indicate

8  Accustom; ethical; citrus fruit

9  Introductory; fatal

10  Placid; dispatch; uncooked; recline lazily

11  Agent's fee; overshadow

12  Sloping script; upright; public speaker

13  Fork prong; ___ lights, aurora borealis; European nationality

14  Imperil; portent; wander off

15  Young deer; smear; two-wheeled vehicle; limb

16  Trade union; mother's ruin; young eel; deafening sound

17  Lower limb; build an annex; clarinet's mouthpiece; army canteen

## DOWN

1  Serious; detergent; malicious

2  London shopping road (6,6); senseless

3  Remove errors from; choose; task; hairpiece

4  Important principle (6,4); purify

5  Six deliveries in cricket; Chester's river; number in a nonet; tavern; carton

6  Holiday town; Middle-Eastern republic; forcefully convincing

7  Alternatively; gentleman's title; brink

8  Sea off Greece; charged particle; head of corn; coach

9  Water nymph; peculiar; hunting dog

10  Swimming stroke; burn slightly; twelfth month

11  Princess Royal; before; stringed instrument; boy's singing voice

12  Metric measure; fragrance; plot together

13  Sprite; serpent; move stealthily; hazarded

14  Tidier; rowing blade; fibber; division of school year

15  Raised platform; ache; spinning toy; rant

16  Concurring; too; Indian dresses

17  Sunbeam; marry; vote counter; songs of praise

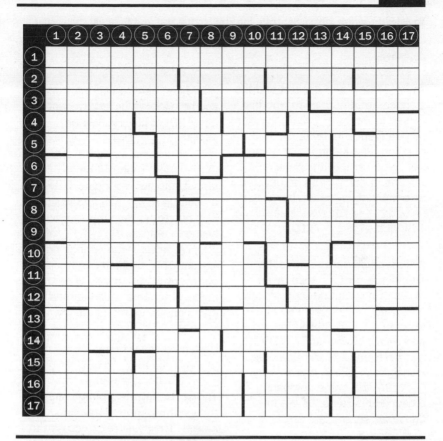

# RIDDLE ME REE

My first is in SHIVER and also in SHAKE,

My second's in ICING not in FLAKE,

My third's in both BLIZZARD and BLOW,

My fourth's in SLEET though not in SNOW,

My fifth's in GLACIER and also FREEZE,

My sixth is in CHILBLAINS but not in SNEEZE,

My seventh's in ARCTIC but not in WINTRY,

My whole is a very cold place indeed to be.

# STORY CROSSWORD

Transfer the words which complete the story to the grid and then put the circled letters in the right order to discover the name of the famous person therein described.

The ___ (12A) of a general and the grandson of a nobleman who had settled in Santo ___ (22A), he was born in France in 1802. He had little formal education but found work as a clerk to the duke of Orléans in Paris. Here he became an enthusiastic reader, particularly enjoying ___ (4D) stories set in the 16th and 17th ___ (11D).

While working for the duke, he attended a performance by an English Shakespearean company, an ___ (8A) which inspired him to try to ___ (2D) plays. His play *Henry III and His ___* (15A) was performed by the Comedie Francaise in 1829. A year ___ (19A) the same company produced his romantic drama, *Christine*.

He considered writing an ___ (6A) career and, over the ___ (13A) few years, he went on to write more plays including *The Tower of Nesle, Catherine ___* (1A) and *The Alchemist*. He wrote a huge number of novels, too, many of them ___ (1D). His best-known works are *The ___* (14A) *Musketeers* and *The Count of ___* (18D)-*Cristo*, which both appeared in 1844. They were translated into English in 1846. ___ (23A) of both of these books were ___ (9D).

His writing earned him a fortune, and he adopted an extravagant ___ (12D) of life. He was an intelligent ___ (18A) and he soon realised that he would be able to earn more money if he could produce books more quickly. He dreamt up a ___ (5D) that would help him to achieve this aim and began to employ a ___ (21D) of ___ (7A) writers who penned books for him. This enabled him to bring out about 1,200 novels under his name, a scheme which earned him enormous amounts of money.

He ran an estate near Paris where he lived like a ___ (16A). He ___ (20D) bought many works of art and set up a variety of businesses, though most made large financial losses. Their failure forced him to ___ (17A) a considerable amount of his earnings to cover business liabilities. In addition, he supported numerous ___ (24A), one of whom was the mother of his son who grew up to become a writer, too.

He ___ (3D) in 1870 at the age of sixty-eight, by which time his extravagance had brought him to the brink of bankruptcy. Some of his books are still in print today and he is considered ___ (10A) of France's finest writers of the Romantic Period.

# BOXWISE

Put these three-letter groups into the twelve numbered boxes to produce twelve six-letter words, each of which starts in one box and finishes in another as indicated by an arrow. For instance, 2 and 5 make a six-letter word, but not 5 and 9. One group has been filled in to start you off.

ATE  DER  EST  GOS

HON  MIT  PEL  PER

PRO  SEN  SIP  TEN

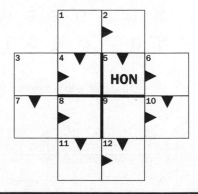

# KEYWORD

This puzzle has no clues in the conventional sense. Instead, every different number printed in the main grid represents a different letter (with the same number always representing the same letter, of course). For example, if 7 turns out to be a 'V', you can write in V wherever a square contains 7. We have completed a very small part of the puzzle to give you a start, but the rest is up to you.

| 21 | 25 | 9 | 10 | 2 | 17 | | 7 | 13 | 2 | 10 | 11 | 15 |
|----|----|----|----|----|----|----|----|----|----|----|----|----|
| 25 | | 10 | | 22 | 12 | 8 | 21 | 10 | | 19 | | 6 |
| 9 | 10 | 22 | 18 | 12 | 20 | | 2 | 18 | 12 | 11 | 6 | 9 |
| 6 | | 6 | | 25 | 18 | 20 | 12 | 9 | | 18 | | 7 |
| 3 | 18 | 9 | 25 | | 11 | 18 | 19 | | 20 | 12 | 26 | 18 |
| 10 | 16 | 17 | 6 | 11 | | 7 | | 22 P | 10 | 9 | 12 | 11 |
| | 12 | | 17 | 12 | 23 | | 1 | 18 A | 22 | | 19 | |
| 7 | 6 | 22 | 10 | 20 | | 4 | | 17 T | 6 | 25 | 18 | 11 |
| 18 | 7 | 12 | 20 | | 2 | 18 | 19 | | 17 | 6 | 9 | 10 |
| 20 | | 10 | | 17 | 24 | 9 | 6 | 5 | | 26 | | 25 |
| 19 | 6 | 9 | 25 | 10 | 18 | | 3 | 6 | 16 | 12 | 25 | 23 |
| 18 | | 19 | | 2 | 14 | 12 | 9 | 11 | | 19 | | 17 |
| 22 | 11 | 10 | 25 | 17 | 13 | | 18 | 15 | 9 | 10 | 2 | 24 |

## A B C D E F G H I J K L M
## N O P Q R S T U V W X Y Z

(The small grid is provided for ease of reference only)

| 1 | 2 | 3 | 4 | 5 | 6 | 7 | 8 | 9 | 10 | 11 | 12 | 13 |
|----|----|----|----|----|----|----|----|----|----|----|----|----|
| 14 | 15 | 16 | 17 | 18 | 19 | 20 | 21 | 22 | 23 | 24 | 25 | 26 |

# CROSSWORD

## ACROSS

1 State of neglect (9)
9 Learned institution (7)
10 Betting suggestion (3)
11 Massive person (5)
12 Long hilltop (5)
14 Breed of dog favoured by the Queen (5)
16 Exuberant enjoyment, zest (5)
18 Centre of a wheel (3)
19 Provide weapons to (3)
21 Hot and damp, as of weather (5)
22 Eskimo snow-hut (5)
23 Downright (5)
25 Passed on to another tenant (5)
26 Idiot (3)
27 Stand-off (7)
28 Edict (9)

## DOWN

1 Sever (6)
2 Wonderful (6)
3 UK flower? (7,4)
4 Mixture of diverse elements (7)
5 Brown rodent (3)
6 Relating to a diet thought to promote well-being and longevity (11)
7 Ward (off) (4)
8 Rubber wheel-covering (4)
13 Banking system (4)
15 Depose (4)
17 Maker of seats for horse riders (7)
19 Non-acidic substance (6)
20 Hair application (6)
23 Military division (4)
24 Summits (4)
25 Communist colour (3)

# TINKER, TAILOR ...

To discover who these people are unscramble the words in the verse, which hints at what they do or have done. Write these words into the boxes below, reading across, and, if you've placed them in the correct order, the arrowed column will spell out the occupation.

OCCUPATION:

_____

EACHLIM DRAWHO and MAILWIL WITHWALE,

VADDI BETTLUNK and KCAJ WARTS

Have DEHL this EFFICO for their NOCTURY,

Making law and DERRO a RIPROTYI.

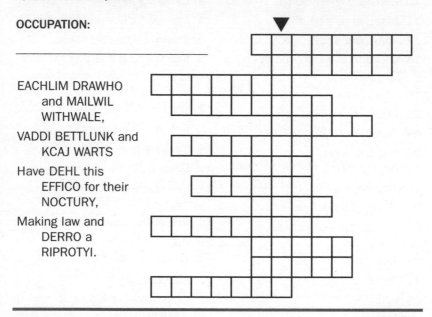

# SILHOUETTE

Shade in every fragment containing a dot - and what have you got?

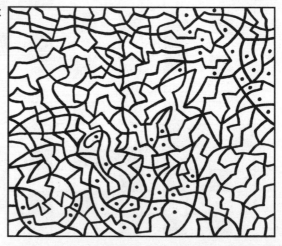

# WORDSEARCH

The 39 different kinds of aircraft have all been hidden in the diagram. They have been printed across (backwards or forwards), or up or down, or diagonally, but always in a straight line without letters being skipped. You can use the letters in the diagram more than once. You will probably find it helpful to mark the words in the diagram and cross them off the list as you find them.

```
V I S C O U N T H P E N C M X V
R R C D A K O T A L V O T J I G
M E V O D K O U G E N T R K L G
O T D Q N M H A G C L G I A R V
H N N N R S E A O T R N D O B C
A U M E A N T R R A G I E T C B
W H G B E M D E U R A L N I A R
K I W D L E A G L T I L T U N I
T W L R L E A L O L R E H Q B T
Y O A G E J N R A O A W R S E A
G D S H V K E H T S B T A O R N
S K Y H A W K C E O I M I M R N
F S A B R E E O Z I D O U O A I
A R A V A V S P F X M A J J N A
T E M O C T L O B R E D N U H T
K I T T Y H A W K K E G A R I M
M E R L I N I H S U Y L I U O Q
L E K N I E H N O C L A F L R T
```

| | | | |
|---|---|---|---|
| ARAVA | FALCON | KITTY HAWK | THUNDERBOLT |
| BLENHEIM | FOKKER | MERLIN | TIGER MOTH |
| BRITANNIA | GLADIATOR | MIG | TORNADO |
| CANBERRA | GOLDEN EAGLE | MIRAGE | TRIDENT |
| CARAVELLE | HARRIER | MOHAWK | VECTOR |
| COMET | HEINKEL | MOSQUITO | VEGA |
| CONCORDE | HUNTER | SABRE | VIKING |
| CONSTELLATION | ILYUSHIN | SALAMANDER | VISCOUNT |
| DAKOTA | JAGUAR | SEAHAWK | WELLINGTON |
| DOVE | JUMBO | SKYHAWK | |

Just like a Jig-word – but instead of letters, numbers.

| 3-figures | | 6-figures | 7-figures |
|---|---|---|---|
| 209 | 5460 | 146640 | 2336540 |
| 253 | 6325 | 298017 | 3231183 |
| 392 | 6632 | 299163 | 3410601 |
| 418 | 7340 | 305621 | 4316299 |
| 423 | 8033 | 376418 | 5401012 |
| 873 | 9057 | 419382 | 8432199 |
| 911 | | 431701 | 9530373 |
| | | 571206 | |
| | **5-figures** | 650279 | |
| **4-figures** | 13623 | 763041 | |
| 1132 | 20223 | 842077 | |
| 2575 | 35221 | 925717 | |
| 2650 | 69676 | 972926 | |
| 3308 | 93284 | | |

# BRACER

The first part of each clue gives a six-letter answer, five of whose letters make up the five-letter answers to the second part and four of which make up the four-letter answer to the third part. The unused letter from the first answer is entered into column A, and that from the second answer into column B. The two columns when completed, spell out the names of two ballet dancers.

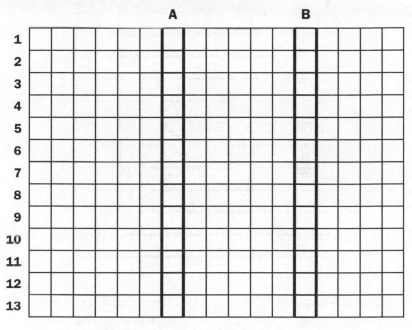

1 Young girl; excavated; eat supper

2 Indication; profits; serenade

3 Esteem; reverie; honey drink

4 Strong-smelling bulb; Holy ___, cherished goal; deceiver

5 Far East; cosmetic lotion; torn

6 Do again; Princess Anne's son; member of the nobility

7 Solemn, official; plant-life; by mouth

8 Waterproof jacket; holy book; grade

9 Hire charge; tilted; overdue

10 Cavalier; end of day; nearby

11 Hi-fi; guide; remainder

12 Carry; rabbit-skin; ice-cream holder

13 Sailor; minister's home; sewn edge

# SPIRAL

Every answer (except the first) uses the last letter of the preceding answer as its initial letter, the chain thus formed following a spiral path to the centre of the grid. The diagonals spell two drinks.

**START**

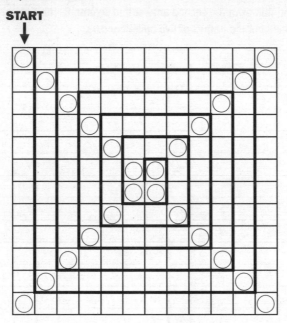

Disney character (6,5)

Soil (5)

The Netherlands (7)

Small rodent (8)

Female ruler (7)

Robert Burns' country (8)

Tooth doctor (7)

Venomous spider (9)

Huge ocean (8)

Whitehall monument (8)

Tirade, lecture (8)

"___ my dear Watson" – Sherlock Holmes saying (10)

Cowardly colour (6)

Charles, Prince of ___ (5)

Long thin dagger (8)

Fruit garden (7)

Spanish chaperone (6)

Operatic song (4)

Come into view (6)

Niche (6)

Spanish wine punch (7)

___ and Crafts, movement (4)

Quick gulp of drink (4)

Clothing (4)

Sheep's noise (3)

Swiss mountain (3)

# CROSSWORD

## ACROSS

1 Detonate (2,3)

5 See the sights (4)

6 Summertime star sign (6)

7 Altercations (4)

8 Complete in natural development (6)

9 Hair at the front of the head (8)

12 Sedimentary rock (9)

15 Body part containing a lobe (3)

16 Olympic stadium (5)

17 Landowner (5)

18 Whitish timber (3)

19 Decorative roof slab (5,4)

21 Pass judgement on (8)

24 Unfledged (6)

25 Tiny skirt (4)

26 Share (6)

27 Horrible (4)

28 Unmoving (5)

## DOWN

2 Culinary herb (7)

3 Breakdown (7)

4 Rampart (7)

5 Exhausted (5,3)

9 Hoax call (5,5)

10 Tied the knot again (9)

11 Multi-talented sportsman (10)

13 Bind (in cloth) (7)

14 Piece of surgery (9)

20 Extermination of a race (8)

21 Petition (7)

22 Animate (7)

23 Fish stew (7)

# JIG-WORD

No clues – just pattern and answers – but can you fit them in?

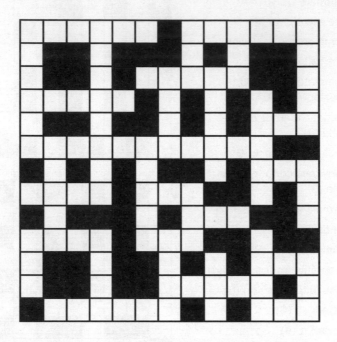

| 3-letter words | 4-letter words | SLOPE |
|---|---|---|
| AIM | BATH | TENSE |
| ASS | ECHO | TROUT |
| BAN | ISLE | |
| DAB | MEET | **6-letter words** |
| GAS | NODE | FURORE |
| HIT | TOUR | INSTEP |
| INN | | INSURE |
| MAN | | WITHIN |
| MET | **5-letter words** | |
| OLD | AISLE | **8-letter word** |
| PAY | DEALT | UNDULATE |
| TAG | FORTH | |
| THE | NAKED | **11-letter word** |
| WON | RADII | PARATROOPER |

# DROP-OUT

In the top picture, the antique dealer is selecting a vase. In the bottom picture he has made his choice. Which vase did he choose?

# PATHFINDER

Starting from the bold centre letter, move up or down or sideways (but NOT diagonally) using all the letters to find the path through the names of twenty-two native British wildlife creatures.

| T | A | E | R | R | E | T | L | E | I | F |
|---|---|---|---|---|---|---|---|---|---|---|
| S | G | F | R | R | A | W | D | M | O | Y |
| G | O | T | A | E | T | R | H | S | U | N |
| E | H | E | S | W | W | E | S | E | P | O |
| G | M | L | A | E | Q | U | I | R | R | E |
| D | O | R | E | T | **S** | A | R | R | D | G |
| E | L | B | O | T | O | T | L | E | A | B |
| H | E | R | A | A | T | R | M | A | R | E |
| B | A | R | T | B | D | O | O | H | O | T |
| B | F | O | A | C | D | S | U | T | A | S |
| I | T | X | W | I | L | E | T | O | A | D |

# DOT-TO-DOT

Join the dots in numerical order to reveal the hidden picture.

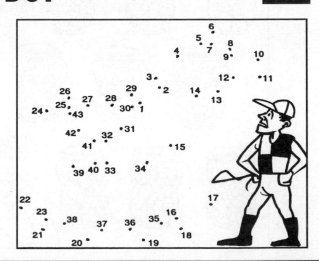

# PURPLE PASSAGE

In a Purple Passage, the grid of letters consists of an entertaining short story, reading across the rows from left to right and from top to bottom. However, some letters have been missed out. Not only that, but there are no spaces between words and no punctuation. Can you fill in the missing letters and work out where the word-breaks are to reveal the story?

| A | □ | A | T | W | A | S | L | □ | I | N | G | I | N | A | □ | A | T | C |
|---|---|---|---|---|---|---|---|---|---|---|---|---|---|---|---|---|---|---|
| □ | O | F | □ | U | N | L | I | G | H | □ | A | N | □ | G | E | T | T | I | N |
| □ | V | E | □ | Y | H | □ | T | □ | H | Y | D | O | N | T | □ | O | U |
| □ | O | V | E | O | U | T | O | □ | T | H | E | □ | U | N | □ | F | Y | O |
| □ | R | E | T | O | □ | H | O | □ | A | S | K | E | D | H | I | □ | F |
| □ | I | E | N | D | W | □ | Y | S | H | □ | U | L | D | I | R | E | □ | L | I | E | D |
| □ | H | E | C | A | □ | I | □ | A | S | □ | E | R | E | F | □ | R | S | T |

# SO COMPLETE

ARTHUR, MICKEY, LESLEY, FREDA, BERT, GREG, MEG, MILDRED, BUNTY, and TIM were remembering their favourite nursery-rhyme characters. Use the letters of their names once each to reveal the names.

```
TH_    G__ND   O__    D_K_   OF   _O__

HU_P__    DU_P__

O__   K___   _OL_

L__T__   _IS   M__F__

OL_   _OT_E_   HU____D

G_O__I_   PO____
```

# TWO-TIMER

Two sets of clues to the same answers. Cryptic clues below and straight clues beneath the grid.

## ACROSS

6 Paddy, before morning, about ten, his natural disposition (11)

8 Bend weapon (3)

9 Monthly return of tropical food (3)

10 Admires intricate weapon (7)

12 Perfume despatched as announced (5)

13 Make light of getting to the point (5)

14 Tiny Scotch (3)

16 Handy way to demonstrate a pet affection (6)

17 Inspiration from Bertha (6)

18 Move up and down, to and fro (3)

20 Higher cut? (5)

22 What kangaroo has gently expressing pain (5)

23 Strike section of fortification (7)

24 Reptile amongst the cobras perhaps (3)

26 Turned up with band-leader at inn (3)

27 Stuffy preservationist? (11)

## DOWN

1 Tree second person mentioned (3)

2 It's separate, this decision (5)

3 Architectural feature to leave you cold, it is reported (6)

4 Clever sergeant-major had skill (5)

5 Unspecified number stuck in the canyon (3)

6 Come into contact with one working in the pool? (5-6)

7 One on the lookout for gifts (6,5)

10 One might need a rest during this game (7)

11 Companion very much supporting seaman (7)

14 Flycatcher on the internet (3)

15 Some pebbles might be exposed by it (3)

19 Bird that circles over its victim (6)

21 Fanatical bard I disconcerted (5)

22 Get ready to fire first (5)

25 Apt sort of tap! (3)

26 Greek character Penny is in reflective mood (3)

## ACROSS

6 Moodiness (11)
8 Front of a ship (3)
9 US sweet potato (3)
10 Handgun (7)
12 Odour (5)
13 Waxed spill (5)
14 Very small (3)
16 Sweep of an oar (6)
17 Inhalation (6)
18 Short haircut (3)
20 Superior (5)
22 Pocket (5)
23 Defensive mound (7)
24 Venomous snake (3)
26 Tavern (3)
27 One who stuffs animals (11)

## DOWN

1 Churchyard plant (3)
2 Diverge (5)
3 Decorative band (6)
4 Quick-witted (5)
5 Whichever (3)
6 Office worker (5-6)
7 Entertainments recruiter (6,5)
10 Indoor game (7)
11 Sailor (7)
14 Tangle (3)
15 Recede (3)
19 Fish-eating hawk (6)
21 Zealous (5)
22 Chief (5)
25 Gentle 16 Across (3)
26 23rd Greek letter (3)

# KEYWORD

This puzzle has no clues in the conventional sense. Instead, every different number printed in the main grid represents a different letter (with the same number always representing the same letter, of course). For example, if 7 turns out to be a 'V', you can write in V wherever a square contains 7. We have completed a very small part of the puzzle to give you a start, but the rest is up to you.

| 25 | 15 | 1 | 3 | 7 | 22 | 5 | | 17 | 12 | 1 | 8 | 8 |
|----|----|----|----|----|----|----|----|----|----|----|----|----|
| 2 | | 21 | | 22 | | 9 | | 12 | | 3 | | 12 |
| 4 | 21 | 8 | 20 | 8 | | 8 **S** | 12 | 21 | 4 | 20 | 15 | 6 |
| 19 | | 1 | | 1 | | 12 **H** | | 20 | | 9 | | |
| 21 | 18 | 8 | 2 | 4 | 18 | 1 **E** | 11 | | 8 | 22 | 21 | 20 |
| 13 | | | | 13 | | 11 | | 23 | | 5 | | 15 |
| 7 | 19 | 21 | 5 | 1 | 8 | | 18 | 9 | 4 | 1 | 21 | 9 |
| 26 | | 11 | | 11 | | 8 | | 26 | | | | 22 |
| 1 | 22 | 26 | 6 | | 8 | 16 | 9 | 1 | 1 | 14 | 1 | 11 |
| | | 21 | | 23 | | 9 | | 22 | | 2 | | 1 |
| 18 | 21 | 22 | 11 | 21 | 22 | 21 | | 7 | 22 | 22 | 1 | 4 |
| 7 | | 17 | | 17 | | 10 | | 15 | | 1 | | 1 |
| 18 | 15 | 1 | 21 | 24 | | 24 | 22 | 1 | 21 | 11 | 1 | 11 |

## A B C D E F G H I J K L M
## N O P Q R S T U V W X Y Z

**(The small grid is provided for ease of reference only)**

| 1 | 2 | 3 | 4 | 5 | 6 | 7 | 8 | 9 | 10 | 11 | 12 | 13 |
|----|----|----|----|----|----|----|----|----|----|----|----|----|
| 14 | 15 | 16 | 17 | 18 | 19 | 20 | 21 | 22 | 23 | 24 | 25 | 26 |

# ARROWORD

The arrows show the direction in which the answer to each clue should be placed.

| Major city on the Caspian Sea ▼ | | Weak Long Island politician ▼ | | Loosened ▼ | | Big rooms ▼ | |
|---|---|---|---|---|---|---|---|
| | | | | | | | |
| Spanish ranch ▶ | | Form a surface for walking on ▼ | | 1970 hit for the Kinks ▼ | | Fringes ▼ | |
| Came up with | __ Gay, famous US bomber ▼ | | Likelihood ▶ | | | | |
| Wrong live broadcast ▶ | | | | Flurry | | | Magical or mystical Hindu text ▼ |
| | | | Aid illegally ▶ | | ▼ | | ▼ |
| Capricorn __, 1978 film ▶ | | Darts players' line ▼ | Crikey, it's hot! ▼ | Uncle Sam's initials? (inits) ▶ | | | |
| Runs with easy strides ▶ | | | | | | __ Lingus, Irish plane company ▼ | |
| | | | | Shabby articles ▶ | | | |
| 18th-century German composer ▶ | Former Austrian coin ▶ | | | | | | |
| Person of Hebrew origin | | | | Generation ▶ | | | |

# CRYPTIC CROSSWORD

## ACROSS

1 Spectacular holiday wear? (4,7)
7 Wicked deliveryman? (5,6)
8 Endlessly tense ballet-step (3)
10 Service address (6)
12 Responded when Swede ran amok (8)
13 Speak falsely with fellow in confidence (6)
14 A weapon in catalogue for scaremonger (8)
17 Penny, this cheap storybook, how terrible (8)
18 From mixed maintop, remove name having most favourable points (6)
19 Replaced at recent interval (8)
21 In spring, Dan skied in Poland (6)
23 Fashion of the century (3)
24 Unsympathetic and tough in the middle? (4-7)
26 Ubiquitous honour in returning gift (11)

## DOWN

1 Mother, almost noble lady (3)
2 Hurry to get things planted and become exhausted (3,2,4)
3 Shine but scowl unhesitantly (4)
4 Everything together that's fashionable taken in by a pair of learners twice (3,2,3)
5 Animal shut up about beginning of winter (5)
6 Foreman's oversight? (11)
7 Being insubordinate, ordered inside to bed (11)
9 Distracted, having been removed from mainline (11)
11 Becoming slower when dealing with notes (11)
15 Reject idea put re reconstruction (9)
16 Flatter now fat's increased (6,2)
20 Anglo-Saxon layer of wood (5)
22 Last home for woman with many children (4)
25 Bird entitled to appear within (3)

# SKELETON CROSSWORD

Have double the fun with this puzzle: you've got to fill in the answers and the black squares! We've given you the bare bones to start and it will help you to know that the black squares in the finished grid form a symmetrical pattern, so that every black square has at least one other corresponding black square.

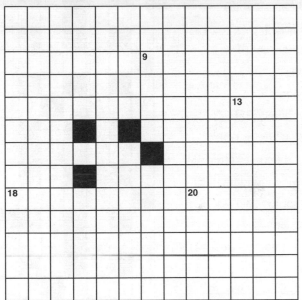

## ACROSS

1 Murmur
5 Mendacious
8 Short poem evoking rustic life
9 Self-mortification
10 Obesity
12 Up to the time of
14 Sagging
16 Frill
18 Low-ranking office worker
19 Wide pasta strips
22 Skewered
24 Top
26 Old silver coin
27 Day of rest

## DOWN

1 Unpleasant smell
2 Frosty
3 Regular beat
4 Lie back
5 Slow, relaxed
6 Coaching house
7 Species of goose
11 Treasure ___, valuable find
13 Object, item
14 Adorning, dressing
15 Small flat crumpet
17 Dashing fellows!
20 Firework
21 Drive (a fox) to its underground lair
23 Non-amateur
25 Small round vegetable

# CROSSWORD

## ACROSS

**5** Sporty (8)

**7** Tell porkies! (3)

**8** Award for valour (5)

**9** Caper (8)

**11** Important test (4)

**12** Con (4)

**14** Soap bars (5)

**15** Park yourself (3)

**16** Female inheritor (7)

**20** Go ___, become rotten (3)

**21** Underlying foundation (5)

**23** Claptrap, twaddle (4)

**24** Drifting ice (4)

**26** Active support (of a cause) (8)

**28** Vex (5)

**29** Once round a track (3)

**30** Candidate (8)

## DOWN

**1** Topples (5)

**2** Style of knot (10)

**3** Edible flesh from cattle and sheep (3,4)

**4** Incorrect identification of a disease (12)

**6** Lessen (9)

**10** Thaw out (2-3)

**13** Impute (7)

**17** Display of great gratitude or approval (12)

**18** ___ work, deep-level dental procedure (4-5)

**19** Burnt remains (5)

**22** Part of a cruet set (4,6)

**25** Synthetic fibre (7)

**27** Sudden outbreak (5)

# BACKWARDS

For this puzzle, we've filled in the answers, but there are letters in the grid, where the black squares should be. You need to black out the unwanted letters to make a symmetrical grid to match the clues, which are listed in random order.

| C | H | I | R | O | P | O | D | I | S | T |
|---|---|---|---|---|---|---|---|---|---|---|
| O | E | N | A | D | A | R | U | T | T | E |
| N | R | S | N | I | G | G | E | R | E | L |
| T | O | O | W | N | E | E | G | O | W | E |
| E | L | F | E | N | T | M | U | M | A | P |
| N | O | T | E | R | O | E | S | A | S | H |
| T | I | E | L | F | E | W | A | N | T | O |
| M | R | S | E | A | S | H | I | C | A | N |
| E | H | T | A | D | P | O | L | E | V | I |
| N | O | R | M | O | U | S | A | M | O | S |
| T | E | M | P | E | R | A | M | E | N | T |

**ACROSS**

— Young frog
— Be in debt (to)
— Musical symbol
— Maiden name indicator
— Foot health expert
— Pixie
— Remains of a fire
— Pale
— Half-suppressed laugh
— Woman's title
— Female relation
— As well
— Disposition
— Is able to
— Low marshy land
— Sliding window

**DOWN**

— Fashion, trend
— Beat
— Happiness
— Jewel
— World power
— Boy servant
— Unit of electrical current
— Novel about love
— Country hotel
— Moved swiftly
— Switchboard operator
— Urge on
— Most yielding
— Expected
— Which person
— Snake-like fish

# JOLLY MIXTURES

In this puzzle, each clue is simply an anagram of the answer – but watch out! There might be more than one possible solution to each clue. For instance, the clue 'TALE' might lead to the answer 'LATE' or 'TEAL'. You'll have to look at how the answers fit into the grid to find out which alternative is correct.

**ACROSS**

1 PIERCE
4 RIVING
9 ART
10 SCION
11 ITS
12 EARN
14 GORE
16 ARE
18 ZONED
19 REGAL
21 ODE
24 BEAD
25 NEAT
28 PIT
30 NAMED
31 DOH
32 SUNDER
33 CRONES

**DOWN**

1 NEUTER
2 ARC
3 SHOP
5 CHIN
6 SAG
7 TENTED
8 RUNIC
13 OATEN
15 ANGLE
16 DEN
17 LEA
20 RATTAN
22 ENDOW
23 REEFED
26 CAME
27 LIED
29 RAP
31 ASH

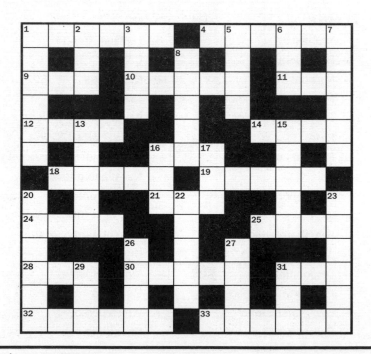

# DOUBLE CROSS

When the letters of the answers from the upper grid are transferred to the lower grid, they give a quotation. Reading down column 'A' will give the name of its author.

|   | A | B | C | D | E | F | G | H | J | K |
|---|---|---|---|---|---|---|---|---|---|---|
| **1** Perimeter fence |  |  |  |  |  |  |  |  | ■ |  |
| **2** Following; warmth |  |  |  |  |  | ■ |  |  |  |  |
| **3** Sabre; reckless |  |  |  |  |  |  |  |  |  |  |
| **4** Make up; auction item |  |  |  |  |  |  | ■ |  |  |  |
| **5** Slack; pledge |  |  |  |  |  | ■ |  |  |  |  |
| **6** Paradise; foot digit |  |  |  |  |  |  | ■ |  |  |  |
| **7** Beneath; tender |  |  |  |  |  | ■ |  |  |  |  |
| **8** Unite; display |  |  |  |  |  | ■ |  |  |  |  |
| **9** Proof |  |  |  |  |  |  |  |  | ■ |  |

| 3B | 8B |    | 1D | 5E | 6K | 3E |    | 2J | 9F | 5B | 6H | 8H | 4D | 7E |
|----|----|----|----|----|----|----|----|----|----|----|----|----|----|----|
|    |    |    |    |    |    |    |    |    |    |    |    |    |    | ,  |
| 1B | 2E |    | 8J | 7K | 5K | 9E | 1G | 3J |    | 2C | 5C |    |    |    |
|    |    |    |    |    | ,  |    |    |    |    |    |    |    |    |    |
| 7G | 5H | 4F | 9C | 3A | 2B | 1H |    | 2K | 6A | 9H |    |    |    |    |
|    |    |    |    |    |    |    |    |    |    |    |    |    |    |    |
| 9G | 3D | 2A | 6D | 4A | 7B | 8D | 5D |    | 3C | 7J |    | 6J | 7A | 8C |
|    |    |    |    |    |    |    |    |    |    |    |    |    |    |    |
| 3K | 1C | 8A | 6C | 4B |    | 2G | 9A | 1F | 3G | 4K | 8G |    | 8K | 2D |
|    |    |    |    |    |    |    |    |    |    |    | .  |    |    |    |
| 6F | 7D | 2H | 9D |    | 5J | 7H |    | 4H | 5G | 4C | 8E |    |    |    |
|    |    |    |    |    |    |    |    |    |    |    |    |    |    |    |
| 3H | 4E | 1E |    | 1A | 6B |    | 5A | 4J | 9B | 6E | 7C |    |    |    |
|    |    |    |    |    |    |    |    |    |    |    | .  |    |    |    |

# ROUND TOUR

A fantastic puzzle in which each square counts at least twice – some count three or four times! The answer-words form two continuous chains, each of them starting at the top left-hand corner and following the directions of the arrows to and fro along alternate rows, and down and up along alternate columns. Moreover, the last letter of one word is the first letter of the next one. For example, the three consecutive words GINGER, RED and DAVID would appear in the completed puzzle as GINGEREDAVID, so be careful – it's not an easy puzzle!

## TO AND FRO

- Original letter (7)
- Jemmy left Eve right (5)
- Reel around British revolutionary (5)
- Cover learner and one deputy head (3)
- Maiden changed me, lads! (6)
- Spikes shoestrings (5)
- Give voice to South African youth leader (3)
- Thread account (4)
- Love east Egyptian flower (4)
- Mires muddy Arabian rulers (5)
- See round in French river (5)
- One new vast age (3)
- Mesh after tax (3)
- Underground small pipes (5)
- Alarms temptresses (6)
- Small elf ego (4)
- Little lie about thread (5)
- A teen messily consumed (5)
- Northern primate scruff of neck (4)
- Reg oddly gets new yen for vitality (6)
- Closely unite obscure returned toy (3)
- Lukewarm new soft diet (5)
- Doctor, for example wine sediment (4)
- Silence joke (3)
- Leg back to take shape (3)
- Jumps over strange lapse (5)
- Dispatched perfume, we hear (4)
- Drink the health of brown bread (5)
- Stepped in retro device (4)
- Overshadow midget (5)
- Feathery leafed plant right in fen (4)
- On after no midday (4)
- No British toff (3)
- Scottish feature where there was a vicar, we hear (4)
- Big Australian bird you hear behind 'em (3)
- New World article after us (1,1,1)
- Al gets left every one (3)
- Hawaiian garland that is left around (3)
- Saint follows in present month (4)
- Pasta, possibly Spanish snacks (5)
- Sport new leather razor sharpener (5)
- Tack in softly before (3)
- No point at the moment (3)
- We are endlessly dressed in (4)
- Corruption to right coming back (3)

## DOWN AND UP

- Beg Eric to stir frozen mass (7)
- Chat about American petrol (3)
- Season old sailor (4)
- Russian author from lost toy (7)
- Affirmative you old son! (3)
- Girl is a sun's creation (5)
- Love duck (3)

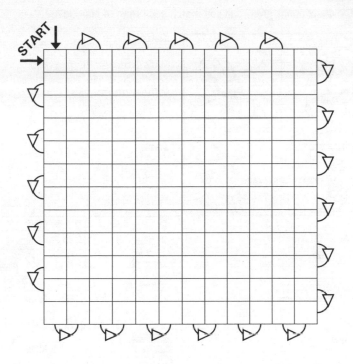

- The French can for language (5)
- No time for negation (3)
- Rue after time constant (4)
- Pause before a time period (3)
- Point gun at first class male (3)
- US city changed re my note (8)
- Yes it disturbed legendary Himalayan beasts (5)
- Sean becomes rational (4)
- Points around gym sword (4)
- Need new paradise garden (4)
- Topical material sewn round (4)
- Cuts old sayings (4)
- Snap new bridge arch (4)
- Norma got left as usual (6)
- Roads in Milan especially (5)
- Cut off bargain (4)
- Separate component (4)
- A hundred not returned (3)
- Seize new head sailor (3)
- Small nail British Rail advert (4)
- Comedian Jack or river (3)
- Dine out Miss Blyton (4)
- Bad end with evil Satan (5)
- Cheerful song till adapted! (4)
- Time referee is not kosher (4)
- Penny of backward dandy (3)
- Just beat hard seed (3)
- New plane console (5)
- Odd elf on a sheet of paper (4)
- One who touches antenna (6)
- About a thousand sun radiation units (4)
- Blockade inside Aussie gear (5)
- Sore about Greek god (4)
- Classify type (4)
- Chinese guild gripping device endlessly (4)
- Grab assorted clothes (4)
- Bung British rib east (5)

# WHO'S WHO?

**143**

Using the descriptions given, can you match each man to his wife?

MY WIFE JUNE HAS DARK HAIR — JOHN

MY WIFE IS JOAN — JACK

MY WIFE KAY WEARS EARRINGS — IAN

RICHARD

**John**

Wife No: _____

Wife's name: _____

**Jack**

Wife No: _____

Wife's name: _____

**Ian**

Wife No: _____

Wife's name: _____

**Richard**

Wife No: _____

Wife's name: _____

MY HUSBAND HAS A BEARD — 2

1

3

I'M MIA — 4

# 4-SQUARE

**144**

Solve these four clues and then rearrange the solutions into a sixteen-letter phrase, for which a clue is given. The two diagonals also make four-letter words.

HEAVY WOOD

PIQUANT FLAVOUR

WATER TUBE

SEVEN DAYS

Clue: Lose strength in joints? (2,4,2,3,5)

# POT LUCK

Two of these pictures are exactly the same, while each of the other two differs in one small detail from the rest. Which are the 'twins' and what are the differences?

# TAKE FIVE

The three answers in this mini-crossword read the same across and down. We've given you clues to the three words, but NOT in the right order. See how quickly you can solve it.

**1** Distribute in portions

**2** Praise highly

**3** Talk foolishly

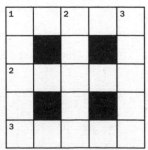

This puzzle has no clues in the conventional sense. Instead, every different number printed in the main grid represents a different letter (with the same number always representing the same letter, of course). For example, if 7 turns out to be a 'V', you can write in V wherever a square contains 7. We have completed a very small part of the puzzle to give you a start, but the rest is up to you.

| 18 | 17 | 5 | 13 | 15 | 12 | 20 | | 8 | 14 | 21 | 12 | 3 |
|----|----|----|----|----|----|----|----|----|----|----|----|----|
| 11 | | 26 | | 17 | | 12 | | 12 | | 14 | | 22 |
| 6 | 3 | 14 | 8 | 9 | | 5 | 26 | 14 | 15 | 17 | 5 | 12 |
| 15 | | 17 | | 2 | | 14 | | 13 | | 3 | | |
| 17 | 9 | 9 | 11 | 12 | 9 | 20 | 19 | | 25 | 12 | 14 | 7 |
| 25 | | | | 3 | | 12 | | 5 | | 25 | | 14 |
| 26 | 22 | 6 | 3 | 17 | 20 | | 24 | 19 | 3 | 4 | 12 | 23 |
| 12 | | 3 | | 12 | | 5 | | 9 | | | | 17 |
| 3 | 19 | 11 | 4 | | 7 | 14 | 3 | 16 | 19 | 3 R | 14 A | 7 M |
| | | 25 | | 16 | | 7 | | 11 | | 14 | | 17 |
| 12 | 25 | 1 | 11 | 17 | 3 | 12 | | 2 | 14 | 10 | 12 | 25 |
| 8 | | 11 | | 15 | | 3 | | 14 | | 19 | | 12 |
| 12 | 24 | 12 | 9 | 4 | | 14 | 15 | 15 | 11 | 3 | 12 | 20 |

## A B C D E F G H I J K L M
## N O P Q R S T U V W X Y Z

(The small grid is provided for ease of reference only)

| 1 | 2 | 3 | 4 | 5 | 6 | 7 | 8 | 9 | 10 | 11 | 12 | 13 |
|----|----|----|----|----|----|----|----|----|----|----|----|----|
| 14 | 15 | 16 | 17 | 18 | 19 | 20 | 21 | 22 | 23 | 24 | 25 | 26 |

# CROSSWORD

## ACROSS

1 False head of hair (3)
8 Maze-like (12)
9 Drink taken with milk or lemon (3)
11 Selected randomly (5)
12 Absorb (7)
14 Challenge to do something risky (4)
15 Cigarette container (6)
18 Metalworker (6)
20 Corrosive liquid substance (4)
23 Release your grip (5,2)
25 Make one (5)
27 Number of seats on a tandem (3)
28 Soft (drink) (3-9)
29 Make ___ while the sun shines, proverb (3)

## DOWN

1 Aquatic ball game played by swimmers (5,4)
2 Happy (4)
3 Wear away by friction (6)
4 Crush (5)
5 Facial expression of scorn or contempt (5)
6 Ruffian, hoodlum (4)
7 Countless (6)
10 Space science (9)
13 In mint condition (3)
16 Colouring pencil (6)
17 Label showing a product's price (3)
19 Fit to be eaten (6)
21 ___ potato, person who watches a lot of television (5)
22 Territory of a nobleman (5)
24 GCSE, eg (4)
26 Engrave (4)

# MISSING LINKS

The answer to each clue is a word which has a link with each of the three words listed. This word may come at the end (eg Head linked with Beach, Big and Hammer), at the beginning (eg Black linked with Beauty, Board and Jack) or a mixture of the two (eg Stone linked with Hail, Lime and Wall).

## ACROSS

3 Bare, Needle, Worm (6)
6 Career, Rope, Step (6)
7 Branch, Constable, Offer (7)
8 In, Lounge, Van (7)
9 Band, Chair, Pit (3)
12 Form, Gallery, Nouveau (3)
13 Addict, Dealer, Store (4)
14 Birth, Blind, Dinner (4)
16 Noon, School, Sky (4)
18 Board, Gazer, Shooting (4)
19 Bath, Guard, Skipper (3)
20 Cauliflower, Mark, Ring (3)
22 Intervals, Triangle, Verb (7)
23 Fish, Sea, Wood (7)
25 Scout, Ship, Union (6)
26 Lamp, Level, Measure (6)

## DOWN

1 Point, Take, Unfair (9)
2 Cabinet, Manner, Table (7)
3 Hat, Notch, Secret (3)
4 Breaker, Company, Hit (6)
5 Far, Game, Run (4)
7 Bone, Molecular, Social (9)
10 Breakfast, Orange, Tree (9)
11 Bird, Poppy, Vessel (4)
12 Head, Heart, Tooth (4)
15 Finger, Happy, Off (7)
17 Home, Sledge, Yellow (6)
21 Cold, Dragon, Shot (4)
24 Cracker, Hazel, Roast (3)

# TWIN TIME

Can you see which two of these cockerels are exactly the same?

# WIRED UP

Can you work out which plug should be inserted in the socket to operate the kettle?

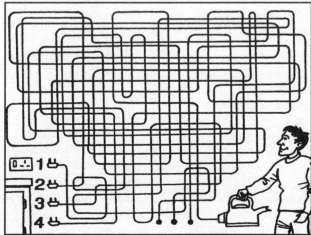

# SKELETON CROSSWORD

Have double the fun with this puzzle: you've got to fill in the answers and the black squares! We've given you the bare bones to start and it will help you to know that the black squares in the finished grid form a symmetrical pattern, so that every black square has at least one other corresponding black square.

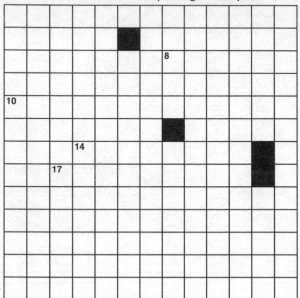

**ACROSS**

1 Originally a long open vehicle
5 Afternoon meal
7 Move around an axis
8 Troops' assigned quarters
9 ___ volatile, smelling salts
10 Euro-Asian mountain range
12 W Indian song, often improvised
13 Larva of a louse adhering to human hair
14 Old Russian autocracy
18 Add (up)
20 Just arrived (baby)
23 Main heart artery
24 Jailbird
25 Obstruct
26 Famous Florence art gallery
27 Wander about
28 One who delivers to homes

**DOWN**

1 Avoiding
2 Robert ___, director of M*A*S*H
3 Performers
4 Slight fever
5 Spring flowers
6 Official go-ahead
8 Bleat of a sheep
9 Terrifying
11 Ignited
15 Managed (by)
16 Make a noise like a cow
17 Took without permission
19 Axiom
21 1997 George Michael hit
22 John ___, 19th-century Arctic explorer

# FOURSOME

This man would like to buy four identical ornaments. Which design will he choose?

# SILHOUETTE

Shade in every fragment containing a dot – and what have you got?

# DATELINE

A number jig with a difference: with clues to figure out (with the help of a calculator if you wish!) to discover the date in the shaded line – in this case, a notable day in sporting history.

## ACROSS

1 Add 3 Across to 5 Across

3 Subtract 1,745 from 12 Down

5 Divide 10 Down by 12,000

7 Square root of 6,724

8 Subtract 33 Across from 9 Across

9 Digits of 3 Across reversed

11 Add 130 to 1 Across

13 Spots on eight dice

14 Multiply 26 Down by eight

16 Subtract 136,017 from 20 Down

21 Add 84,196 to one-third of 16 Across

22 Add 3,520 to the square of 5 Across

25 Add 311 to 8 Across

27 Multiply 7 Across by four

28 Sum of all whole numbers from one to fifteen

30 24 baker's dozens

31 Add four to years in a diamond wedding

32 Add 500 to 29 Down

33 Roman CIII

34 Digits of 5 Across reversed

## DOWN

1 Multiply 33 Across by 27

2 Multiply 26 Down by the square root of 34 Across

4 Feet in 74 yards

5 Multiply 3 Across by nine

6 Pounds in 343 stones

9 Square of 1 Down

10 Seconds in twenty days

12 Digits of 1 Down reversed

15 Subtract bingo's 'legs' from 1 Down

17 25 per cent of 10,100

18 Add 1 Across to 5 Across, then subtract three

19 Subtract 8 Across from 26 Down

20 Multiply 2 Down by four

23 Multiply 29 Down by twenty, then subtract 1,561

24 Add 1 Down to one-tenth of 29 Down

26 Add 6 Down to 23 Down

29 Subtract 27 Across from 8 Across

# SYMBOLIC

Can you work out which symbol should logically appear in the empty box, and which way up it should be?

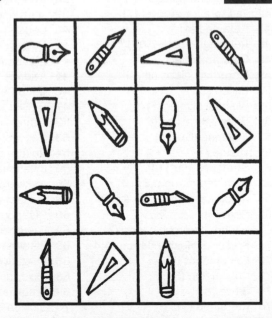

# GIANT CROSSWORD

## Across

1 Change in appearance (9)
5 Scenery at rear of stage (8)
9 Head of corn (3)
10 Colourless gas (5)
11 Funeral director (8)
12 Shoulder blade (7)
14 Game played on a course (4)
16 Collector of discarded material (8)
18 Worker who belongs to a trades group (8)
20 Pelt or hide (4)
22 Outlet of river to sea (7)
23 Poppycock! (8)
26 Archaeological relic (6)
29 Lost (7)
32 Hen's produce (3)
33 Tutoring (8)
34 Law officer (7)
35 Enchant (7)
37 Vow (4)
38 Nine-sided polygon (7)
42 Fall to a lower level (7)
45 Retained (4)
46 Relating to pottery (7)
48 Conforming (7)
49 Extremely pleasing (8)
50 Epoch (3)
51 Wishful thinker (7)
55 Brownish-yellow (6)
57 Angering (8)
59 Tussle (7)
61 Stretches (out) (4)
63 Commemoration (8)
64 Relocate (8)
66 Seat (4)
67 Written communication (7)
71 Preset explosive device (4,4)
72 Full amount (5)
73 Conclusion (3)
74 Sieve (8)
75 Refrained (9)

## Down

1 Narrow depressions (7)
2 Looks (4)
3 Vegetable (lady's fingers) (4)
4 Bill of fare (4)
5 Bosom (6)
6 Rectangular road stones (7)
7 Ms Smith, of culinary fame (5)
8 Depiction (9)
13 Dry red Italian table wine (7)
15 Smokestack of a ship (6)
17 Drinking vessel (5)
19 Call for help (1,1,1)
21 Bird of New Zealand (4)
24 Badly behaved (7)
25 Devon city (6)
26 Delicate, fragile (5)
27 Educational establishments (7)
28 Set alight (7)
29 Stonecutter (5)
30 Rear of ship (5)
31 Resistance against attack (7)
36 Run away (7)
39 Herb used in cooking (7)
40 Cause to be amazed (7)
41 Ruler (7)
43 Mode of expression (5)
44 Avid (5)
46 Circus entertainer (5)
47 Deliverance (6)
52 Lifting (7)
53 Heavenly beings (6)
54 Relieve (4)
55 Inflammation of the stomach (9)
56 Awkward, stupid people (5)
58 Maiden name indicator (3)
60 Disappointment (7)
62 Fastened with a metal pin (7)
63 Person in a group (6)
65 Purgative (5)
68 Mixer drink (4)
69 Unfortunately (4)
70 Sicilian volcano (4)

# KEYWORD

This puzzle has no clues in the conventional sense. Instead, every different number printed in the main grid represents a different letter (with the same number always representing the same letter, of course). For example, if 7 turns out to be a 'V', you can write in V wherever a square contains 7. We have completed a very small part of the puzzle to give you a start, but the rest is up to you.

| 10 | 1 | 16 | 5 | 8 | 15 | | 26 | | 5 | 24 | 19 | 4 |
|----|----|----|----|----|----|----|----|----|----|----|----|----|
| 16 | | 20 | | 7 | 4 | 21 | 6 | 10 | 15 | | 4 | |
| 12 | 24 | 4 | 20 | 5 | 25 | | 22 | | 4 | 10 | 14 | 10 |
| 24 | | | 4 | | 11 | | 3 | 16 | 18 | 5 | | 4 |
| 16 | 22 | 7 | 14 | 16 | | 16 | | 18 | | 20 | | 1 |
| 22 | | 20 | | 9 | 24 | 13 | 5 | 4 | 14 | 7 | 10 | 16 |
| | | 6 | | 16 | | 14 | | 8 | | 1 | | |
| 16 | 21 | 21 | 6 | 8 | 6 | 16 | 18 | 5 | | 16 | | 25 |
| 3 | | 6 | | 5 | | 22 | | 10 | 16 | 3 | 2 | 16 |
| 2 | | 8 | 4 | 10 | 5 | | 19 | | 4 | | | 4 |
| 16 | 23 | 16 | 18 | | 20 | | 4 | 16 | 20 | 6 I | 4 | 22 |
| | 7 | | 5 | 20 | 24 | 10 | 5 | 11 | | 8 C | | 7 |
| 5 | 17 | 16 | 16 | | 16 | | 10 | 16 | 22 | 16 E | 8 | 5 |

A B C D E F G H I J K L M

N O P Q R S T U V W X Y Z

(The small grid is provided for ease of reference only)

| 1 | 2 | 3 | 4 | 5 | 6 | 7 | 8 | 9 | 10 | 11 | 12 | 13 |
|---|---|---|---|---|---|---|---|---|----|----|----|----|
| 14 | 15 | 16 | 17 | 18 | 19 | 20 | 21 | 22 | 23 | 24 | 25 | 26 |

# CROSSWORD

## ACROSS

1 Female aristocrat (8)

6 17th-century soldier with a firearm (9)

7 Collection of items for auction (3)

8 Foolishly sentimental (5)

9 Wind instrument (8)

12 Naked and unclothed (4)

13 Reflection of sound waves (4)

16 Alternative therapist (9)

18 Course plotter (9)

19 Plan (4)

20 Units of electrical resistance (4)

23 Having a rough texture (8)

26 Refill (3-2)

27 Voice disapproval (3)

28 Expanse of brushwood (9)

29 Give rise to (8)

## DOWN

1 Pleasing (6)

2 Restless (9)

3 Store of valuable things (8)

4 Make higher (7)

5 Hunter's victim (4)

10 Bristled stick for mouth care (10)

11 Inconsiderate (10)

14 Shoreline (5)

15 Large branch (5)

17 Cinema film (5)

21 Bed's endpiece (9)

22 Guilty (8)

24 Common painkiller (7)

25 Owner (6)

26 Elephant's long tooth (4)

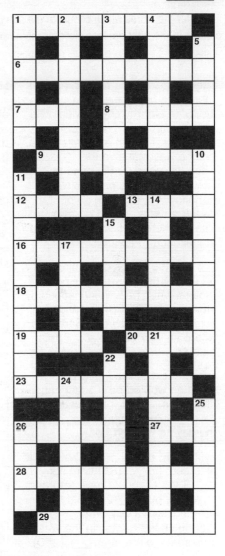

# STORY CROSSWORD

Transfer the words which complete the story to the grid and then put the circled letters in the right order to discover the name of the famous person therein described.

The ___ (12A) of a farmer, he is thought to have been born in about 1635, in Llanrhymny in Wales. He grew up in the ___ (22A) of the English civil war in a Royalist area, and he was still a young ___ (20A) when he made up his mind to join the army. His parents would not allow ___ (23D) to go but but he left anyway, ___ (31A) away to Bristol where he hoped to catch a stagecoach to London.

___ (6A) his hopes of winning glory on the battlefield were dashed though, when he was kidnapped by slave ___ (17D) in Bristol and taken across the ___ (15A) to Barbados, where he was sold to a ___ (5D) master.

For the next seven ___ (7D) years he worked on a sugar cane plantation, a brutal existence that gave him plenty of time to ___ (28A) the day he had left home.

Eventually, at the ___ (9A) of about nineteen, he ___ (8A) from his ___ (33A). He could have returned to Wales, but ___ (26A) old life seemed such a long time ___ (29D) that he chose to stay in the West Indies and join a pirate ___ (25D).

By 1666, he was in command of his own ship and became a feared but ___ (18D) figure. Held in great ___ (14D) by women and highly respected by his own ___ (10A), he was the scourge of the Spanish, attacking their ships and towns in ___ (4D) of savage piracy.

He would never attack British vessels though and ___ (32A) always willing to ___ (27D) to the assistance of the British navy when their ships came under attack from the Spanish. After driving the Spanish away from the British fleet near Cuba, he was made ___ (6D) of the Jamaican navy.

Shortly afterwards, Britain and Spain signed a peace treaty and Charles II ordered him to stop attacking the Spanish. He ___ (11D) already made plans to attack ___ (13A) though – a country reputed to contain fabulous wealth.

Ignoring the king's command, he ___ (3D) off for South America, determined to ___ (21D) his goal to ___ (16A) more gold to his treasure store.

He sacked Panama, but on his return to Jamaica he was arrested for piracy and taken to prison in ___ (2D) to face a possible ___ (18A) sentence. In his cell, he wrote numerous letters to Charles II entreating him to consider his ___ (24A).

For two ___ (1A) he had no reply, then the Spanish launched an attack on the British fleet and the war between Britain and Spain broke out again.

He was ___ (30A) out of prison and knighted for his loyalty. Charles II awarded him a ___ (19D) job, making him governor of Jamaica.

He died in 1688.

# KNOT SO

Can you work out how many of the tangles will form a knot when their ends are pulled?

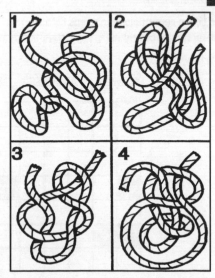

# MIRROR, MIRROR

Four of these super-heroes have mirror images. Can you see which are the four pairs and which is the odd-one-out?

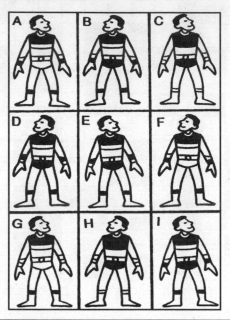

# STAIRCASE

When the seven communication words listed here in a mixed-up order are correctly placed along the horizontal rows, the letters in the diagonal 'staircase' will spell out an eighth word.

RADIO   MISSIVE   CHANNEL   ADDRESS   MEMO   POSTAGE   AERIAL

# WHAT'S MISSING?

Each picture is missing a detail that is present in the other seven. Can you spot all eight missing details?

# TWO-TIMER

Two sets of clues to the same answers. Cryptic clues below and straight clues beneath the grid.

## ACROSS

**1** Absolutely delighted in space (4,3,4)

**9** Run off to fasten the door (4)

**10** Not an upright desire? (11)

**11** Departed, but not right (4)

**14** Lie about bran (5)

**17** Means to move house (5)

**18** Pole composed motet (5)

**19** Five, giving shout of pain, testify (5)

**20** She might tend to make others feel better (5)

**21** Each number had been taken in (5)

**22** It turns back and forth (5)

**25** Some advertisements featuring drink (4)

**29** Sticky fruit? (6-5)

**30** Upsetting Leon at Christmas time (4)

**31** It's topping for the hunter (11)

## DOWN

**2** Violet takes nearly new vegetation (4)

**3** Usual thing for a government to do (4)

**4** Some North Indian language (5)

**5** Tom takes up alternative form of transport (5)

**6** Money some took to Bologna (4)

**7** Person of little importance had ninety-ton monstrosity (9)

**8** Formal account from New Testament (9)

**12** Ten madmen corrected alteration (9)

**13** Asked to enter date wrongly (9)

**14** Alternatively leaving forever having infectious disease (5)

**15** Frank is not keen (5)

**16** Theatrical number (5)

**23** Make a tender suggestion? (5)

**24** Open using ball on the green (5)

**26** One is not at work to receive this pay (4)

**27** Old friend's gem (4)

**28** True colour? (4)

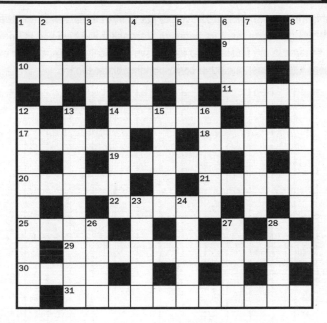

## ACROSS

1 Elated (4,3,4)
9 Dash, escape (4)
10 Tendency (11)
11 Abandoned (4)
14 Thread (5)
17 Minister's home (5)
18 Carved pole (5)
19 Bear witness (5)
20 Medical assistant (5)
21 Consumed (5)
22 Revolving aerofoil (5)
25 Wine made with honey (4)
29 Caramel-coated fruit on a stick (6-5)
30 Yuletide (4)
31 Peaked hat (11)

## DOWN

2 Grape plant (4)
3 Reign (4)
4 Indo-European language (5)
5 Car (5)
6 Ancient Greek coin (4)
7 Insignificant person (9)
8 Declaration (9)
12 Improvement (9)
13 Beseeched (9)
14 Extreme state of excitement (5)
15 Plain-spoken (5)
16 Upper air (5)
23 Bid (5)
24 Public (5)
26 Unemployment pay (4)
27 Milky stone (4)
28 Sad (4)

# SKELETON CROSSWORD

Have double the fun with this puzzle: you've got to fill in the answers and the black squares! We've given you the bare bones to start and it will help you to know that the black squares in the finished grid form a symmetrical pattern, so that every black square has at least one other corresponding black square.

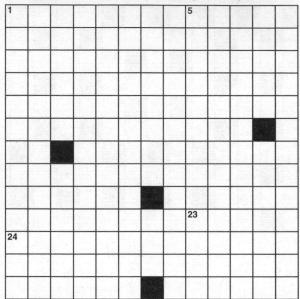

## ACROSS

1 *Little* ___, film directed by Bernardo Bertolucci
4 Looked into
8 James ___, fifth US president
10 Exceed
11 Court card
12 Song in an opera
14 Social insects
15 Marring
17 Called to mind
20 German industrial valley
21 Part of a ladder
22 Tilted
24 Concrete floor-finishing
25 Ground (the teeth)
26 One who enjoys inflicting cruelty
27 2002 film starring Ralph Fiennes as a disturbed man

## DOWN

1 Former name of an Indian port
2 ___ Minogue, Aussie pop star
3 Small town east of Basingstoke
5 Rake
6 Revealing
7 ___ Van Outen, TV presenter
9 Caught up
10 Employing excessively
13 *My Cherie* ___, Stevie Wonder song
14 Extreme displeasure
16 Moment of danger
17 Buttressed
18 Removed powder from
19 Moroccan seaport
22 Relay stages
23 Excursion

# JIG-WORD

No clues – just pattern and answers – but can you fit them in?

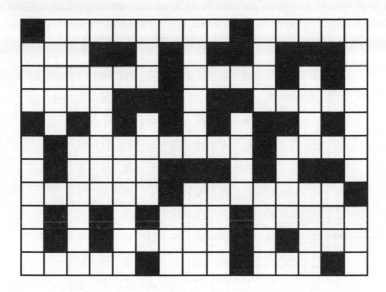

**3-letter words**
ASH
FAT
FIT
FLO
MAO
MOA
NUT
SHY
TOR
YES

**4-letter words**
ALTO
BLOB
BYRE
ECHO

GOAT
LAME
LOAF
LORE
OGEE
PIER
POOR
RELY
TALC
TOLL

**5-letter words**
CORGI
CREEP
ERATO
OBOES
SHEAR
TOWER

**6-letter words**
ALLURE
ARMPIT
CACTUS
CELLAR
EXTORT
PETROL
TRADER

**7-letter words**
APOLOGY
RIPPLED

**8-letter words**
ARTISTIC
CLEANSER

# BACKWARDS

For this puzzle, we've filled in the answers, but there are letters in the grid, where the black squares should be. You need to black out the unwanted letters to make a symmetrical grid to match the clues, which are listed in random order.

| S | T | A | R | T | U | S | A | B | R | E |
|---|---|---|---|---|---|---|---|---|---|---|
| A | I | S | U | I | C | I | D | E | O | N |
| U | P | P | E | R | O | T | O | A | S | T |
| C | U | E | B | E | R | E | T | S | E | E |
| E | R | N | E | T | H | O | S | T | A | R |
| A | S | H | W | H | I | T | E | A | S | T |
| P | U | C | E | R | N | E | T | H | I | N |
| O | I | L | R | F | O | B | C | O | D | E |
| S | T | A | L | E | R | R | U | L | E | R |
| E | A | S | I | A | M | E | S | E | N | V |
| R | I | S | E | R | O | W | A | S | T | E |

## ACROSS

— Lubricate
— Before
— Billiards stick
— From Thailand
— Begin
— Diocese
— Rancid
— Part of a shoe
— Poem set to music
— Squander
— Celebrity
— Sea eagle
— Monarch
— Drink one's health
— Not fat
— Sword
— Part of a stair
— Watch chain
— Self-destruction
— Pure colour
— Purplish-red

## DOWN

— Fatigue
— America's initials
— The coast
— Female sheep
— Make beer
— Creature
— Regret
— Untruth
— Building land
— School form
— Commotion
— Trembling poplar
— Coagulate
— Teaser
— Go in
— Horned African creature
— Gaps
— Ketchup, for example
— Dread
— Daring
— Chase

# JOLLY MIXTURES

In this puzzle, each clue is simply an anagram of the answer – but watch out! There might be more than one possible solution to each clue. For instance, the clue 'TALE' might lead to the answer 'LATE' or 'TEAL'. You'll have to look at how the answers fit into the grid to find out which alternative is correct.

**ACROSS**

7 PEDANT
8 NEARER
9 DEN
10 MOAT
11 TOED
12 ART
14 DEALT
17 BAGEL
19 CODER
20 THESE
22 HATED
24 DAD
26 RITE
28 MODE
29 GNU
30 SACHET
31 GLIDER

**DOWN**

1 TABLET
2 MITE
3 TAPED
4 RACED
5 RAID
6 LINTEL
13 NAMED
15 EEL
16 CAT
17 DOG
18 BAR
21 EIGHTH
23 PELMET
24 GLEAN
25 DOING
27 SORE
28 READ

# DATELINE

A number jig with a difference: with clues to figure out (with the help of a calculator if you wish!) to discover the date in the shaded line – in this case, the birthdate of a comedian.

## ACROSS

**1** Twice 5 Across

**5** Square root of 26 Down

**7** Multiply 25 Across by 249, then add 96

**8** Add 39,317 to 11 Down

**9** Square 30 Across

**11** Square root of 49,284

**13** First three digits of 5 Down

**15** Square 2 Down

**20** Multiply 2 Down by 5 Down

**21** Divide 9 Across by 4

**23** Multiply 1 Across by 5 Across

**25** Half of 4 Down

**27** Multiply 5 Across by 1,000

**28** Multiply 25 Across by 501, then subtract 10,000

**30** Divide 31 Across by 3

**31** Square root of 4,356

## DOWN

**1** Half of 31 Across

**2** Multiply 30 Across by 25 Down

**3** Twice 11 Across

**4** Multiply 31 Across by 4

**5** Half of 2 Down

**6** Add 2 to 31 Across

**10** Add 3,534,539 to 15 Across

**11** Square 151

**12** Add 24,000 to 21 Across

**13** Multiply the first two digits of 26 Down by 593

**14** Multiply 13 Across by 102

**16** Last three digits of 7 Across

**17** Subtract 618 from 16 Down

**18** Add 74 to 11 Across

**19** Multiply 30 Across by 37

**22** Multiply 21 Across by 30 Across

**24** Multiply 5 Across by 21 Across

**25** Next in series 59, 73, 87, ...

**26** Multiply 1 Across by 8

**27** Divide 7 Across by 2,747

**29** Add 4 to 30 Across

# PATHFINDER

Starting from the bold centre letter, move up or down or sideways (but NOT diagonally) using all the letters to find the path through eighteen nautical terms.

# CRYPTIC CROSSWORD

**ACROSS**

1 It is outdated as a painkiller for lumbago, perhaps (4-6)
8 Another girl from Aileen (6)
9 Song won't upset slum district (6,4)
10 Separate act he'd developed (6)
11 Like the youngest daughter, perhaps, at the back of the queue (4,2,4)
12 Keep the soldiers in check (6)
13 Head on one's shoulders (4)
15 One who stirs up public interest endlessly is excited when dealing with notes (7)
19 First male worker is intransigent (7)
21 We split on a Welshman (4)
22 Whistling when it's very hot (6)
25 World-shattering experience (10)
27 Obliquely across like the French book (6)
28 I'd hum at first if I took the queen a moistener (10)
29 String of invective from one in business (6)
30 Vote to submit the last part to Greek character returning (10)

**DOWN**

1 Herb finds many in Iowa church (8)
2 Youth leader following form that is elegant (6)
3 Coypu had fruit before getting the wind up (6)
4 Silver encountered Capone (5)
5 Having done the plastering, submitted an account (8)
6 Handyman – fellow to perform outside with hesitation (8)
7 Idleness indeed (8)
13 Keep under – lower! (3)
14 Severely criticise the cooking vessel (3)
16 Denied that profits help (8)
17 One hurried to adjust the sails first of the boat (8)
18 Three got tipsy at the same time (8)
20 Met large eccentric with an urgent message (8)
23 Landowner's singers, we hear (6)
24 A diverse change without the last two – diverse (6)
26 You're slim, egghead! (5)

# FOOD FUN

Arthur has cooked a cake, Bernard is wearing a scarf, Charles isn't wearing an apron, Daniel is wearing a low hat and Edward is standing next to Bernard. Can you put the names to the numbers?

# DOT-TO-DOT

Join the dots from 1 to 35 to reveal the hidden picture.

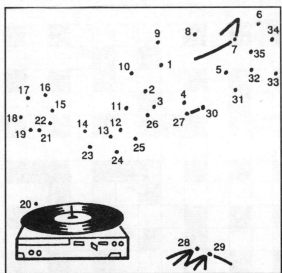

# CROSSWORD

## ACROSS

- **4** Science of reasoned thinking (5)
- **9** Lithely (7)
- **10** For all to see (5)
- **11** Sprint, hurry (3)
- **12** Idiot (3)
- **13** Antagonist (3)
- **14** Hinted (7)
- **15** Professional varnishing (6,9)
- **19** Principal city (7)
- **20** Bed for a baby (3)
- **21** Mate (3)
- **22** In time past (3)
- **23** Children's entertainment (5)
- **24** Door attachment (7)
- **25** Sibling's daughter (5)

## DOWN

- **1** Make redundant (3,3)
- **2** Musical rhythmic phrase (4)
- **3** Process of making into a god (11)
- **4** Medieval harp-like instrument (4)
- **5** Friendly (6)
- **6** Formation, construction (11)
- **7** Summertime star sign (6)
- **8** Breeding establishment (4)
- **16** Dilate (6)
- **17** Official residence of a sovereign (6)
- **18** Aplenty (6)
- **19** Manage (4)
- **20** Solid fuel (4)
- **21** Early infantry weapon (4)

# SAMPLER

A sample has been cut from each of the three rolls of cloth. Can you tell which sample belongs to which roll?

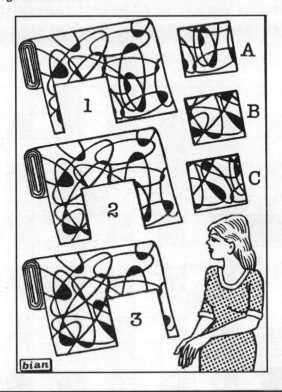

# 4-SQUARE

Solve these four clues and then rearrange the solutions into a sixteen-letter phrase, for which a clue is given. The two diagonals also make four-letter words.

CURVE, ARC

CHRISTMAS

MAKE AIRTIGHT

SMALL ARROW

Clue: He doesn't even come for the rent? (8,8)

This puzzle has no clues in the conventional sense. Instead, every different number printed in the main grid represents a different letter (with the same number always representing the same letter, of course). For example, if 7 turns out to be a 'V', you can write in V wherever a square contains 7. We have completed a very small part of the puzzle to give you a start, but the rest is up to you.

| 20 | 5 | 17 | 1 | 24 | 10 | 13 | 10 | 13 | ■ | 23 | 8 | 10 |
|---|---|---|---|---|---|---|---|---|---|---|---|---|
| 2 | ■ | 25 | ■ | 13 | ■ | 10 | ■ | 17 | ■ | 5 | ■ | 24 |
| 21 | 15 | 12 | 24 | 17 | ■ | 17 | 18 | 2 | 3 | 15 | 24 | 9 |
| 15 | ■ | 12 | ■ | 11 | ■ | 20 | ■ | 5 | ■ | 1 | ■ | 10 |
| 17 A | 11 N | 24 T | 2 | 21 | 15 | 10 | 1 | ■ | 16 | 9 | 17 | 13 |
| 11 | ■ | ■ | ■ | 15 | ■ | 7 | ■ | 6 | ■ | 10 | ■ | ■ |
| 24 | 15 | 13 | 11 | 2 | 20 | ■ | 23 | 12 | 17 | 13 | 7 | 1 |
| ■ | ■ | 10 | ■ | 5 | ■ | 23 | ■ | 5 | ■ | ■ | ■ | 8 |
| 26 | 2 | 5 | 24 | ■ | 22 | 12 | 11 | 7 | 13 | 12 | 15 | 1 |
| 10 | ■ | 17 | ■ | 22 | ■ | 22 | ■ | 25 | ■ | 19 | ■ | 24 |
| 17 | 11 | 4 | 2 | 10 | 24 | 8 | ■ | 2 | 3 | 17 | 6 | 10 |
| 11 | ■ | 10 | ■ | 17 | ■ | 10 | ■ | 1 | ■ | 24 | ■ | 3 |
| 1 | 17 | 7 | ■ | 14 | 10 | 13 | 16 | 9 | 2 | 10 | 25 | 1 |

A B C D E F G H I J K L M

N O P Q R S T U V W X Y Z

(The small grid is provided for ease of reference only)

| 1 | 2 | 3 | 4 | 5 | 6 | 7 | 8 | 9 | 10 | 11 | 12 | 13 |
|---|---|---|---|---|---|---|---|---|---|---|---|---|
| 14 | 15 | 16 | 17 | 18 | 19 | 20 | 21 | 22 | 23 | 24 | 25 | 26 |

# ADD-A-LETTER

Insert or add a letter to these four-letter words to make five-letter words which fit the rhyming clues. The six added letters should spell out a word.

| LUSH | | A velvety fabric of rich quality |
| SPAN | | Madrid's the capital of this country |
| QUID | | Tentacled creature of the ocean |
| HEAR | | Vital organ – keeps blood in motion |
| CAST | | Cliffs and beaches bordering the shore |
| OVER | | Romantic interest, paramour |

# BLACK OUT

Can you see which one of the six letters was printed by the reverse stamp which is shown at the top?

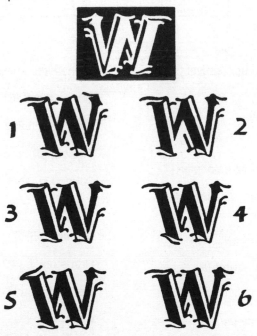

# SPIRAL

Every answer (except the first) uses the last letter of the preceding answer as its initial letter, the chain thus formed following a spiral path to the centre of the grid. The diagonals spell out the names of two colours.

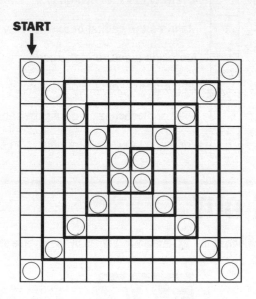

START

Late December festival (9)

Inactive, taking little exercise (9)

Cede (5)

Explanatory figure or plan (7)

___ Navratilova, Wimbledon champion (7)

Covered with water (5)

Occurrence, event (9)

Deity (7)

Take large steps (6)

Of the highest excellence (9)

Less difficult (6)

Stiff, unbending (5)

Twofold (6)

Deceptive, shifty (7)

Mistake (5)

Monarch (5)

Lion's noise (4)

List of duties (4)

Upper limb (3)

# BOXWISE

Put these three-letter groups into the twelve numbered boxes to produce twelve six-letter words, each of which starts in one box and finishes in another as indicated by an arrow. For instance, 2 and 5 make a six-letter word, but not 5 and 9. One group has been filled in to start you off.

HOR   TER   SET   PER

BAN   SON   NER   TEE

ROR   TAM   NET   ~~COR~~

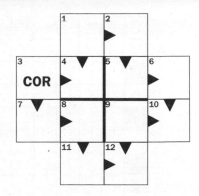

# IN THE ABSTRACT

George has bought one of the four abstract paintings shown here, but he can't remember which one it is or which way up it is supposed to go. Can you help him?

# SKELETON CROSSWORD

Have double the fun with this puzzle: you've got to fill in the answers and the black squares! We've given you the bare bones to start and it will help you to know that the black squares in the finished grid form a symmetrical pattern, so that every black square has at least one other corresponding black square.

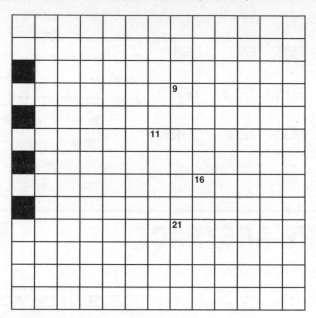

## ACROSS

7 Felony expert
8 Distorts into knotty lumps
9 Native American dwelling
10 Bet ___, former *Coronation Street* barmaid
11 In a high-handed manner
14 Proposals
16 Explosive weapons
19 Fruit acid
21 Winds up by hand
22 Potteries county

## DOWN

1 Stylish
2 Included
3 Star ___, spice used in Chinese cooking
4 Layered board
5 Very eager
6 Middle Eastern state
12 Puts up with
13 Heat food beforehand
15 Throws out of a house
17 Place where bread is made
18 Missiles formerly used by Iraq
20 Rampant

# WORDSEARCH

The surnames of 48 male tennis players have all been hidden in the diagram. They have been printed across (backwards or forwards), or up or down, or diagonally, but always in a straight line without letters being skipped. You can use the letters in the diagram more than once. You will probably find it helpful to mark the words in the diagram and cross them off the list as you find them.

```
S S S P N D T D R E D B E R G A
T G M L E T R E R P R S Y F N S
O G I A W R D O E O A E A A E E
L I T V C E R T F T B L T R O I
L R H E O B R Y S W K N T E R X
E E O R M A V A O E A I Y P N A
A S H S B R N O N S L R C O E S
N C E C E T D B I D Z S C O C F
S I B D O W U Y E L N I K C M B
E P T D G R A N E S L E I N U G
D E E S G M U L L I G A N N R H
O J T M U M A U L D R B G O M K
K X W S E A K N U Y O E B T R O
C O N N O R S B N T R C L A L D
T E H C O C S H Q T O K M N D E
S E N I V N A O E A T E O N N M
R A L S T O N L N P R R G E E L
T R T T I V A S F R A S E R L O
```

| | | | |
|---|---|---|---|
| ASHE | EDBERG | NASTASE | SAVITT |
| AUSTIN | EMERSON | NEWCOMBE | SCHROEDER |
| BECKER | FALKENBURG | NIELSEN | SEDGMAN |
| BORG | FRASER | OLMEDO | SEIXAS |
| BOROTRA | KODES | PATTY | SMITH |
| BUDGE | KRAMER | PERRY | STOLLE |
| BUNGERT | LACOSTE | PETRA | TANNER |
| COCHET | LAVER | RALSTON | TILDEN |
| CONNORS | LENDL | RIGGS | TRABERT |
| COOPER | McENROE | ROCHE | VINES |
| CRAWFORD | McKINLEY | ROSEWALL | VON CRAMM |
| DROBNY | MULLIGAN | SANTANA | WOOD |

# STORY CROSSWORD

Transfer the words which complete the story to the grid and then put the circled letters in the right order to discover the name of the famous person therein described.

Although he was born in rural Kent, his early life was quite ___ (6D). He was first off to Ceylon where his father worked, then to America with his mother and sister, settling in San Francisco. Six months later, they moved on to Canada and eventually to New York. All this was before he was eight years old.

His mother decided he needed a proper education and brought him back to England, to Clifton College, Bristol. Here he had a ___ (12A) to show more ___ (7A) in sport rather than ___ (14A) work so, when the time came to leave, he had no idea what to do, but he decided on acting and enrolled with RADA. However, he would have to ___ (5D) before pursuing his theatrical life as, in 1940, his call-up papers arrived.

Desperate to see some action, he joined the Red Berets. There followed a ___ (23A) of ___ (13D) tests, until eventually he was declared unsuitable and was invalided out, much to his dismay.

___ (1D) on launching himself in films, he approached the director Carol Reed for a part, albeit a ___ (16D) one, in *The Way Ahead*. It was, however, the ___ (22A) his

___ (15D) needed. 1945 saw the release of *Brief Encounter*, which made him a ___ (11A), and he was to ___ (3D) this success in the equally ___ (24A) *The Third Man*.

When Jose Ferrer, the American actor-director, asked him to appear in the war picture *Cockleshell Heroes*, he could hardly ___ (9A), as he considered it to be the perfect opportunity to ___ (4D) international fame, and he was ___ (20A) right.

During the sixties and seventies, he was still ___ (21D) much in demand, although he wasn't always ___ (10A) in choosing film roles, as in the forgettable *Pope Joan*. But *Sons and Lovers* and ___ (18A) *Ryan's Daughter*, in which he was ___ (2D) to shed his military image and play a priest, are two of his finest.

The last years of his life were as busy as ever and, whereas many would have found the ___ (19D) too much, he kept working right up to his death, which came on January 7th, 1988, when he was ___ (8A) 71. His actress wife, Helen Cherry, was at his bedside. Together, they had remained a devoted ___ (17D) for more than forty years.

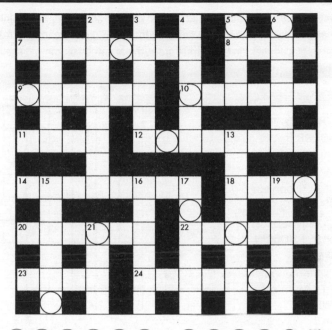

# VISIGRID

Can you see which one of these seven impressions was made by the stamp?

# TINKER, TAILOR ...

To discover who this person is unscramble the words in the verse, which hints at what the person does. Write these words into the boxes below, reading across, and, if you've placed them in the correct order, the arrowed column will spell out the occupation.

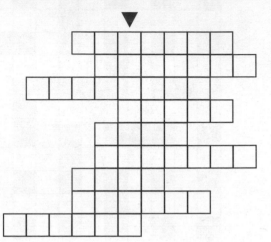

Visit this RATSIS'T LAPOURR if your whim

Is a colourful GINNAIPT on your KINS

CESETL a SINGED: an anchor, PHODLIN or bird,

And for sentimental PESTY, Mum's the DOWR.

OCCUPATION: _____

---

# SILHOUETTE

Shade in every fragment containing a dot - and what have you got?

# WINDOW SHOPPING

Four of these women in Fashion Street are actually wearing identical outfits to those displayed in the windows. Can you match them up? In each case, the wearer is in a different picture from the one in which the respective outfit is displayed.

# DILEMMA

Two straightforward crosswords – but their clues have been mixed up. You have to decide which clue belongs to which grid, but two words have been entered to give you a start.

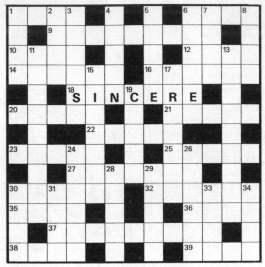

## ACROSS

| | |
|---|---|
| **1** Conceal | **1** Manager |
| **6** Applaud | **6** Swiss mountains |
| **9** Black sweet | **9** Out of sight |
| **10** Multi-coloured gem | **10** Small garden bird |
| **12** Dray | **12** At a distance |
| **14** Well-mannered | **14** Accounts book |
| **16** Business syndicate | **16** Wigwam |
| **18** Eternal | **18** Genuine |
| **20** Core | **20** Walter ___, writer of *Ivanhoe* |
| **21** Bar seat | **21** Sacred song |
| **22** Latin American dance | **22** Concur |
| **23** Nearby | **23** Not dirty |
| **25** Sam ___, film star | **25** Arrive at |
| **27** Choral work | **27** Alike |
| **30** Love apple | **30** Complete failure |
| **32** Marzipan flavour | **32** Universe |
| **35** Ancient Peruvian | **35** Shortly |
| **36** Flan | **36** Notion |
| **37** Important event | **37** Paper seller |
| **38** Simple to do | **38** Lean over, list |
| **39** 'Great' US lake | **39** Back part |

**DOWN**

| | | | |
|---|---|---|---|
| 1 | Circular band | 1 | Basin |
| 2 | Toboggan | 2 | Clock face |
| 3 | Join up | 3 | Vocalist |
| 4 | Sentry | 4 | Flax cloth |
| 5 | Segment | 5 | Box |
| 6 | Red wine | 6 | Entry |
| 7 | Jump | 7 | Abandoned |
| 8 | Knitting stitch | 8 | Building plot |
| 11 | Uprising | 11 | Fine pottery |
| 13 | Air transport | 13 | Light on a bicycle |
| 15 | Huge | 15 | Plead |
| 17 | Strong Spanish grass | 17 | Munitions store |
| 19 | Welsh dog | 19 | Restriction |
| 24 | Attack | 24 | Sparse |
| 26 | Spring festival | 26 | Stoat fur |
| 28 | Cash | 28 | Compass point |
| 29 | Stage player | 29 | Church members |
| 30 | Angle | 30 | Story |
| 31 | Highest point | 31 | Simple plant |
| 33 | Female horse | 33 | German river |
| 34 | Agitate | 34 | Risk |

# NUMBER JIG

Just like a Jig-word – but instead of letters, numbers.

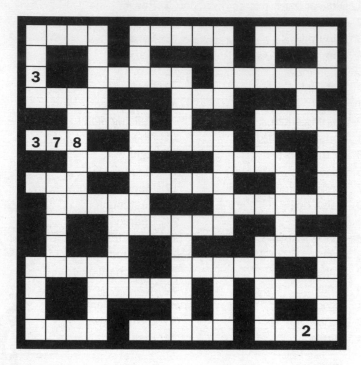

| **3-figures** | 3745 | **5-figures** | 79943 |
|---|---|---|---|
| 331 | 3928 | 23333 | 84731 |
| 378 | 4788 | 28355 | 89033 |
| 511 | 5623 | 28814 | 93400 |
| 592 | 6442 | 35676 | |
| 732 | 7084 | 37389 | |
| 782 | 7113 | 38380 | |
| 791 | 7723 | 39005 | **6-figures** |
| 905 | 7830 | 40298 | 371972 |
| | 8037 | 41173 | 378224 |
| **4-figures** | 8129 | 42798 | 473211 |
| 1112 | 8387 | 61555 | 597826 |
| 2363 | 9327 | 68917 | 717775 |
| 3335 | 9893 | 77806 | 724520 |

# KEYWORD

This puzzle has no clues in the conventional sense. Instead, every different number printed in the main grid represents a different letter (with the same number always representing the same letter, of course). For example, if 7 turns out to be a 'V', you can write in V wherever a square contains 7. We have completed a very small part of the puzzle to give you a start, but the rest is up to you.

| 1 | 2 | 3 | 4 | 5 | 6 | 7 | 8 | 9 | | 10 | 11 | 12 |
|---|---|---|---|---|---|---|---|---|---|----|----|----|
| 11 | | 11 | | 11 | | 8 | | 2 | | 4 | | 2 |
| 3 | 11 | 13 | 2 | 14 | | 10 | 7 | 15 | 15 | 13 | 11 | 10 |
| 16 | | 7 | | 17 | | 17 | | 11 | | 18 | | 17 |
| 7 | 8 | 19 | 20 | 3 | 3 | 11 | 5 | | 16 | 7 | 17 | 11 |
| 8 | | | | 4 | | 1 | | 21 | | 8 | | |
| 9 | 6 | 1 | 10 | 20 | 22 | | 23 | 7 | 8 | 9 | 13 | 11 |
| | | 2 | | 10 | | 24 | | 11 | | | | 13 |
| 13 | 20 | 3 | 16 | | 13 | 2 (L) | 19 (A) | 3 (C) | 4 | 10 | 10 | 11 |
| 20 | | 25 | | 26 | | 17 | | 19 | | 13 | | 19 |
| 8 | 4 | 20 | 3 | 7 | 10 | 26 | | 11 | 8 | 2 | 19 | 17 |
| 9 | | 11 | | 10 | | 11 | | 10 | | 10 | | 11 |
| 11 | 21 | 17 | | 10 | 19 | 3 | 2 | 17 | 19 | 26 | 11 | 5 |

**A B C D E F G H I J K L M**

**N O P Q R S T U V W X Y Z**

(The small grid is provided for ease of reference only)

| 1 | 2 | 3 | 4 | 5 | 6 | 7 | 8 | 9 | 10 | 11 | 12 | 13 |
|----|----|----|----|----|----|----|----|----|----|----|----|----|
| 14 | 15 | 16 | 17 | 18 | 19 | 20 | 21 | 22 | 23 | 24 | 25 | 26 |

# SYMBOLIC

Which two of the smaller rectangles contain the same four symbols?

# VISIGRID

Can you see which one of the seven prints was made by the roller?

# CROSSWORD

**ACROSS**

4 Spider's snare (3)
8 Talk rapidly and incoherently (8)
9 Make clear (6)
10 Arise (4,2)
11 Steer (8)
13 Title of Russian emperors (4)
15 Alternative (5)
16 Rounded roof (4)
18 Name applied to a great Indian prince (8)
20 Underground exploring (6)
22 Direct (descendant) (6)
23 Make frail (8)
24 Conclusion (3)

**DOWN**

1 Pinnacles (6)
2 Swallow greedily (4)
3 Prevent (4)
4 Misguided (5-6)
5 Large dam-building rodent (6)
6 ___ on, revolved around (6)
7 Hare's tail (4)
12 Female farm animal (3)
13 Male domestic cat (3)
14 Wanderer (6)
15 Word of a god (6)
17 Shawl (6)
19 Barren, parched (4)
20 Small restaurant (4)
21 Suddenly change direction (4)

# TWO-TIMER

Two sets of clues to the same answers. Cryptic clues below and straight clues beneath the grid.

## ACROSS

1 Pack member not meant to be taken seriously (5)

4 Stage show featuring terrible act – going round undressed! (7)

8 Barber's vessel (7)

9 Fruit drink, about two pence (5)

10 Bit of a scrap (5)

11 Flower faeries dancing (7)

13 One of some found in avenues or streets (4)

15 Sweet, well-dressed person has the same point repeated (6)

17 New Delhi's protection (6)

20 A, B, C, D, F or G! (4)

22 Fine goal (7)

24 Bridget's heart is in the mountains (5)

26 Man of parts (5)

27 Eat nuts, strangely causing disease (7)

28 Can rule out a type of energy (7)

29 Encourage singularly good health (5)

## DOWN

1 Kitty shot by sailor (7)

2 If Ken moves, it will cut (5)

3 Salesman allowed leading exporter to be well-stocked (7)

4 Gunner in the restaurant has a bottle (6)

5 How one might welcome you thus (5)

6 Swift, sharp reply to tripe so awful (7)

7 Character from Greece in the Territorial Army (5)

12 Support the others (4)

14 Split the hire charge (4)

16 In fact, a crazy, over-enthusiastic type (7)

18 Eric the Terrible doesn't follow the accepted doctrine (7)

19 Welsh theatre attendant? (7)

21 Peculiar story about Gravesend shellfish (6)

22 It's obvious there's one in the plot (5)

23 At which one has a lot of freedom (5)

25 Square ball? (5)

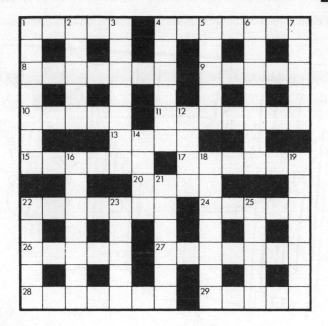

## ACROSS

1 Jester (5)
4 Night-club entertainment (7)
8 Sailing ship (7)
9 Green or red fruit (5)
10 Part (5)
11 Iris (7)
13 Woody plant (4)
15 Chewy sweet (6)
17 Plate of armour (6)
20 Message (4)
22 Forfeit (7)
24 Crest (5)
26 Performer (5)
27 Lockjaw (7)
28 Subatomic (7)
29 Applaud (5)

## DOWN

1 Top prize (7)
2 Piece of cutlery (5)
3 Completely filled (7)
4 Wine-flask (6)
5 Courageous (5)
6 Rejoinder (7)
7 Greek letter (5)
12 Relaxation (4)
14 Torn (4)
16 Zealot (7)
18 One with an unconventional belief (7)
19 Sideboard (7)
21 Bivalve (6)
22 Evident (5)
23 Great (5)
25 Move to music (5)

# THAT BIT OF DIFFERENCE

There are eight differences between these two cartoons. Can you spot them?

# BACK-HANDER

Can you tell which one of these five cooks is seen from the back as shown in the top left-hand corner?

---

# TWO-BY-TWO

Each word in a clue can be preceded by the same two letters to spell out another word. For instance INTER, LATE and TENT can be preceded by PA to make PAINTER, PALATE and PATENT. Can you solve the three clues below, then spell out the three pairs of letters to make a six-letter word?

ARROW   HERE   RIG

ALLY   BUS   CITE

DICTION   DRESS   JUST

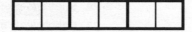

# CROSSWORD

## ACROSS

1 Beastly (7)
7 Picture stand (5)
8 Place of underground excavation (3)
9 After all others (4)
10 Alcoholic drink (4)
12 Be an onlooker (8)
14 Clothing retailer (9)
15 Minor planet (8)
18 Gourd (8)
21 Corporate label (9)
23 Functioning (8)
25 Long-billed wading bird (4)
26 Steep rugged rock (4)
28 Fiery (3)
29 Muslim scriptures (5)
30 Fatty (7)

## DOWN

2 Stinging insects' home (5,4)
3 Void (4)
4 Having an irrational fear of the unknown (13)
5 Isolated retreat (9)
6 Affected (5)
11 Make a great effort (6)
13 Wear away (5)
16 (In a position) on one's own say-so (4-9)
17 High-pitched (5)
19 Tired-looking (6)
20 Aircraft propulsion device (3,6)
22 Whale product used in perfume-making (9)
24 Brief and profound (5)
27 Deliberately omit (4)

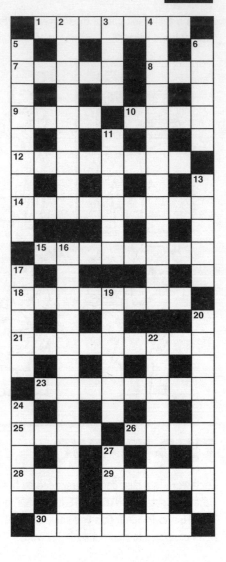

# CROSSWORD

**ACROSS**

1 Evasive behaviour (13)
9 Unctuous (6)
10 Unseen danger for motorists (5,3)
11 Ankle-length skirt (4)
12 Number-calling game (5)
13 Person controlled by others (4)
14 Liquid mineral (3)
15 Bring charges against (3)
16 Small British garden bird (4)
18 Indicate or suggest without stating directly (5)
20 Slight mark (4)
22 Provide (a foreign film) with a written translation (8)
24 Blood fluid (6)
25 Deep thinking (13)

**DOWN**

2 Ballroom dance (5)
3 Particular way of telling a story (7)
4 Shaft of light (3)
5 Hut, cottage (5)
6 Cover for a brewing vessel (3,4)
7 Tree which grows from an acorn (3)
8 Flat-bottomed boat (4)
12 Burn mark (7)
13 Long narrow flag (7)
17 Profligate, rake (4)
19 Journalistic profession (5)
21 Brief film role (5)
23 Darken in the sun (3)
24 Baked pastry dish (3)

# TINKER, TAILOR ...

To discover who this person is unscramble the words in the verse, which hints at what the person does. Write these words into the boxes below, reading across, and, if you've placed them in the correct order, the arrowed column will spell out the occupation.

This person ASSUMERE you with a PEAT,

SUDJATS the UMDYM to your HASPE

And SKROW away with TAPLE and TRAD

To make a FAINOSH REMGNAT smart.

OCCUPATION: _____

---

# TAKE FIVE

The three answers in this mini-crossword read the same across and down. We've given you clues to the three words, but NOT in the right order. See how quickly you can solve it.

1  Beneath

2  Mistake

3  Small rodent

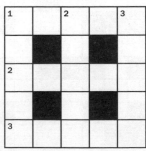

# JIG-WORD

No clues – just pattern and answers – but can you fit them in?

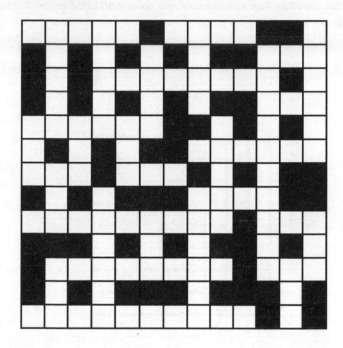

### 3-letter words
AIL
AND
BOX
EMU
ERR
NAP
NUN
PAR
PEA
RAM
RED
SET
TAG
VIA

### 4-letter words
AFAR
FREE
ROTA
SIDE

### 5-letter words
APACE
ARROW
COSTA
PINCH

### 6-letter words
EXILES
LEGEND

PHRASE
RECOIL
WRECKS

### 8-letter words
ELEVATOR
SPITEFUL

### 9-letter word
INTERVIEW

### 10-letter words
BLANCMANGE
QUADRUPLET

# LETTER SET

Every answer (except the first) uses the last letter of the preceding answer as its initial letter, the chain thus formed following a spiral path to the centre of the grid. The diagonals spell two English ports.

**START**

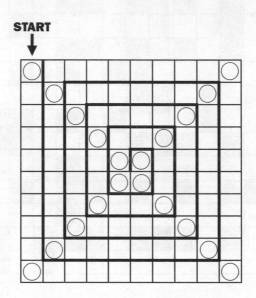

- Patron saint of animals (7)

- Rarely (6)

- Pilgrim Fathers' ship (9)

- Rice dish (7)

- Fertile desert spot (5)

- Extend (7)

- Soft felt hat (7)

- Male goose (6)

- Contrite (9)

- Bother (7)

- King Arthur's sword (9)

- Heating device (8)

- Round building (7)

- Similar (5)

- Join the army (6)

- Warty amphibian (4)

- Varied (7)

The arrows show the direction in which the answer to each clue should be placed.

| Sections of a play ▼ | | Organ with which a fish steers ▼ | | Interfered ▼ | | Reproductive cell ▼ | Pinpoints |
|---|---|---|---|---|---|---|---|
| | | | | ▼ | | | ▼ |
| ▶ | | | | | | | |
| Economised wherever possible | | Keanu Reeves' role in *The Matrix* ▶ | ▶ | | | Indigo dye | |
| ▶ | | | Exclamation of annoyance ▶ | | | ▼ | |
| __ Sheridan, Warner Bros' 'Oomph girl' | | __ Geller, showman | Lairs ▶ | | | | |
| ▶ | | ▼ | | | Person renting | | Allotted periods of work |
| *The __ Suspects*, 1995 film | Ugly old women | | Measures of cloth ▶ | | ▼ | | ▼ |
| ▶ | ▼ | | | | | Abounding | |
| Young aristocrat | | This thing's | Bigwig (inits) | __ Lanka, Asian country ▶ | | ▼ | |
| Concedes defeat (5,2) ▶ | | ▼ | ▼ | | | | |
| ▶ | | | | Alternative name for a newt ▶ | | | |
| Sparkling wine | Lively outings ▶ | | | | | | |

# GIANT CROSSWORD

## Across

1 Casino card game (9)
6 Down-payments (8)
10 Adam's Biblical partner (3)
11 Accurate (5)
12 Manufacturer (8)
13 Blood-red (7)
15 Metallic element (4)
17 Traditional practices (8)
19 Investigation (8)
21 Tells (4)
23 Took for granted (7)
24 Portable defence from rain (8)
27 More lustrous (8)
30 Members of a ship's crew (7)
33 Existed, lived (3)
34 Foot digit (3)
35 Illustrations, instances (8)
36 Land of fifty states (7)
37 Entertainment venue (7)
39 Consumes (4)
40 Transition (7)
44 External (7)
47 Ova (4)
48 Night attire (7)
50 Trying out (7)
51 Logs for burning (8)
52 Put into service (3)
53 Alcoholic beverage (3)
54 Attained (7)
58 Insistence (8)
60 Abandoned (8)
62 Relieve an itch (7)
63 Detritus (4)
65 Fabric (8)
66 Win approval or support for (8)
68 Reverberation (4)
70 Discharge (7)
74 Member of one's family (8)
75 Walk about stealthily (5)
76 Saucepan cover (3)
77 In a grave, sedate manner (8)
78 Twenty-four hours ago (9)

## Down

1 Gentle winds (7)
2 Once more (5)
3 Outfits (4)
4 Continent (4)
5 Main beam of a vessel (4)
6 Lowest regions (6)
7 Dither (13)
8 Difficult or unusual feat (5)
9 Give up (9)
14 Enclosed space (7)
16 Cursory (6)
18 Let in (5)
20 Unwell (3)
22 Domain (4)
25 Depressed (7)
26 Missing (6)
28 Occurs (7)
29 Chosen by vote (7)
30 Postal token (5)
31 Units, pieces (5)
32 Statuesque (7)
38 Adult male chicken (7)
41 More furious (7)
42 Female siblings (7)
43 Quantities (7)
45 Native to Eire (5)
46 Bordered (5)
48 Manner of uttering a word (13)
49 Adjudicated (6)
55 Competition submissions (7)
56 Embrace lovingly (6)
57 Greek love god (4)
58 Vital travel documents (9)
59 Mistake (5)
61 Epoch (3)
64 Basket on wheels (7)
65 Only just (6)
67 Cause fear in (5)
69 Combination of notes (5)
71 Noblewoman (4)
72 Requests (4)
73 Duelling sword (4)

# BODY LANGUAGE

The Across clues consist of jumbled-up words relating to the body. The Down clues and answers are normal.

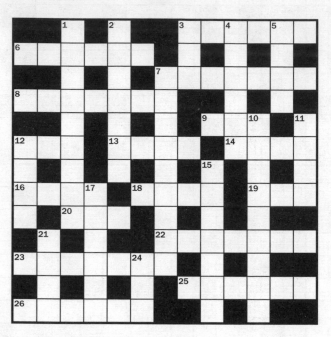

**ACROSS**

**3** FURSCF

**6** ODNENT

**7** LEADBDR

**8** TAPEALL

**9** ARE

**12** MUG

**13** PEAT

**14** MILB

**16** STUB

**18** SIIR

**19** TUG

**20** OTE

**22** SHEYLEA

**23** SHUMREU

**25** DIMELD

**26** USITSE

**DOWN**

**1** Person skilled in dissection (9)

**2** Servings of ice-cream (7)

**3** Roman sun god (3)

**4** Type of tyre (6)

**5** Jumping insect (4)

**7** Electrical cells (9)

**10** River forming border between the US and Mexico (3,6)

**11** Assist in crime (4)

**12** Hurtful remark (4)

**15** One who lives austerely (7)

**17** Tall structures (6)

**21** Dame ___ Dench, Oscar-winning actress (4)

**24** Function (3)

# KEYWORD

This puzzle has no clues in the conventional sense. Instead, every different number printed in the main grid represents a different letter (with the same number always representing the same letter, of course). For example, if 7 turns out to be a 'V', you can write in V wherever a square contains 7. We have completed a very small part of the puzzle to give you a start, but the rest is up to you.

| 23 | 5 | 8 | 13 | 15 | 13 | 25 | 23 | | 20 | 23 | 23 | 14 |
|---|---|---|---|---|---|---|---|---|---|---|---|---|
| 25 | | 22 | | 22 | | 12 | | 21 | | 9 | | 13 |
| 8 | 13 | 17 | 13 | 9 | | 6 | 18 | 12 | 16 | 16 F | 9 | 19 |
| 3 | | 7 | | 12 | | 6 | | 24 | | 4 I | | 10 |
| | 1 | 12 | 4 | 17 | 25 | 23 | 21 | 21 | 23 | 17 N | 8 | 23 |
| 13 | | 18 | | 25 | | 26 | | 23 | | | | 17 |
| 8 | 3 | 23 | 2 | 23 | 26 | | 21 | 1 | 12 | 4 | 18 | 25 |
| 18 | | | | 23 | | 18 | | 12 | | 17 | | 21 |
| 4 | 17 | 25 | 23 | 18 | 16 | 23 | 18 | 23 | 17 | 8 | 23 | |
| 10 | | 4 | | 4 | | 14 | | 17 | | 23 | | 10 |
| 22 | 18 | 6 | 13 | 17 | 11 | 13 | | 25 | 13 | 17 | 6 | 22 |
| 17 | | 23 | | 6 | | 4 | | 9 | | 21 | | 21 |
| 19 | 13 | 18 | 17 | | 6 | 18 | 23 | 19 | 17 | 23 | 21 | 21 |

A B C D E F G H I J K L M
N O P Q R S T U V W X Y Z

(The small grid is provided for ease of reference only)

| 1 | 2 | 3 | 4 | 5 | 6 | 7 | 8 | 9 | 10 | 11 | 12 | 13 |
|---|---|---|---|---|---|---|---|---|---|---|---|---|
| 14 | 15 | 16 | 17 | 18 | 19 | 20 | 21 | 22 | 23 | 24 | 25 | 26 |

# WORK FORCE

Can you see which three of these vases are exactly the same?

# WATERWORKS

Each of the eight pictures is lacking in one detail that is in the other seven. Can you spot all eight missing details?

# ROUNDABOUT

Solutions to Radial clues (1 to 24) either start from the outer edge of the circle and read inwards, or start from the inner ring and read outwards to the edge (so they are all five-letter words). Solutions to Circular clues read in either a clockwise or an anticlockwise direction around the circle.

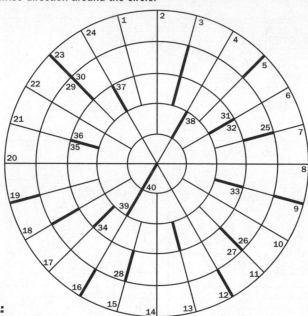

## RADIAL:
### INWARDS
2 Intended
3 Representative
5 King with a golden touch
6 Debtors
7 Russian emperors
8 ___ Enfield, comedian
9 Journal
10 Monastery
11 Full of punctures
12 Lock of hair
13 Pile up
15 Seasons
20 Unit of length
21 Lighthouse
24 Rainy snow

### OUTWARDS
1 Abrupt, concise
4 Canonised person
14 Soak
16 Acer tree
17 Manufacturer
18 Skinflint
19 Florida city
22 Gives out
23 Ant

## CIRCULAR:
### CLOCKWISE
5 Night-flying insect
16 Go astray
19 Little demons
27 Great ___, feature of Llandudno

28 Beer
30 Otherwise
32 Organ of hearing
33 Competent
36 Objective
37 Period of time
38 Take into custody
39 Pilots

### ANTICLOCKWISE
4 Most domesticated
11 Possessed, owned
15 Tiff
25 Flying appendage
26 Prejudice
29 Topic
31 Perish
34 Earnest prayer
35 Assignment
40 Modus operandi

# MISSING LINKS

The answer to each clue is a word which has a link with each of the three words listed. This word may come at the end (eg Head linked with Beach, Big and Hammer), at the beginning (eg Black linked with Beauty, Board and Jack) or a mixture of the two (eg Stone linked with Hail, Lime and Wall).

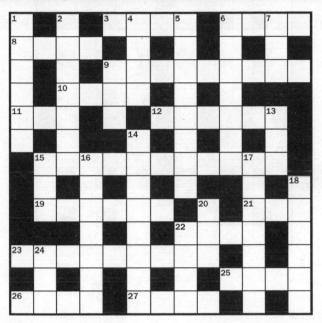

## ACROSS

3 Granny, Iron, Tyre (4)
6 Nymph, Pile, Pulp (4)
8 Acid, Check, Dance (4)
9 Earnings, Ink, Man (9)
10 Jumble, Price, Room (4)
11 Instructor, Jump, Lift (3)
12 Book, Comedy, Rough (6)
15 Hostile, Natural, Working (11)
19 Launcher, Science, Sky (6)
21 Afternoon, Break, Urn (3)
22 Bishop, Duke, Enemy (4)
23 Action, Picketing, School (9)
25 Garden, Reef, Slip (4)
26 Club, Express, Pit (4)
27 Calendar, Financial, Leap (4)

## DOWN

1 Elbow, Gun, Paint (6)
2 Bell, Mercy, Statement (7)
4 Assembly, Judge, Washing (4)
5 Cap, Quick, Time (8)
6 Penny, Stop, Wolf (7)
7 Crude, Filter, Olive (3)
9 Feeling, Fitting, Wind (3)
13 Flush, Spot, Water (3)
14 Fire, Persuasion, User (8)
15 Drum, Piercing, Trumpet (3)
16 Ceremony, Hollow, Roll (7)
17 Doing, Else, Much (7)
18 Belt, Net, Razor (6)
20 Small, Stir, Up (3)
22 Code, Office, Play (4)
24 Alter, Boost, Maniac (3)

# DILEMMA

Two straightforward crosswords – but their clues have been mixed up. You have to decide which clue belongs to which grid, but two words have been entered to give you a start.

Grid entries shown: **DONOR** (18 Across)

## ACROSS

| | |
|---|---|
| 1 Motive | 1 Smashed |
| 5 Mute | 5 Acquire |
| 9 School punishment | 9 Lebanese tree |
| 10 Spurn | 10 American space-station |
| 11 Natural fibre | 11 Cause to remember |
| 12 Uses sparingly | 12 Cricket team |
| 15 Many, lots | 15 Sheriff |
| 17 Sprint | 17 Barrel |
| 18 Giver | 18 Young man |
| 19 However | 19 Wager |
| 20 Droop | 20 US author |
| 22 Sifting implement | 22 Immunisation fluid |
| 24 Baby's bed | 24 Take a drink |
| 26 Found, discovered | 26 Isolated area |
| 27 Angel | 27 Tough coating |
| 28 Fix firmly | 28 Drums |
| 30 Guardian | 30 Ravel piece |
| 31 Speak | 31 Areas |
| 32 Main course | 32 Being |
| 33 Revolve | 33 Deprived |

**DOWN**

| | | | |
|---|---|---|---|
| 1 | Street musician | 1 | Most scarce |
| 2 | Life-giving gas | 2 | Abut |
| 3 | Inhabit | 3 | Overjoyed |
| 4 | Mesh | 4 | Pen tip |
| 5 | Dry, as wine | 5 | Rowing blade |
| 6 | Gap | 6 | Line on a weather map |
| 7 | Bury | 7 | Bee colony |
| 8 | Naturist | 8 | Leaseholder |
| 13 | Of the moon | 13 | Prestige |
| 14 | Famous | 14 | Hard, dense |
| 15 | Cooker | 15 | Waterlily |
| 16 | Uncanny | 16 | Fable writer |
| 20 | Sea-rover | 20 | Constant, firm |
| 21 | Red gemstone | 21 | Bring out |
| 22 | Nap | 22 | Start a journey (3,3) |
| 23 | Recollection | 23 | Enclose |
| 24 | Photographer's box | 24 | Blot |
| 25 | Celestial body | 25 | Royal seat |
| 29 | Pig-house | 29 | Fish eggs |
| 30 | Implore | 30 | Spider's lair |

Crossword grid with partial answer **YOUTH** filled in at 18.

# PIECEWORD

With the help of the Across clues only, can you fit the 35 pieces into their correct positions in the empty grid (which, when completed, will exhibit a symmetrical pattern)?

## ACROSS

1 Meal; flatfish

2 Coax, cajole through flattery

3 Light rainstorm; spring festival

4 Charles _____, Victorian author

5 Coal spade; craving for liquid

6 Tall and thin

7 Fable; peak

8 Forerunner

9 Water vapour; trim feathers (of birds)

10 Flower's stem

11 Cooking instructions; young child

12 Female

13 Foundation; woodland clearing

14 Forged

15 Rural thoroughfare; brief letter

16 Command

17 Earthquake; morals

18 Heavy artillery, bombardment

19 Sorrow; maim

20 Unspecified person

21 More difficult; capital of Greece

| | | | | | | | | |
|---|---|---|---|---|---|---|---|---|
| T | H | ■ | I | C | E | R | E | T |
| R | E | D | N | ■ | R | ■ | S | O |
| A | M | ■ | T | E | R | D | E | R |

| | | | | | | | | |
|---|---|---|---|---|---|---|---|---|
| I | S | ■ | R | D | E | T | A | L |
| O | U | N | ■ | O | ■ | ■ | R | ■ |
| N | E | ■ | R | R | A | O | M | A |

| | | | | | | | | |
|---|---|---|---|---|---|---|---|---|
| ■ | D | I | B | A | S | A | S | T |
| V | E | L | E | ■ | C | ■ | W | H |
| ■ | L | ■ | ■ | L | A | W | E | R |

| | | | | | | | | |
|---|---|---|---|---|---|---|---|---|
| D | ■ | S | C | ■ | ■ | ■ | M | ■ |
| I | P | E | R | E | C | M | E | O |
| T | ■ | W | I | ■ | ■ | ■ | R | ■ |

| | | | | | | | | |
|---|---|---|---|---|---|---|---|---|
| R | ■ | ■ | R | E | G | A | D | E |
| E | T | H | C | ■ | E | T | ■ | R |
| G | E | ■ | H | A | R | T | E | ■ |

| | | | | | | | | |
|---|---|---|---|---|---|---|---|---|
| E | X | ■ | P | L | A | ■ | A | P |
| R | ■ | A | L | E | ■ | S | S | O |
| E | E | N | E | A | S | ■ | P | R |

| | | | | | | | | |
|---|---|---|---|---|---|---|---|---|
| L | ■ | N | ■ | G | L | E | ■ | A |
| E | C | E | F | E | I | R | S | T |
| R | ■ | E | ■ | N | O | F | ■ | A |

| | | | | | | | | |
|---|---|---|---|---|---|---|---|---|
| K | ■ | T | S | ■ | V | C | K | E |
| I | N | F | T | R | E | ■ | O | ■ |
| N | ■ | O | A | ■ | N | A | N | K |

204 |

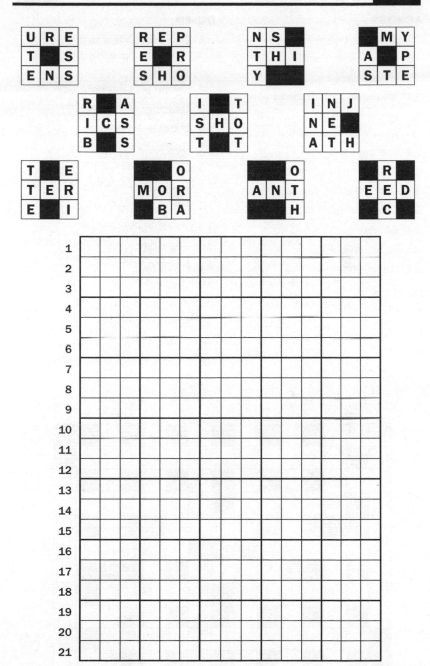

# CROSSWORD

## ACROSS

1 Front part of overalls (3)
8 Putting in the picture (12)
9 Have regret for (3)
11 Shrimp-like crustacean (5)
12 Scramble to get on by fair means or foul (3,4)
14 Lasting flavour (4)
15 S American fruiting tree (6)
18 Older relative, familiarly (6)
20 Central church section (4)
23 Be very sure (3,4)
25 Prose piece (5)
27 No longer in jail (3)
28 Wastefulness (12)
29 Rower's tool (3)

## DOWN

1 Don't touch it with a ___, refuse to have anything to do with it! (9)
2 Sound of a car horn (4)
3 Delicate, of a fabric (6)
4 Middleman (5)
5 Unrelenting (5)
6 Sea mile (4)
7 Baby or young child (6)
10 Future state (9)
13 Turkish governor (3)
16 Showing curiosity (6)
17 Including (3)
19 Overlooked (6)
21 In agitation (5)
22 Spookily odd (5)
24 Skilful (4)
26 Child's toy on a string (2-2)

# CROSSWORD

## ACROSS

5 Unity, solidarity (8)

7 Wet-weather garment (3)

8 Staple Italian food (5)

9 Cue (8)

11 Exclude (4)

12 Amend proofs (4)

14 Study intensively within a short period (3,2)

15 Miss the mark (3)

16 Harmful (7)

20 Curve section (3)

21 Sub-machine gun (5)

23 Plus (4)

24 Former Indian coin (4)

26 Imagine, picture (8)

28 Weapon of chivalry (5)

29 Alcoholic drink distilled from sugar cane (3)

30 Ambitious person (8)

## DOWN

1 Idle or mischievous person (5)

2 Cooking additive (10)

3 Sterile (7)

4 Lack of balance (12)

6 Inland Revenue form (3,6)

10 Insect larvae (5)

13 In large amounts (7)

17 Unswerving quality (12)

18 Trinket (9)

19 Obscure or secluded path (5)

22 Relating to administration (10)

25 Hermit (7)

27 Forge worker (5)

# JIG-WORD

No clues – just pattern and answers – but can you fit them in?

**3-letter words**
ACT
APE
ERR
ION
LEA
POT
SAY
SUN
TAG
TOY

**4-letter words**
BEST
EDIT

FREE
FRET
POST
ROTA
RUIN
RUSE
SATE
SOFT

**5-letter words**
DELTA
FLEAS
TIFFS

**6-letter words**
ADDING
LAMENT
TRADER

**7-letter word**
TRANCED

**8-letter words**
CASEMENT
TREASURE

**9-letter words**
DETERGENT
REPORTAGE

# SUM-UP

Using the totals given, can you calculate the price of each envelope, pen, stamp and roll of tape?

# 4-SQUARE

Solve these four clues and then rearrange the solutions into a sixteen-letter phrase, for which a clue is given. The two diagonals also make four-letter words.

THIN STRIP OF WOOD

BEARDED FARM ANIMAL

PIT

LADDER STEP

Clue: Serious affair (2,8,6)

# CONTINUITY

No black squares – heavy bars mark the ends of words.

## ACROSS

1 Dawn and Jennifer, comediennes (6,3,8)

2 Fate; in existence; merit; of hearing

3 Attribute; glowing coal; Black _____, police van

4 Prophet; garden feature; snake-like fish; serpent

5 Empty talk (3,3); solar body; person being tested

6 Worry; former (3-4); loan provider

7 Seldom found; diplomacy; annul; veto

8 Het up (2,1,6); river bird; Ireland

9 Concur; weird; quack medicine

10 Come into view again; police informer; lying face down

11 Edition of a book; _____ of Wight, county; pulled along

12 Sleuth; topic; Adam's mate

13 Establish by law; abhorrent thing; pare

14 Of the type mentioned; corner; solemn vow; *Rule Britannia* composer

15 Hollywood film award; strong wind; Russian mountain range; festival

16 Series shown again; fibbing; railway track support

17 Cereal fibre; Wimbledon favourite; precipitous; university official

## DOWN

1 Urgent news report; monk; fateful date in March; globe

2 England's flower; citrus fruit; male adults; consumer

3 And so on (2,6); entranced; Ghana's capital

4 Tell a story; Irish sprite

5 Short film extract; tiny amount; heroic tale; mountain lakes

6 Sleep through the winter; become knotted

7 Opposed; breaking the rules; vote in favour

8 Born as; rainwater channel; contender; container top

9 Devilish; wash lightly; adolescent years

10 Black fur; outer husk of nutmeg; despite the fact

11 Region; inert gas; practise for a play

12 Dreamlike; chef; garment edge; yarn

13 Nominate; encounter; health resort; Austrian symphonic composer

14 Twofold; creek; regret; bleeped

15 Purposeful mission; ballpoint pen; lustful gaze; primate

16 Lift up; organ of hearing; rough; meadow

17 Sharp hit; sea eagle; ancient Iranian; acquire knowledge

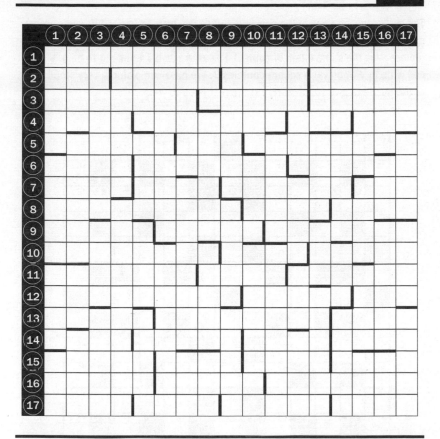

# RIDDLE ME REE

My first is in PUPIL but not in EYE,

My second's in FASTEN but not in TIE,

My third is in SISTER but not in BROTHER,

My fourth is in FATHER but not in MOTHER,

My fifth is in COUCH but not in SEAT,

My sixth is in GRAVY but not in MEAT,

My seventh's in MAIZE but not in CORN,

My whole by some workers you'll see is worn.

# KEYWORD

This puzzle has no clues in the conventional sense. Instead, every different number printed in the main grid represents a different letter (with the same number always representing the same letter, of course). For example, if 7 turns out to be a 'V', you can write in V wherever a square contains 7. We have completed a very small part of the puzzle to give you a start, but the rest is up to you.

| 19 | 2 | 14 | 6 | 24 | 1 | | 26 | 16 | 24 | 13 | 6 | 1 |
|----|----|----|----|----|----|----|----|----|----|----|----|----|
| 18 | | 16 | | 18 | | 21 | | 4 | | 12 | | 18 |
| 4 | 24 | 2 | 6 | 26 | | 2 | | 6 | 10 | 23 | 18 | 12 |
| 12 | | 3 | | 19 | 18 | 1 | 19 | 20 | | 3 | | 23 |
| 6 | 21 | 14 | 6 | 1 | | 13 | | 1 | 2 | 14 | 7 | 19 |
| 19 | | | 12 | | 25 | 16 | 4 **B** | | 14 | | | 6 |
| | 5 | 6 | 4 | 24 | 18 | | 2 **I** | 3 | 12 | 18 | 20 | |
| 18 | | | 16 | | 8 | 23 | 14 **G** | | 16 | | | 9 |
| 26 | 12 | 16 | 22 | 3 | | 3 | | 1 | 16 | 4 | 6 | 24 |
| 26 | | 23 | | 6 | 17 | 2 | 1 | 19 | | 24 | | 2 |
| 18 | 3 | 14 | 6 | 24 | | 19 | | 24 | 16 | 16 | 8 | 1 |
| 2 | | 7 | | 15 | | 20 | | 18 | | 16 | | 16 |
| 24 | 18 | 19 | 7 | 6 | 24 | | 1 | 9 | 16 | 11 | 6 | 3 |

A B C D E F G H I J K L M
N O P Q R S T U V W X Y Z

(The small grid is provided for ease of reference only)

| 1 | 2 | 3 | 4 | 5 | 6 | 7 | 8 | 9 | 10 | 11 | 12 | 13 |
|----|----|----|----|----|----|----|----|----|----|----|----|----|
| 14 | 15 | 16 | 17 | 18 | 19 | 20 | 21 | 22 | 23 | 24 | 25 | 26 |

# CROSSWORD

**ACROSS**

1 Another term for the navy (6,7)
9 Flick through (pages) (6)
10 Happening (8)
11 Amaze (4)
12 Small flat savoury Indian cake (5)
13 Young animals (4)
14 Mongrel (3)
15 Only even prime number (3)
16 Eccentric (4)
18 Carved decoration (5)
20 Cylindrical hand warmer (4)
22 Remain firmly where you are (3,5)
24 Connect up to the electrical system (4,2)
25 Alternative (medicine) (13)

**DOWN**

2 Be (5)
3 First stage of human life (7)
4 Grass similar to wheat (3)
5 Girl's name or heather (5)
6 Mindlessness (7)
7 Much-eaten sea fish (3)
8 Small portion (of butter) (4)
12 Look after, rear (5,2)
13 Set fire to (7)
17 Dead keen (4)
19 Metric fluid measure (5)
21 Roving monk (5)
23 As well, besides (3)
24 Dish enclosed in pastry (3)

# STORY CROSSWORD

Transfer the words which complete the story to the grid and then put the circled letters in the right order to discover the name of the famous person therein described.

The son of a civil servant who made his name ___(27A) Arabia, he was born in Ambala, ___(8A) in 1911. He was educated at Westminster ___(1D), then went on to Trinity College, ___(7A), where he ___(16D) Guy Burgess, Donald Maclean and Anthony Blunt. They all shared an interest in communism and it soon became clear that the Soviet agents were keen to ___(3D) his name to their list of spies. He became an agent for them in 1933.

Following the outbreak of the Spanish civil ___(14A) in 1937, he went to Spain as a freelance journalist and a Soviet ___(25D). He was later employed by *The Times*.

In 1940 he returned to London and managed to ___(17D) a post with the British Secret Intelligence Service (MI6). This job gave him the opportunity to pass on secret information to his Soviet contacts. In 1944, he achieved the ___(15D) of head of the anti-communist counter-espionage unit. He used his position to prevent the defection to the west of ___(17A) of the KGB's senior officials, an occurrence which would have caused ___(11A) difficulties for the Soviet Union if it ___(5D) gone ahead. His part in the matter was ___(28A) detected and when World War II ended, he was awarded an ___(2D) for his wartime services.

In 1949 he ___(11D) off for the United ___(6D) to take up a post as the first secretary of the British embassy in Washington, where he worked closely with the CIA. Burgess ___(13A) posted to Washington by the Foreign Office, but before long he discovered that the security services were interested in Maclean's activities. He sent Burgess home to encourage Maclean to ___(26D) to get ___(24D) of Britain before it was too ___(12A). The ___(22A) men defected in 1951 and he was interrogated about his part in the affair. He denied all knowledge of any wrongdoing by either man. The investigators doubted that anyone ___(19A) was involved, but there was not ___(20D) evidence ___(21A) him to bring a successful prosecution. He was asked to resign from his post.

He worked as foreign correspondent for the *Observer* and the *Economist* in ___(4D), then took ___(9A) for the Soviet Union in 1963. He was granted political asylum and became a Soviet citizen. His wife ___(18D) to join him in Moscow, but she ___(10D) disenchanted with life there and returned to the West in 1965, leaving him ___(23A). In 1968 ___(5A) book, *My Silent War*, was published. He died in 1988.

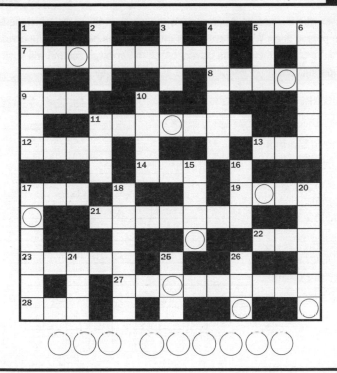

# BOXWISE

Put these three-letter groups into the twelve numbered boxes to produce twelve six-letter words, each of which starts in one box and finishes in another as indicated by an arrow. For instance, 2 and 5 make a six-letter word, but not 5 and 9. One group has been filled in to start you off.

GER ~~HAL~~ HUN LED

LEN LET PAL SUL

TED TIL TRY VES

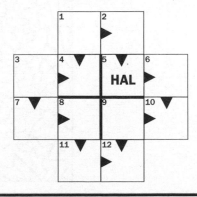

# TINKER, TAILOR ...

To discover who this person is unscramble the words in the verse, which hints at what the person does. Write these words into the boxes below, reading across, and, if you've placed them in the correct order, the arrowed column will spell out the occupation.

BROIS KERBEC and
    MIT MANNHE

Are famous stars of
    DONEBLIMW.

FESTIF FRAG and
    SLAYDIN
    EVANDROPT

RENTHAL the
    CAUDIEEN when
    they are on the
    CUROT.

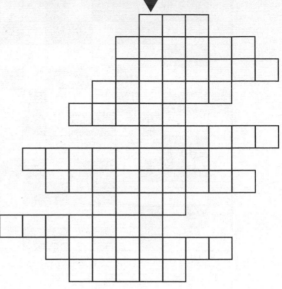

OCCUPATION: _____

# SILHOUETTE

Shade in every fragment containing a dot – and what have you got?

# WORDSEARCH

The 40 names and words on a motor-racing theme have all been hidden in the diagram. They have been printed across (backwards or forwards), or up or down, or diagonally, but always in a straight line without letters being skipped. You can use the letters in the diagram more than once. You will probably find it helpful to mark the words in the diagram and cross them off the list as you find them.

```
L U S S H A K K I N E N Q G D V
A L E S I H C T A H S D N A R B
O L W I L L I A M S M I P I A O
P L S J W N V G Z I C F I C H E
R E R I A L X E E A L A T N T H
A S L A L Z M H R A C N S A L E
C N A R C O N A G S S G T L U N
T A P O L E P O S I T I O N O O
I M S G K Y T A M E I O P I C A
C I R C U I T N N A R P N G S L
E I O T S O R P O A I A R E N U
D H R A C R O T O M I A T O T M
R E H C A M U H C S N D I I R R
L A H S R A M L I D G P N T A O
D B R A B H A M P M M B M I W F
F E R R A R I R F A O A N N E S
G N A P E S I L H U S L E K T Q
V H U N T X O C L J S W A T S N
```

| | | | |
|---|---|---|---|
| ALESI | GRAND PRIX | MANSELL | PROST |
| BRABHAM | GRID | MARSHAL | RACING |
| BRANDS HATCH | HAKKINEN | MASERATI | SCHUMACHER |
| CHAMPION | HILL | McLAREN | SENNA |
| CIRCUIT | HOCKENHEIM | MONTE CARLO | SEPANG |
| COULTHARD | HUNT | MONZA | SILVERSTONE |
| FANGIO | IMOLA | MOTOR-CAR | STEWART |
| FERRARI | INDIANAPOLIS | PIT STOP | STIRLING MOSS |
| FLAG | LANCIA | POLE POSITION | TEAM |
| FORMULA ONE | LAPS | PRACTICE | WILLIAMS |

# NUMBER JIG

Just like a Jig-word – but instead of letters, numbers.

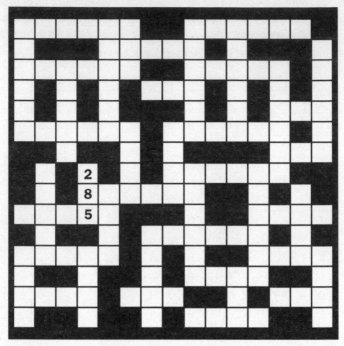

| 3-figures | 4-figures | 5-figures | 253231 |
|-----------|-----------|-----------|--------|
| 124 | 1886 | 15284 | 328419 |
| 208 | 2172 | 23051 | 342100 |
| (285) | 3124 | 31066 | 397162 |
| 406 | 3169 | 40122 | 416294 |
| 613 | 3943 | 55315 | 472851 |
| 737 | 4746 | 65119 | 502831 |
| 759 | 4840 | 81309 | 519639 |
| 801 | 5221 | | 623881 |
| | 6386 | **6-figures** | 683148 |
| | 8356 | 106394 | 762305 |
| | 8505 | 135028 | 830136 |
| | 9278 | 248339 | 944271 |

# BRACER

The first part of each clue gives a six-letter answer, five of whose letters make up the five-letter answers to the second part and four of which make up the four-letter answer to the third part. The unused letter from the first answer is entered into column A, and that from the second answer into column B. When completed, the two columns spell out two plants.

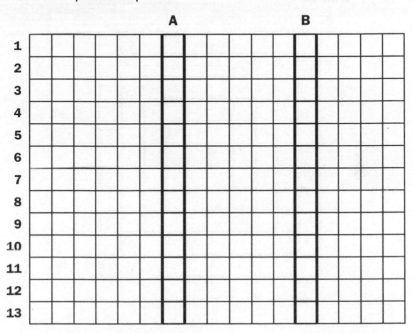

1 Travelled by boat; slip; fibbed
2 Stumble; amend; rip
3 Minister; malice; nuisance
4 Partnered; peeled; expensive
5 Costed; conceit; travel by bicycle
6 Consuming; dye, shade; small bell sound
7 _____ of Eden, OT paradise; category; old
8 Endeavoured; large shop; remainder
9 Choux pastry cake; Irish county; delicate fabric
10 Eye part; lifting gear; close by
11 Animal's guiding rope; our planet; speed
12 Extol; French capital; ship's mast
13 Hesitate; leased; inheritor

# SPIRAL

Every answer (except the first) uses the last letter of the preceding answer as its initial letter, the chain thus formed following a spiral path to the centre of the grid. The diagonals spell two singers.

**START**

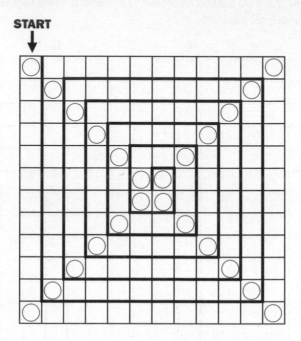

- Rejection (9)
- Daily publication (9)
- Set of beliefs (8)
- Taper (6)
- Timber (4)
- Miserable, sad (8)
- Bedroom wear (8-4)
- NE British city (9)
- Fan, devotee (10)
- Quisling (7)
- Old name for a soldier (7)

- Deadly spider (9)
- Overbearing (8)
- Glass beaker (7)
- Admired, esteemed (9)
- Prudent, tactful (8)
- Teaching (8)
- Original site of the Royal Observatory (9)
- Rented vehicle (4,3)
- Florid architectural style (6)
- Killer whale (4)

# CROSSWORD

## ACROSS

1 Something worth having (5)
4 Table of months (8)
11 Adaptable system of working hours (9)
12 Precious stone, often yellow (5)
13 Aspiring to be creative (4)
14 Ground particles (6)
16 Customer's courtesy title (3)
18 Final part (3)
19 Disconcert (3,3)
22 Whip mark (4)
24 Boredom (5)
26 Journal and magazine kiosk (4-5)
27 Informer (8)
28 Wear away, destroy gradually (5)

## DOWN

2 Exuded perspiration (7)
3 Outlet (4)
5 Alter (5)
6 Cafe (6)
7 Immerse briefly (3)
8 Shaving accessory (5,5)
9 Blotting out, deletion (10)
10 Metric measurement (4)
15 Court (3)
16 Overseer (7)
17 Rigid support for a broken bone (6)
20 Based on harmony (5)
21 Pale brown (4)
23 Title of the emperor of Russia (4)
25 Score of nothing in sport (3)

# JIG-WORD

No clues – just pattern and answers – but can you fit them in?

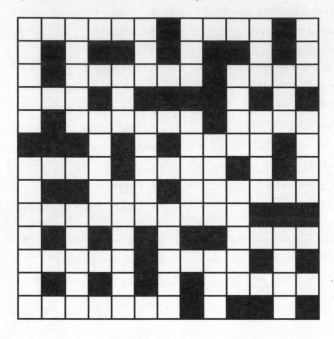

**3-letter words**
END
ERA
LAY
LEA
LOG
MET
NOT
TEA
TWO

**4-letter words**
ATOP
CRAB
DODO
EGGS
GOBI

LOUD
OGLE
OPEN
SALT
SEAT
SLED
SOLO
TROT

**5-letter words**
ADORE
ALBUM
EASEL
MESSY
PALMS
READY
RILED

STOOL
TITAN
UMBEL

**6-letter words**
ENTAIL
NODDER
NUTRIA
RESIST
TOMATO

**7-letter words**
CLEARED
DESTROY

**10-letter word**
EMPLOYMENT

# DROP-OUT

In the top picture, the conductor is choosing his sheet music. In the bottom picture, he has made his choice. Which did he take?

# TWO-TIMER

Two sets of clues to the same answers. Cryptic clues below and straight clues beneath the grid.

## ACROSS

1 Accidentally catching something perhaps (11)

9 Skinny swimmers (4)

10 Bartender on board? (11)

11 Drop rent (4)

14 Knew rat had got inside cape in Scotland (5)

17 Noted drama (5)

18 A minor trophy (5)

19 According to leading heavy drinker (5)

20 Strained in time (5)

21 Not how cruise passengers feel if there is one? (5)

22 Not an inaccessible part of river? (5)

25 Knot just below the surface of the sea? (4)

29 Remains to be studied in this (11)

30 Patient has some luggage (4)

31 Soldier of an area? (11)

## DOWN

2 Extremely quivery at the end (4)

3 Profligate has nothing to be sorry about (4)

4 Number three replaced (5)

5 Replant shaky trees (5)

6 Unwatered stock (4)

7 Produced out of great need (9)

8 A non-committal position on a horse perhaps (9)

12 One sharing top billing with one accountant in the country (5,4)

13 Vegetarians' festive occasion? (9)

14 Liquid Walter initially leaked out (5)

15 A letter from Corinth (5)

16 Lehar's hardest section was grating (5)

23 Here's another place near London (5)

24 Leading climber has breather on ridge (5)

26 Not at any price (4)

27 Slight legato effect (4)

28 Some vagrants hiding in the city (4)

## ACROSS

- **1** Eavesdropping (11)
- **9** Long fishes (4)
- **10** Graphic designer (11)
- **11** Rip (4)
- **14** Anger (5)
- **17** Musical play (5)
- **18** Prize (5)
- **19** Drunkard (5)
- **20** Taut (5)
- **21** Distend (5)
- **22** Attain (5)
- **25** Chain of rocks (4)
- **29** Study of human antiquities (11)
- **30** Box (4)
- **31** ___ Army, part-time force (11)

## DOWN

- **2** Terribly (4)
- **3** Rake (4)
- **4** Anaesthetic (5)
- **5** Change the reading (5)
- **6** Tidy (4)
- **7** Originated (9)
- **8** With legs wide apart (9)
- **12** Central American country (5,4)
- **13** Jollification (9)
- **14** Adam's ale (5)
- **15** Greek A (5)
- **16** Severe (5)
- **23** Surrey town (5)
- **24** Emblem (5)
- **26** Costing nothing (4)
- **27** Pass over lightly (4)
- **28** Site of the Taj Mahal (4)

# KEYWORD

This puzzle has no clues in the conventional sense. Instead, every different number printed in the main grid represents a different letter (with the same number always representing the same letter, of course). For example, if 7 turns out to be a 'V', you can write in V wherever a square contains 7. We have completed a very small part of the puzzle to give you a start, but the rest is up to you.

| | 18 | 26 | 3 | 22 | | 18 | 6 | 1 | 14 | 13 | | 24 |
|---|---|---|---|---|---|---|---|---|---|---|---|---|
| 4 | | 7 | | 3 | 23 | 7 | | 14 | | 26 | | 14 |
| 3 | 15 | 3 | 20 | 8 | | 1 | 14 | 11 | 16 | 20 | 14 | 11 |
| 1 | | 5 | | 18 | | 1 | | 12 | | 24 | | 3 |
| 1 | 11 | 14 | 18 | 4 | 14 | 8 | | 25 | 17 | 18 | 20 | 8 |
| 14 | | 11 | | | | 14 | | 11 | | | 8 | |
| 10 | 7 | 13 | 20 | 17 | 23 | | 16 | 14 | 18 | 18 | 8 | 14 |
| | 15 | | | 14 | | 2 | | | | 22 | | 6 |
| 2 | 3 | 13 | 18 | 14 | | 3 | 21 | 19 | 25 | 20 | 11 | 14 |
| 7 | | 26 | | 10 | | 8 | | 25 | | 17 | | 8 L |
| 22 | 3 | 11 | 2 | 8 | 14 | 13 | | 3 | 17 | 16 | 8 | 14 E |
| 14 | | 25 | | 14 | | 3 | 11 | 16 | | 8 | | 18 T |
| 8 | | 2 | 14 | 13 | 7 | 9 | | 14 | 15 | 14 | 17 | |

A  B  C  D  E  F  G  H  I  J  K  L  M

N  O  P  Q  R  S  T  U  V  W  X  Y  Z

(The small grid is provided for ease of reference only)

| 1 | 2 | 3 | 4 | 5 | 6 | 7 | 8 | 9 | 10 | 11 | 12 | 13 |
|---|---|---|---|---|---|---|---|---|---|---|---|---|
| 14 | 15 | 16 | 17 | 18 | 19 | 20 | 21 | 22 | 23 | 24 | 25 | 26 |

# ARROWORD

The arrows show the direction in which the answer to each clue should be placed.

| Pearl __, 1960s singer ▼ | ▼ | Mrs __, famous cook | ▼ | Strip of wood | Large desert stop | ▼ | Modern Siamese |
|---|---|---|---|---|---|---|---|
| Reddening ▶ | | ▼ | | | ▼ | | Sounded |
| Chris __, *The Road to Hell* singer ▶ | | | | Part of the head ▶ | | | ▼ |
| ▶ | | | | | | | |
| S African city | 1937 Garbo film | | Contrary to the law | Ben __, US *Hell's Angels* actor | | Keanu Reeves' role in *The Matrix* | |
| Winding in rings ▶ | ▼ | | ▼ | ▼ | | ▼ | |
| ▶ | | | | | Radioactiv-ity-emitting (rays) | | Taking legal action |
| Dignified | | The Word of God ▶ | | | ▼ | | ▼ |
| Obtain by deception | | __ Sharples, ex-*Street* character ▶ | | | | Pop star's follower | |
| ▶ | | | | Flat-pack home store (inits) ▶ | | ▼ | |
| Derek __, ex-racing driver | | Jordan's capital city ▶ | | | | | |
| ▶ | | | | __ Lee, Taiwanese film director ▶ | | | |

# STYLE CHALLENGE

This woman would like to buy two identical hats. Which two should she choose?

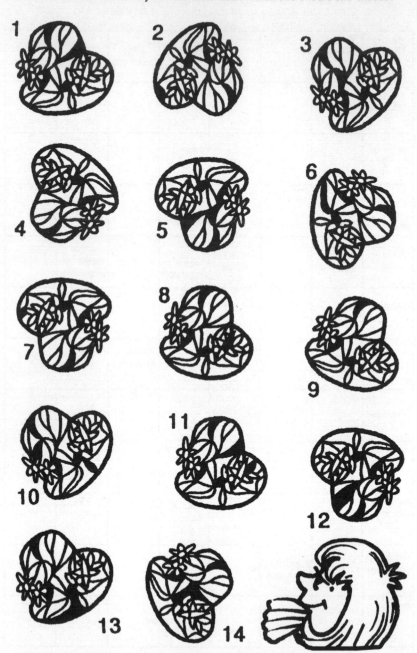

# ROUNDABOUT

Solutions to Radial clues (1 to 24) either start from the outer edge of the circle and read inwards, or start from the inner ring and read outwards to the edge (so they are all five-letter words). Solutions to Circular clues read in either a clockwise or an anti-clockwise direction round the circle.

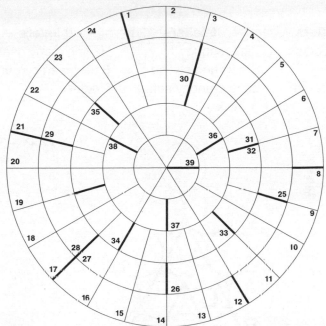

## RADIAL:
### INWARDS

1 Buying and selling
3 Spooky
4 Transparent
6 Sequence, arrangement
7 Gambol, frolic
8 Magic formula
9 Tortoise's home
10 Horrify, dismay
11 To do with the Pope
12 Theatrical play
17 Small weasel-like mammal
19 Added small photo
20 Rear of a ship
21 Scottish child
22 Trembling poplar
23 Shine, lustre
24 Multitude

### OUTWARDS

2 Duck noted for its feathers
5 Man-made fibre
13 Spanish word for 'friend'
14 Archer's missile
15 Crime of fire-raising
16 Shabby, poor-quality
18 Opinion, principle

## CIRCULAR:
### CLOCKWISE

12 Covered with fluffy hair
21 Beat, hit hard
28 Camper's shelter
29 On dry land
32 Look slyly or surreptitiously
33 Sets of two
34 Twenty hundredweight

### ANTI-CLOCKWISE

7 Musical performance
11 Overtake
20 Takes a seat
25 Conditional release of a prisoner
26 Symbolic diagram
27 As well
30 Challenge to do something risky
31 Fabric stainer
35 Filled pastries
36 Diplomatic assistant
37 Masculine
38 Back part
39 Cost of hire

# FRAME UP

Solve the clues and then fit the three nine-letter words around the outside of the pyramid, two words starting from the top and one across the base. Do the same with the three six-letter and three-letter words. The shaded letters will spell out an illness.

| **3 letters** | **6 letters** | **9 letters** |
|---|---|---|
| Clumsy person | Picturesque | Having many uses |
| Possess | Smart and stylish | Blue-green colour |
| Cooling device | Long crunchy salad stick | Fiddler |

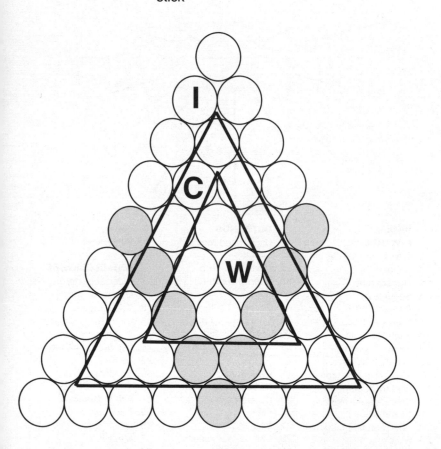

# CROSSWORD

## ACROSS

1 Incite (3,2)
4 Legless lizard (4-4)
11 Helped out (7,2)
12 ___ Jacobi, *I, Claudius* actor (5)
13 ___ Duncan Smith, ex-Tory leader (4)
14 Deep emotion (6)
16 Mass of water (3)
18 Swine (3)
19 Member of the clergy ranking lower than a priest (6)
22 Money paid for a wrongdoing (4)
24 Computer data (5)
26 District of LA (9)
27 Queen of Denmark and mother of Hamlet (8)
28 Sneeze-inducing substance (5)

## DOWN

2 Burning to a shell (7)
3 Line behind which darts players stand (4)
5 Midday meal (5)
6 Largest in scope (6)
7 Boat paddle (3)
8 Compensate (4,6)
9 Illlumination projected towards the ceiling (10)
10 Barry Humphries' Dame (4)
15 Facial spasm (3)
16 Side effect (4-3)
17 Magazine boss (6)
20 Was protractedly painful (5)
21 Night birds (4)
23 Tatum O'Neal's father (4)
25 For each (3)

# MISSING LINKS

The answer to each clue is a word which has a link with each of the three words listed. This word may come at the end (eg HEAD linked with BEACH, BIG and HAMMER), at the beginning (eg BLACK linked with BEAUTY, BOARD and JACK) or a mixture of the two (eg STONE linked with HAIL, LIME and WALL).

**ACROSS**

1 GUEST, ILLNESS, SHOPPER (7)
5 BAG, CASTLE, PIT (4)
7 BITTER, POTATO, TROLLEY (5)
8 FORWARDING, HOME, LABEL (7)
9 ACHE, DRUM, TRUMPET (3)
10 REASON, STREET, WATER (4)
12 BOOK, MARK, SECURITY (4)
15 RODEO, SELF, TEST (5)
17 CRAB, PIE, TREE (5)
18 CHANGE, CUT, FOOT (5)
19 BAND, BARN, SQUARE (5)
20 CODE, OFFICE, PLAY (4)
22 CABIN, CUT, NECK (4)
23 HATE, NAME, SHOP (3)
25 LETTER, OUTLAY, REACTION (7)
26 ACTIVE, DIGITAL, LOCAL (5)
28 GREEN, MORE, PRESENT (4)
29 BOMB, POWER, REACTOR (7)

**DOWN**

1 HYSTERIA, MEDIA, PRODUCTION (4)
2 SAW, SIGHT, THROUGH (3)
3 FAMILY, HIGHLIGHTS, WARRANTY (8)
4 BOOK, NEW, PLANNER (4)
5 MERCHANT, PAPER, YARD (5)
6 COURT, MOVIE, WALKING (8)
11 FUNDS, OPPORTUNITY, TIME (5)
13 BOARD, GROUND, SUSPICION (5)
14 GLOSSY, PARISH, RACK (8)
16 BLANKET, FIRE, RAZOR (8)
21 ALL, EFFECT, TASTE (5)
23 FLOOR, MASTER, SEATING (4)
24 MAN, MAT, STABLE (4)
27 CAST, DOWN, HARD (3)

# WORDSEARCH

The 30 occupations have all been hidden in the diagram. They have been printed across (backwards or forwards), or up or down, or diagonally, but always in a straight line without letters being skipped. You can use the letters in the diagram more than once. You will probably find it helpful to mark the words in the diagram and cross them off the list as you find them.

```
F E R B B J P H H P S U M F R R
J A N I T O R T R K L A R E W E
P A T O R Z A I B E I U T U A L
J E U E M P H M R D T R M G R T
X U K T O P A S Q E A S L B D U
C A D E H R J N M C H E E K E B
B R M G T O C U A W N C P R N R
V O O I E B R G G G T X T A O Y
H J S U A R C H I T E C T U U F
W T C N P J E N S R E W E R B C
Y A O A N I E G T A M O L P I D
K H O M R E E Y R M L N N S I F
C V K S R E D R A S I A G U I T
M G R E Q S T D T N M T Z R A O
P O H L L E B A E K A R E G I L
H K T A X Y O N L V W M C E I I
D H Q S F L Z I W S A Q E O Z P
G R O C E R M O F N A G E N T X
```

| | | |
|---|---|---|
| AGENT | COOK | JUDGE |
| ARCHITECT | CROUPIER | MAGISTRATE |
| ARTIST | DIPLOMAT | MAID |
| AUTHOR | ENGINEER | MILKMAN |
| BAKER | FIREMAN | PILOT |
| BELLHOP | FORESTER | PLUMBER |
| BREWER | GROCER | SALESMAN |
| BUTCHER | GUNSMITH | SLATER |
| BUTLER | HOMEOPATH | SURGEON |
| CARTER | JANITOR | WARDEN |

# PIECEWORD

With the help of the Across clues only, can you fit the 35 pieces into their correct positions in the empty grid (which, when completed, will exhibit a symmetrical pattern)?

**ACROSS**

1 Tympanum • Moved along noisily
2 Second-largest living bird
3 Sturdier • Let go
4 Female farm animal
5 Old-fashioned 'you' • Seaweed jelly
6 Bore flowers
7 Division of geological time • Card below the Jack
8 Part of a play • Long narrow crest
9 Trail • Tear
10 Next world
11 Writing instrument • Simple

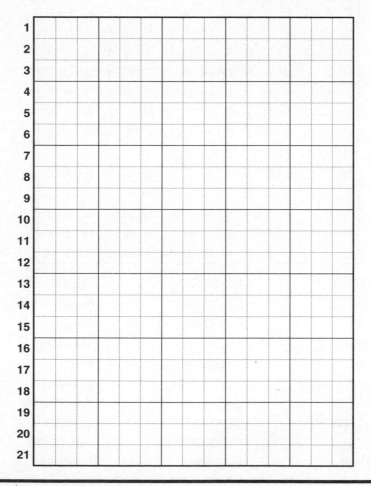

12 Return of cash

13 Parrot's home • Give or send out (energy, eg)

14 More strange • ___ firma, solid ground

15 Fishing item • Grate on

16 Aftermath of a nuclear bomb

17 Having X and Y chromosomes • Ferocious domineering person

18 Cake ingredient added to the creamed fat and sugar

19 Effortful (voice) • Give a claim to

20 Make a blunder

21 Coached • Tuesday to Thursday

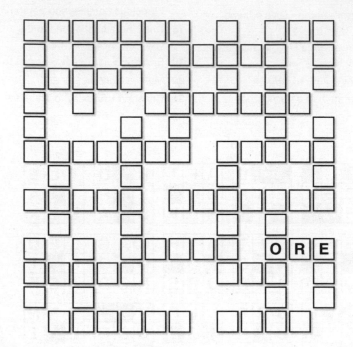

**3 letters**

Ace
Elf
Eve
Get
How
Ore
Win

**4 letters**

Blag
Hare
Knit
Onyx

Oslo
Xmas

**5 letters**

Camps
Fiver
Irate
Tanga
Texan
Wipes

**6 letters**

Gripes
Hard up
Issues

Rioter
Stains
Wading

**7 letters**

Dioxide
Goblets
Regrets
Skivers
Underdo

# RIDDLE ME REE

My first is in CRISPS, but not in SWEETS,

My second's in PARTY and also in TREATS,

My third is in FUN but not in FOOD,

My fourth is in CARDS and also in MOOD,

My fifth is in BALLOONS and in FOLKS,

My sixth is in GAMES and also in JOKES,

My seventh's in MUSIC and in CHEERS,

My whole celebrates a number of years.

# 4 SQUARE

Solve these four clues and then rearrange the solutions into a sixteen-letter phrase, for which a clue is given. The two diagonals also make four-letter words.

**Wine-bottle stopper**

**Snooker sticks**

**In this place**

**Attic**

**Clue: racing official (5,2,3,6)**

# CROSSWORD

## ACROSS

1 Spanish dance (8)
6 Tightly bound (community) (5-4)
7 Produce eggs (3)
8 Keen, sharp (5)
9 Protective skin lotion (3-5)
12 Porridge cereal (4)
13 Comedy sketch (4)
16 Punch and Judy man, perhaps (9)
18 Jury's verdict (3,6)
19 Back of the neck (4)
20 Invalid piece of play in sport (4)
23 Remain firmly where you are (3,5)
26 Distance down (5)
27 Zodiac lion (3)
28 Reverse on a bicycle (4-5)
29 Result of a puncture! (4,4)

## DOWN

1 Flighty, changeable (6)
2 Advice-giving journalist (5,4)
3 Chic or gracefulness (8)
4 Perplex, bewilder (7)
5 Eyelid infection (4)
10 Petrol-driven bike (10)
11 Parts of a machine or vehicle (10)
14 Rest on bended legs (5)
15 ___ de Milo, famous statue (5)
17 ___ with, tolerate (3,2)
21 Having a vacation (2,7)
22 Most enjoyable part (4,4)
24 Of current affairs (7)
25 Keeper, in football (6)
26 Money owing (4)

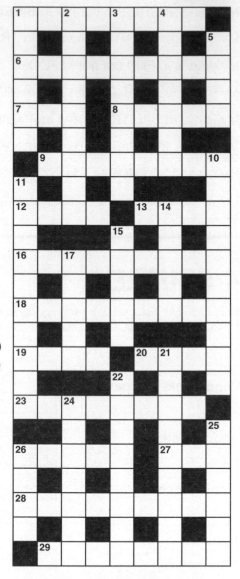

# SUM UP

Using the totals given, can you calculate the price of each bowl, tin of cat food, toy mouse and rubber ball?

# WORDSEARCH

The 30 words which contain CAT have all been hidden in the diagram. They have been printed across (backwards or forwards), or up or down, or diagonally, but always in a straight line without letters being skipped. You can use the letters in the diagram more than once. You will probably find it helpful to mark the words in the diagram and cross them off the list as you find them.

```
C H C K L W O C X D Y N R O A E
H A I L L A C T A C S H H S S Y
R I T T C I L O H T A C C I T T
R E Y C L E N I K T A C H T E L
A G L E H H W M S Y L C A T A C
T C A T A P U L T A E C O V M C
A F T Z R O H F L T Y A Z M M J
C C A T E R E R A K Y T B O B N
X P C L G T I C A T C H W O R D
C Q C H U S T G D S I E U Q A C
C S I S R A H T A C E D Y K A G
A Y T J C T W P A K Z R N T C C
T R C I F A S R L O O A A P A A
A E A U U C T A E G B L S T T T
R T T W V S W H E T O T M H T F
A T N Y Q T T T O G A I A B L I
C A I U A M A A U D N C R C E S
T C P C X C C E C T E J D V B H
```

| | | |
|---|---|---|
| CATACLYSM | CATCHPHRASE | CATHODE |
| CATACOMB | CATCHWORD | CATHOLIC |
| CATALOGUE | CATCHY | CATKIN |
| CATALYTIC | CATECHISE | CATMINT |
| CATAPULT | CATEGORY | CATNIP |
| CATARACT | CATERER | CATSUIT |
| CATARRH | CATERWAUL | CATTERY |
| CATASTROPHE | CATFISH | CATTLE |
| CATBOAT | CATHARSIS | CATTY |
| CATCALL | CATHEDRAL | CATWALK |

# SUDOKU

Place the numbers from 1 to 9 in each empty cell so that each row, each column and each 3 x 3 block contains all the numbers from 1 to 9 to solve this tricky Sudoku puzzle.

| | | | | | | | | |
|---|---|---|---|---|---|---|---|---|
| | | | | | | | | |
| | | | 5 | 8 | | 9 | | |
| | 9 | | | 4 | | | 2 | |
| 6 | | | 3 | | | | | |
| 7 | 5 | | 4 | | | 8 | 6 | |
| 3 | | 4 | 2 | 7 | 6 | | 1 | |
| 1 | 4 | | 7 | | | | | |
| | | 8 | | 3 | | 7 | | |
| 5 | | 6 | 8 | 2 | 1 | | | |

**EASY**

# TINKER, TAILOR...

To discover who this person is, unscramble the words in the verse, which hints at what the person does. Write these words into the boxes below, reading across, and, if you've placed them in the correct order, the arrowed column will spell out the occupation.

If the old joanna doesn't DOUNS so good,

The ABBY DRANG doesn't KINLET like it should,

LICKGINT the ROVISIE BLESSMEER call of moose,

This LIONSSAFEROP will restore all to RUNHOOMSIA CALMSUI use.

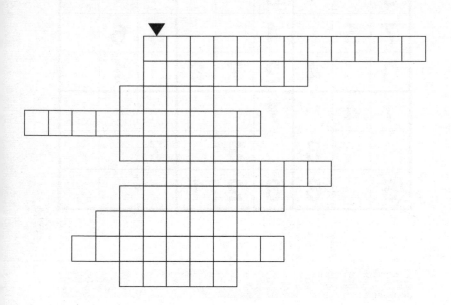

OCCUPATION: _____

# CROSSWORD

## ACROSS

1 Top Olympic award (4,5)
9 Forgot to include (7)
10 Commercials (3)
11 Thing worth having (5)
12 Canvas shelters (5)
14 ___ Gras, Shrove Tuesday carnival (5)
16 Nina ___, perfume company (5)
18 South African golfer (3)
19 Prohibit (3)
21 ___ Garson, star of *Mrs Miniver* (5)
22 Site of the San Marino Grand Prix (5)
23 Bathroom cloth (5)
25 Indian washerman (5)
26 ___ Lanka, country formerly called Ceylon (3)
27 Memory loss (7)
28 Defaming (9)

## DOWN

1 ___ Garden, ex-Goodie (6)
2 Defeated players (6)
3 Without significance (11)
4 Earn (7)
5 Item of an auction (3)
6 Persecuting (11)
7 Shock into a trance (4)
8 Poems (4)
13 Small waterfowl (4)
15 Singing voice, highest for males, lowest for females (4)
17 Share lifts to work (3-4)
19 Japanese dwarf tree (6)
20 Calling, baptising (6)
23 Flat vessel used for carrying articles (4)
24 Departed (4)
25 Beaver's construction (3)

# KEYWORD

This puzzle has no clues in the conventional sense. Instead, every different number printed in the main grid represents a different letter (with the same number always representing the same letter, of course). For example, if 7 turns out to be a 'V', you can write in V wherever a square contains 7. We have completed a very small part of the puzzle to give you a start, but the rest is up to you.

| 12 | 2 | 24 | 25 | 24 | | 24 | 15 | 20 | 2 | 18 | 18 | 24 |
|----|----|----|----|----|----|----|----|----|----|----|----|----|
| 1 | | 1 | | 19 | | 1 | | 23 | | 19 | | 17 |
| 25 | 1 | 18 | 18 | 8 | 19 | 26 | | 10 | 18 | 19 | 25 | 10 |
| 10 | | 9 | | 10 | | | | 2 | | | | 18 |
| 13 | 10 | 12 | 2 | 13 | 7 | 24 | | 3 | 2 | 21 | 1 | 3 |
| 24 | | 19 | | | | 1 | | 10 | | 2 | | 10 |
| | 2 | 13 | 13 | 10 | 24 | 3 (T) | 1 (I) | 23 (N) | 11 | 18 | 14 | |
| 16 | | 22 | | 4 | | 10 | | | | 10 | | 8 |
| 10 | 23 | 24 | 20 | 10 | | 24 | 25 | 2 | 23 | 23 | 10 | 13 |
| 2 | | | | 21 | | | | 22 | | 7 | | 1 |
| 18 | 1 | 22 | 1 | 3 | | 21 | 5 | 2 | 13 | 2 | 7 | 10 |
| 19 | | 2 | | 10 | | 19 | | 16 | | 13 | | 6 |
| 3 | 1 | 13 | 2 | 7 | 10 | 24 | | 10 | 2 | 24 | 10 | 24 |

A B C D E F G H J̸ J K L M N̸ O P Q R S̸ T̸ U V W X Y Z

| 1 (I) | 2 | 3 (T) | 4 | 5 | 6 | 7 | 8 | 9 | 10 | 11 | 12 | 13 |
|----|----|----|----|----|----|----|----|----|----|----|----|----|
| 14 | 15 | 16 | 17 | 18 | 19 | 20 | 21 | 22 | 23 (N) | 24 | 25 | 26 |

# BOX WISE

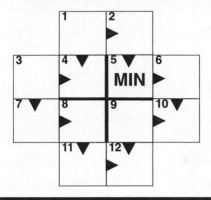

Can you put these three-letter groups into the twelve numbered boxes to produce twelve six-letter words, each of which starts in one box and finishes in another as indicated by an arrow? For instance, 2 and 5 make a six-letter word, but not 5 and 9. One group of three letters has been filled in to start you off.

CER DER EAL GAT GHT HER
IVE (MIN) NOU REV SLI VER

# SILHOUETTE

Shade in every fragment that contains a dot and what have you got?

# NUMBER JIG

Just like a jig-word – but instead of letters, numbers.

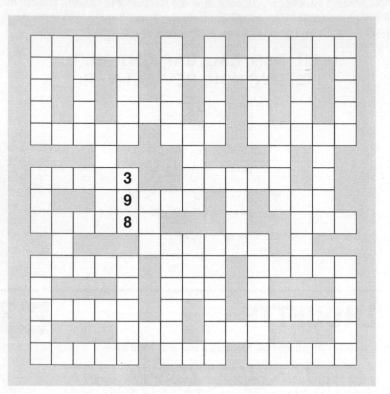

**3-figure**
156
189
215
216
312
(398)
494
502
615
813
830
895
910
937

**4-figure**
1136
1146
1238
2308

**5-figure**
10483
11244
12338
13213
16643
23941
27441
34531

36243
37404
39140
39923
39928
39945
41296
43902
49926
50036
59831
59928
63924
66156

89652
91013
92375
94111
99162

**6-figure**
212483
254509
506384
591324
752562

# WORDSEARCH

The 30 Ancient Greeks have all been hidden in the diagram. They have been printed across (backwards or forwards), or up or down, or diagonally, but always in a straight line without letters being skipped. You can use the letters in the diagram more than once. You will probably find it helpful to mark the words in the diagram and cross them off the list as you find them.

```
Z  J  G  I  F  A  E  T  G  G  N  V  B  T  P  U
E  R  O  S  P  L  T  E  A  A  S  E  S  U  M  O
U  Z  C  O  E  I  R  T  M  R  E  O  D  D  S  F
S  A  L  C  Y  S  I  I  G  S  T  A  I  P  X  D
A  L  T  E  E  U  T  D  O  H  S  A  Y  L  I  J
O  R  S  L  N  T  O  O  S  U  R  L  R  E  E  V
A  O  E  O  A  O  N  R  E  K  A  A  V  U  X  H
M  N  R  C  A  I  H  H  V  C  J  E  T  L  S  N
E  T  A  C  E  H  P  P  O  S  E  I  D  O  N  A
W  J  Y  H  I  R  C  A  E  A  B  H  K  C  R  G
K  R  O  N  O  S  L  D  A  S  O  K  E  E  Q  G
D  N  F  M  S  Z  Z  I  S  U  R  Y  H  P  E  Z
H  E  L  R  I  J  T  O  N  P  E  E  Q  P  S  S
B  M  M  R  M  S  U  N  W  K  A  F  P  B  N  E
V  X  Z  E  E  E  Z  Y  X  W  S  R  N  Q  M  M
Y  L  R  H  T  U  B  S  C  H  R  O  N  O  S  R
Y  T  T  M  R  E  S  U  S  R  K  Y  C  F  E  E
U  L  B  O  A  X  R  S  P  P  X  Q  D  O  W  H
```

| | | |
|---|---|---|
| APHRODITE | ELECTRA | MUSES |
| APOLLO | EROS | NEREUS |
| ARES | GAEA | NYX |
| ARTEMIS | HECATE | PERSEPHONE |
| BOREAS | HELIOS | POSEIDON |
| CALYPSO | HERA | SELENE |
| CHAOS | HERMES | TARTARUS |
| CHRONOS | HESTIA | TRITON |
| DEMETER | KRONOS | ZEPHYRUS |
| DIONYSUS | MORPHEUS | ZEUS |

# LOGISTICAL

Yesterday evening's show did not go well for conjurer Abe Cadabra. He performed five card tricks, each on a different member of the audience, but managed to mess up each trick by accidentally revealing a hidden card before he was supposed to. From the clues given below, can you identify the five audience members who were chosen to take part, working out where each person had been sitting before being called up onto the stage, which card Abe inadvertently revealed to the spectators during the course of each trick and where the magician had been trying to conceal each of the cards?

## Clues

**1** While Gavin was assisting with a trick, a cunningly concealed jack of clubs was accidentally exposed to the audience.

**2** Kenneth's seat was not E14.

**3** It was while Abe was performing a trick with the help of a man from the audience that the ace of diamonds slipped out from its hiding place under the conjurer's hatband.

**4** The spectator from seat A7 was helping Abe when a card slid out from up the performer's right sleeve; the card up the magician's left sleeve was not revealed during the course of the trick involving Maxine, who was from seat C9.

**5** The queen of spades slipped from its hiding place while the person from seat B6 was helping with a trick.

**6** Andrea was the spectator involved in the trick during which the magician carelessly dropped a card that he had been concealing in the palm of his hand; this card was a club.

|  | Seat A7 | Seat B6 | Seat C9 | Seat D12 | Seat E14 | Two of clubs | Jack of clubs | Queen of spades | King of hearts | Ace of diamonds | In hand | Under hatband | Under lapel | Up left sleeve | Up right sleeve |
|---|---|---|---|---|---|---|---|---|---|---|---|---|---|---|---|
| Andrea |  |  |  |  |  |  |  |  |  |  |  |  |  |  |  |
| Gavin |  |  |  |  |  |  |  |  |  |  |  |  |  |  |  |
| Kenneth |  |  |  |  |  |  |  |  |  |  |  |  |  |  |  |
| Maxine |  |  |  |  |  |  |  |  |  |  |  |  |  |  |  |
| Susan |  |  |  |  |  |  |  |  |  |  |  |  |  |  |  |
| In hand |  |  |  |  |  |  |  |  |  |  |  |  |  |  |  |
| Under hatband |  |  |  |  |  |  |  |  |  |  |  |  |  |  |  |
| Under lapel |  |  |  |  |  |  |  |  |  |  |  |  |  |  |  |
| Up left sleeve |  |  |  |  |  |  |  |  |  |  |  |  |  |  |  |
| Up right sleeve |  |  |  |  |  |  |  |  |  |  |  |  |  |  |  |
| Two of clubs |  |  |  |  |  |  |  |  |  |  |  |  |  |  |  |
| Jack of clubs |  |  |  |  |  |  |  |  |  |  |  |  |  |  |  |
| Queen of spades |  |  |  |  |  |  |  |  |  |  |  |  |  |  |  |
| King of hearts |  |  |  |  |  |  |  |  |  |  |  |  |  |  |  |
| Ace of diamonds |  |  |  |  |  |  |  |  |  |  |  |  |  |  |  |

*Record in this grid all the information obtained from the clues, by using a cross to indicate a definite 'no' and a tick to show a definite 'yes'. Transfer these to all sections of the grid thus eliminating all but one possibility, which must be the correct one.*

| Name | Seat | Card | Hiding place |
|---|---|---|---|
|  |  |  |  |
|  |  |  |  |
|  |  |  |  |
|  |  |  |  |
|  |  |  |  |

# ARROWORD

The arrows show the direction in which the answer to each clue should be placed.

| So, therefore | | Place of worship | | Determining | Woody nightshade | Nought | |
|---|---|---|---|---|---|---|---|
| | | | | Honey producer | | | |
| __ Grit, John Wayne film | | T'ai __, movement exercises | | | Soak | | |
| | | | | Number in a duet | | | |
| Talk casually | | Time-honoured ceremony | | | | Scorched | |
| | | | | And so forth (abbr) | | | |
| Grapefruit/tangerine cross | Huge man | Ventilate | | | Quiet, calm | | |
| | | | | Curative mineral spring | | | |
| The Three Wise Men | | More recent | | | | | |
| | | | | Sense organ of balance | | | |
| Antlered male deer | | Nephew's sister | | | | | |
| | | | | __ Hughes, poet | | | |

# CROSSWORD

## ACROSS

1 Typical example (7)
7 Choose (by vote) (5)
8 Hawaiian floral garland (3)
9 Small unit of length (4)
10 Person from Glasgow, eg (4)
12 Young singer in church (8)
14 Small circles as part of a pattern on fabric (5,4)
15 Seafood patty (4-4)
18 Watcher (8)
21 Infant's seat on wheels (4,5)
23 Swaggered (8)
25 Female red deer (4)
26 Long film or novel (4)
28 Ho ___ Minh City, former Saigon (3)
29 Cry like a sheep (5)
30 Creation of select groups (7)

## DOWN

2 Kindergarten (3-6)
3 Turf betting system (4)
4 Light-brown confection (4,9)
5 Submarine's optical device (9)
6 In need of a wash (5)
11 Ring of flowers or foliage (6)
13 Enquired (5)
16 Flimsy (13)
17 Foyer, entrance hall (5)
19 Erase (pencil marks) (3,3)
20 Group of lottery entrants (9)
22 Be printed (2,2,5)
24 Drill part which holds the bit (5)
27 Adjoin, border (4)

# BRACER

The first part of each clue gives a six-letter answer, five of whose letters make up the five-letter answer to the second part and four of which make up the four-letter answer to the third part. The unused letter from the first answer is entered in column A, and that from the second answer in column B. The two columns when completed, spell out two TV quiz programmes.

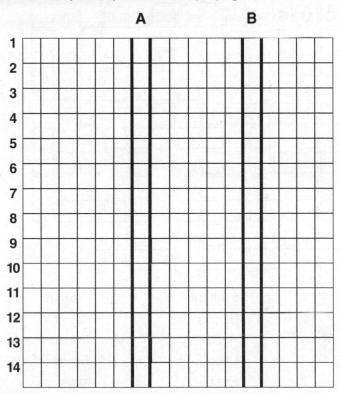

1 Hesitate, stumble; distress signal; authentic

2 Exile; sink; rubbish containers

3 Title; cut grass lightly; rustle

4 Cold season; saltpetre; gull-like bird

5 Unmarried; broken-arm support; chant

6 Lose; oily, muddy; thin

7 Shavings; untrue; transaction

8 *Robinson* ___, Defoe novel; scrub clean; mongrels

9 Reply; Shane ___, Australian bowler; fade, dim

10 Sour; clan; coffin stand

11 Pair; two-door car; manage

12 Illegal drug; wading bird; brave man

13 Dried plums; terrific; goad

14 Yell; draught horse; rent

# JIG-WORD

No clues - just pattern and answers - but can you fit them in?

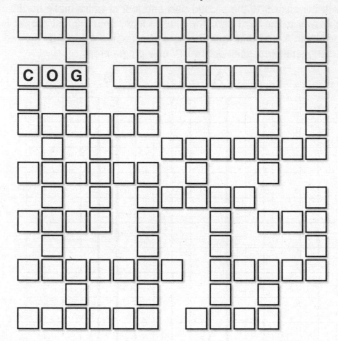

### 3 letters

Cog
Cos
Ink
Pro
Pry
Yen

### 4 letters

Bran
Cord
Edgy
Hide
Ruin

### 5 letters

Dogma
Hoped
Liked
Plied
Reign

### 6 letters

Advise
Caning
Covert
Etched
Porous
Soared

### 7 letters

Digital
Eluding
Fishnet
Idyllic
Ordered
Sulking

# SPIRAL

Every answer (except the first) uses the last letter of the preceding answer as its initial letter, the chain thus formed following a spiral path to the centre of the grid. The diagonals spell an invention and its inventor.

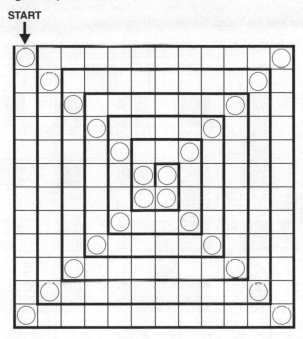

START

- Irregular, variable (7)
- Bread fragment (5)
- Ring road (6)
- Outlast, endure (7)
- Rope-soled shoe (10)
- Ambassador (8)
- Twelve months (4)
- Incoherent phrases (9)
- Plot outline (8)
- Up above (8)
- Study, lair (3)
- Layered ice cream (10)
- Roman sea god (7)
- Christian festival (6)
- Defensive body of troops (9)
- Scalp disorder (8)
- Variable work hours (9)
- Lattice for training fruit trees (8)
- Brightness, shine (8)
- Reveal (6)
- Additional (5)
- Suitable (3)
- Pipe (4)
- Spirit (5)
- After that time (5)

# KEYWORD

This puzzle has no clues in the conventional sense. Instead, every different number printed in the main grid represents a different letter (with the same number always representing the same letter, of course). For example, if 7 turns out to be a 'V', you can write in V wherever a square contains 7. We have completed a very small part of the puzzle to give you a start, but the rest is up to you.

| | 11 | 22 | 5 | 20 | 23 | 10 | 11 | | 15 | 16 | 9 | 24 |
|---|---|---|---|---|---|---|---|---|---|---|---|---|
| 24 | | 13 | | 23 | | 21 | | 9 | | 20 | | 9 |
| 21 | 17 | 9 | | 23 | 20 | 11 | 12 | 26 | 19 | 3 | 9 | 2 |
| 16 | | 25 | | 9 | | 3 | | 10 | | 26 | | 11 |
| 3 | 20 | 21 | 5 | 21 | | 9 | 8 | 22 | 19 | 5 | 3 | |
| 6 | | | | 11 | | | 19 | | 17 | | 21 | |
| 9 | 13 | 9 | 14 | 26 | 16 | | 14 | 5 | 21 | 13 | 9 | 2 |
| 11 | | 21 | | 5 | | | 20 | | | | 7 | |
| | 18 | 5 | 9 | 21 | 23 | 11 | | 18 | 21 | 15 | 16 | 9 |
| 4 | | 11 | | 15 | | 21 | | 21 | | 5 | | 5 |
| 26 | 25 | 22 | 9 | 16 | 10 | 14 | 26 | 16 | | 21 **A** | 10 **P** | 3 **T** |
| 25 | | 19 | | 13 | | 9 | | 16 | | 20 | | 11 |
| 1 | 20 | 3 | 11 | | 18 | 5 | 21 | 13 | 19 | 25 | 11 | |

A B C D E F G H I J K L M N O P Q R S T U V W X Y Z

| 1 | 2 | 3 **T** | 4 | 5 | 6 | 7 | 8 | 9 | 10 **P** | 11 | 12 | 13 |
|---|---|---|---|---|---|---|---|---|---|---|---|---|
| 14 | 15 | 16 | 17 | 18 | 19 | 20 | 21 **A** | 22 | 23 | 24 | 25 | 26 |

# WORD CHAIN

Place the groups of letters listed below into the boxes to form a chain of words, so that each box makes a word when paired up with the next box.

| | | | | |
|---|---|---|---|---|
| ALS | ~~CHES~~ | ED | HER | IN |
| IT | LET | ON | OT | PED |
| PLA | RAIN | ~~RING~~ | ROB | SET |
| ~~TEE~~ | TEND | TER | TH | TY |

```
┌─────┐     ┌─────┐     ┌─────┐     ┌─────┐
│     │ ──► │     │ ──► │     │ ──► │     │
└─────┘     └─────┘     └─────┘     └──┬──┘
                                        │
                                        ▼
┌─────┐     ┌─────┐     ┌─────┐     ┌─────┐
│     │ ◄── │     │ ◄── │ TEE │ ◄── │     │
└──┬──┘     └─────┘     └─────┘     └─────┘
   │
   ▼
┌─────┐     ┌─────┐     ┌─────┐     ┌─────┐
│     │ ──► │     │ ──► │ RING│ ──► │     │
└─────┘     └─────┘     └─────┘     └──┬──┘
                                        │
                                        ▼
┌─────┐     ┌─────┐     ┌─────┐     ┌─────┐
│     │ ◄── │     │ ◄── │     │ ◄── │     │
└──┬──┘     └─────┘     └─────┘     └─────┘
   │
   ▼
┌─────┐     ┌─────┐     ┌─────┐     ┌─────┐
│ CHES│ ──► │     │ ──► │     │ ──► │     │
└─────┘     └─────┘     └─────┘     └─────┘
```

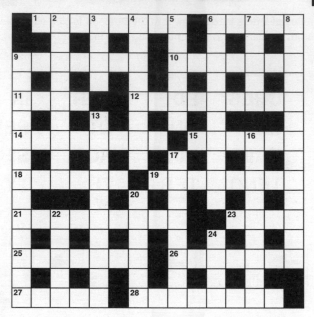

## ACROSS

1 Splendour of elderly relative, terribly rude (8)
6 Hated appalling loss of life (5)
9 More cheeky spaniel I fenced in (7)
10 Circle city motorway with clever paper-folding! (7)
11 Manages to make them at the Oval? (4)
12 Goes faster, like the streaker does? (9)
14 See ship as part of make-up (8)
15 Lint is odd to fix in the mind (6)
18 Most clean up, up before the others (6)
19 Firm cannot get upset about saint (8)
21 Least broad missile in the home (9)
23 Endless danger for a fairy (4)
25 Thankless type tearing round (7)
26 A thought that's funny (7)
27 Manage to overtake (3,2)
28 Pose of bird during a duet, possibly (8)

## DOWN

2 Storyteller managed to take company in? True, sadly (9)
3 Nothing is securing a tack (4)
4 Noble awards for listeners' parts (3,5)
5 Perches up in nest, so organised (6)
6 Satin Enid's fashioned with delicacy (10)
7 Partial dramatisation of a violin family (5)
8 Quibbling given largish pint – it spilt (4-9)
9 Writing being similar (13)
13 Preacher takes journey on a little railway (10)
16 A blow for the market? (5,4)
17 Painting left to judge, say (8)
20 Information woman gets on European city (6)
22 Girth altered the correct way (5)
24 Short axe is about right (4)

# DROP OUT

In the top picture, the man is choosing a polo shirt. In the bottom picture he has made his choice. Which shirt does the man buy?

# SKELETON

Have double the fun with this puzzle: you've got to fill in the answers and the black squares! We've given you the bare bones to start and it will help you to know that the black squares in the finished grid form a symmetrical pattern, so that every black square has at least one other corresponding black square.

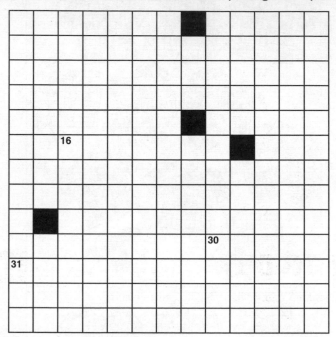

**ACROSS**

1 Break the calm of
5 Forward part
8 Eastern commander
9 Generally liked
10 More elevated
11 None
12 Raised platform
15 Drink usually of Indian or Chinese origin
16 Especially, mainly
18 Woman who wears a wimple
21 Little devil, wicked spirit
23 Success against an opponent
25 Tell fibs
26 Strike
28 Immediately
31 Famous
32 Barbarous
33 Black liquid mineral
34 Drink made from fermented apple juice
35 Modesty

**DOWN**

1 Placed under sedation
2 Poisoned, infected
3 Unpleasant-looking
4 Farm animals' shelter
5 Defective
6 Child with no parents
7 Rotating
13 Shrinking from notice
14 Joined house
17 Tardy
19 Ship which an iceberg sank in 1912
20 With the sceptre, a symbol of royalty
22 Coated, eg with silver
23 Pedlar
24 Early gentlemen farmers
27 Jangly
29 Uninhabited
30 Modish, fashionable

# SO COMPLETE!

LIONEL, ANNIE, GILLIAN, HELEN, PHOEBE, OTTO, PHIL and BOB were in a department store choosing footwear. Use the letters of their names once each to reveal what they bought.

B _ L _ _ T   S _ O _ S

R _ D _ _ G - _ O _ _ S

W _ _ _ _ _ _ T O _ S

F _ O T _ _ _ L   _ O _ _ S

T _ _ _ _ S   S _ _ _ S

F _ _ _ - F L _ _ S

G O _ F   S _ O _ S

---

# DOT TO DOT

Join the dots from 1 to 47 to reveal the hidden picture.

---

# PATHFINDER

Starting from the letter in the box, move up or down or sideways (but NOT diagonally) using all the letters to find the path through the names of eighteen dog breeds.

| P | L | U | R | A | I | R | E | L | E | W |
|---|---|---|---|---|---|---|---|---|---|---|
| U | G | R | O | R | B | A | D | D | O | H |
| E | H | C | D | A | N | L | A | P | O | I |
| R | B | C | O | L | A | I | L | E | P | P |
| A | E | E | N | L | A | T | E | X | E | T |
| G | L | D | A | I | M | D | R | O | U | H |
| S | E | T | S | E | L | A | N | B | S | K |
| A | E | A | P | A | N | I | A | F | A | E |
| L | R | O | R | R | O | E | H | G | G | Y |
| U | G | T | I | G | C | L | R | B | O | D |
| K | I | T | W | E | I | L | E | U | L | L |

| | | |
|---|---|---|
| PUG | BEAGLE | SPANIEL |
| LABRADOR | BOXER | DALMATIAN |
| ROTTWEILER | COLLIE | AIREDALE |
| WHIPPET | GREAT DANE | BULLDOG |
| HUSKEY | POODLE | CORGI |
| AFGHAN | SALUKI | LURCHER |

# JOLLY MIXTURES

In this puzzle, each clue is simply an anagram of the answer – but watch out! There might be more than one possible solution to each clue. For instance, the clue `TALE' might lead to the answer `LATE' or `TEAL'. You'll have to look at how the answers fit into the grid to find out which alternative is correct. None of the solutions are plurals or proper nouns.

## ACROSS

1 IT'S MAD
4 PLEASE
9 SAG
10 WIDER
11 PIT
12 ACRE
14 LOOP
16 ATE
18 LEAST
19 SHAPE
21 TIN
24 REAL
25 MOAT
28 OWN
30 TAPED
31 GUN
32 PRIEST
33 DIRECT

## DOWN

1 A GROAN
2 SIT
3 NEWS
5 IDOL
6 OPT
7 MY POLE
8 DIRGE
13 TRACE
15 STONE
16 NET
17 TAP
20 SENT IN
22 TINES
23 AUNT MO
26 LAST
27 ARTS
29 RAW
31 DOG

# CROSSWORD

## ACROSS

1 Sticky chewy sweet (6)
5 Mocks (6)
9 Fishing port on the Firth of Clyde (3)
11 Reveal (7)
12 Eliminate (7)
13 Careless, light-hearted (4)
15 Haunting spirit! (5)
16 Warmth (4)
17 Farm animals (4)
19 Bushy-tailed wild animals (5)
20 Netting (4)
24 Electoral division (7)
25 Toy made of cloth (3,4)
26 Adam's mate (3)
27 Old Testament queen (6)
28 Followed an eating plan (6)

## DOWN

2 Crop up (5)
3 Number of people in a quintet (4)
4 Fertility goddess (5,6)
5 Redirected (a telephone call) (11)
6 Once ___ a time, story opening (4)
7 Social group (5)
8 Small lump served with tongs (5,4)
10 London street with many government offices (9)
14 OK (3)
16 Make a sound like a bee (3)
18 Sentence components (5)
21 Flee with the intent to marry (5)
22 ___ Grant, *Notting Hill* actor (4)
23 Frightening giant (4)

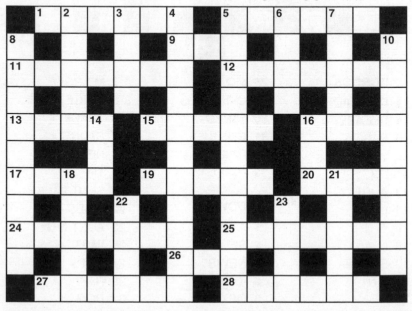

# SUDOKU

Place the numbers from 1 to 9 in each empty cell so that each row, each
column and each 3 x 3 block contains all the numbers from 1 to 9 to solve
this tricky Sudoku puzzle.

| | | | | 6 | | | | 8 |
|---|---|---|---|---|---|---|---|---|
| | | | 9 | 7 | 3 | 6 | 2 | |
| | | 7 | 4 | | 2 | | | |
| | 2 | 4 | | | | | 6 | |
| 8 | 6 | | | | | 4 | | 1 |
| | 7 | 5 | | | | | | |
| | 8 | | 1 | | | | | 2 |
| | 9 | | 7 | | | | | |
| 2 | | | | 4 | | 3 | | |

**MEDIUM**

# GIANT CROSSWORD

## ACROSS

1 Word-perfect, from memory (3,3)
4 Jolly, in a good mood (8)
9 Expected to arrive (3)
10 Droop, hang down in the middle (3)
11 Hula ___, children's toys (5)
12 Informal language, jargon (5)
13 ___ Hayworth, US film star (4)
14 Big, strong and beefy (5)
15 Aid in crime (4)
18 Edible inner part of a nut (6)
20 Idea, thought (6)
23 Old-fashioned kitchen annexe (8)
24 Animal famed for its laugh (5)
26 Portable megaphone (10)
29 Offensively self-satisfied (4)
31 Combine (3)
33 Land for building on (4)
34 Small edible berry (10)
36 Door-chimes (5)
38 Resign, retire (4,4)
40 Mark of disgrace (6)
41 ___ Bullock, actress (6)
44 Exclude, leave out (4)
45 Married women (5)
46 ___ John Silver, pirate (4)
50 Bet or lay a bet (5)
51 EU country shaped like a boot (5)
53 In the ___, eventually (3)
54 Ice-cream holder (3)
55 Borough of New York City (8)
56 Jazz up (6)

## DOWN

1 Refusing to work as a protest (2,6)
2 Scuffle, combat (5)
3 Dull pain (4)
4 Drinking vessel (3)
5 Uncertainty, wavering (9)
6 Simple to do (4)
7 Penniless (4,5)
8 Illuminations (6)
9 Snoozed (5)
16 Sound of mind and body (7)
17 In need of a scratch (5)
19 Enlist (new soldiers) (7)
21 Harsh government (6)
22 Proud, arrogant (7)
25 Near at hand (5,2)
27 Metal saucepan cover (3)
28 Go over (the limit) (6)
30 Made a noise like a cat (7)
32 Slowly progressive (7)
35 Way in which a word or phrase is employed (5)
37 Setting free (7,2)
38 Steadfastness (9)
39 Grouped together (6,2)
42 Spider's trap (6)
43 Turkish meat dish (5)
47 Musical play (5)
48 Star ___, classic sci-fi series (4)
49 Newcastle's river (4)
52 Large beer cask (3)

# ARROWORD

The arrows show the direction in which the answer to each clue should be placed.

| One of the languages of South Africa | Workers' guild | A fast one! | ▼ | Quarrelled, disagreed (4,3) | ▼ | Symbol for Capricorn | Boy at a christening? |
|---|---|---|---|---|---|---|---|
| ► | ▼ | | | Mayonnaise ingredient ► | | ▼ | ▼ |
| Bluish-white metal | | House made from snow ► | | | | | |
| ► | | | | Young boy ► | | | |
| Against | | Units of speed at sea ► | | | | | |
| ► | | | | Wonderment | | Consume | |
| Nocturnal bird of prey | Bats an eyelid | Swallowed ► | | ▼ | | ▼ | |
| ► | ▼ | | Northern girl | | Bangladesh's continent | | Film based on a Thomas Hardy novel |
| __ Sewell, *Black Beauty* author | | Sprang ► | ▼ | | ▼ | | ▼ |
| ► | | | | Use your eyes ► | | | |
| Makes requests | | Leg bones ► | | | | | |
| ► | | | | Com- mercials, in short ► | | | |

266

For this puzzle, we've filled in the answers, but there are letters in the grid, where the black squares should be. You need to black out the unwanted letters to make a symmetrical grid to match the clues, which are listed in random order.

| W | A | R | O | W | E | B | A | L | A | P |
|---|---|---|---|---|---|---|---|---|---|---|
| A | T | O | N | E | Y | E | X | I | L | E |
| S | L | Y | E | S | E | A | E | D | I | N |
| P | A | S | S | T | R | U | M | O | V | E |
| E | S | P | Y | O | U | R | I | C | E | D |
| G | E | A | R | O | M | A | N | O | V | A |
| G | U | R | U | L | B | L | I | D | L | Y |
| A | N | A | P | S | A | L | M | E | E | K |
| B | I | T | O | O | L | A | I | R | A | G |
| A | T | O | L | L | K | S | H | A | V | E |
| N | E | W | O | D | O | T | O | W | E | T |

## ACROSS

- OT hymn
- Damp, moist
- Noise, racket
- Catch sight of
- Spider's trap
- Coral island
- Circuit
- Cleaning cloth
- Armed conflict
- Play a guitar
- In a lazy way
- Piece, portion
- Small spot
- Banish
- Hindu spiritual teacher
- Make amends
- Decorated a cake
- Unused
- Ancient Italian
- Cunning
- Remove hair

## DOWN

- Pull along
- Musical note
- Compass point
- Obtain
- Seventh of a week
- Rob ___, Scottish outlaw
- Prohibition
- Existing, being
- Cuban dance
- Cover
- In the final place
- Used to be
- Depart
- Writing implement
- Fop, dandy
- Exchanged for money
- Join together
- Breakfast food
- Book of maps
- Uncooked
- Thick sweet liquid

# WHO'S WHO?

Using the descriptions given, can you match each man to his wife?

This puzzle has no clues in the conventional sense. Instead, every different number printed in the main grid represents a different letter (with the same number always representing the same letter, of course). For example, if 7 turns out to be a 'V', you can write in V wherever a square contains 7. We have completed a very small part of the puzzle to give you a start, but the rest is up to you.

| 15 | | 11 | | 2 | | 5 | | 15 | | 14 | | 10 |
|----|----|----|----|----|----|----|----|----|----|----|----|----|
| 8 | 5 | 16 | 2 | 9 | 24 | 4 | | 5 | 12 | 17 O | 7 | 24 |
| 5 | | 15 | | 4 | | 26 | | 20 | | 16 N | | 4 |
| 18 | 11 | 2 | 2 | 17 | | 9 | 17 | 5 | 19 | 24 E | 4 | 15 |
| 24 | | 4 | | 16 | | | | 4 | | | | 24 |
| | 15 | 1 | 6 | 6 | 24 | 15 | 2 | 11 | 25 | 24 | 13 | 21 |
| 17 | | 26 | | | | 7 | | | | 16 | | 15 |
| 22 | 24 | 2 | 24 | 17 | 4 | 11 | 26 | 5 | 13 | 13 | 21 | |
| 11 | | | | 4 | | | | 2 | | 5 | | 20 |
| 2 | 4 | 1 | 16 | 18 | 13 | 24 | | 4 | 1 | 4 | 5 | 13 |
| 2 | | 16 | | 24 | | 5 | | 11 | | 6 | | 5 |
| 24 | 13 | 18 | 24 | 4 | | 15 | 3 | 1 | 24 | 24 | 23 | 21 |
| 18 | | 17 | | 15 | | 21 | | 22 | | 15 | | 15 |

A B C D E̶ F G H I J K L M N̶ O̶ P Q R S T U V W X Y Z

| 1 | 2 | 3 | 4 | 5 | 6 | 7 | 8 | 9 | 10 | 11 | 12 | 13 |
|----|----|----|----|----|----|----|----|----|----|----|----|----|
| 14 | 15 | 16 N | 17 O | 18 | 19 | 20 | 21 | 22 | 23 | 24 E | 25 | 26 |

# ROUNDABOUT

Solutions to Radial clues (1 to 24) either start from the outer edge of the circle and read inwards, or start from the inner ring and read outwards to the edge (so they are all five-letter words). Solutions to Circular clues read in either a clockwise or an anti-clockwise direction round the circle.

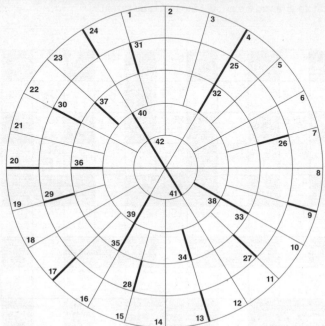

## RADIAL

1 Very overweight
2 Savour
3 Speed
4 Pork product
5 Protective garment
6 Rear end of a boat
7 Cursed
8 Lubricated
9 Trusty mount
10 Harmonious sound
11 Prize
12 Fortune-teller's deck
13 Aviator
14 Vote in
15 Build
16 Feudal lord
17 Actor's platform
18 Spooky
19 Premium Bond picker
20 Attractive woman
21 Banish
22 Soup spoon
23 Confuse
24 Dot-dash code

## CIRCULAR

4 Male opera singer
9 Shoo!
13 Rind
17 Observe
20 ___ Lugosi, film actor
24 Night flier
25 Appropriate
26 Accompanying
27 Mournful cry
28 Ceremony
29 King
30 Bother
31 Sheep's noise
32 West Indian language
33 Paddle
34 ___ Remick, actress
35 Gain by work
36 Hinged cover
37 Attire
38 Fabulous bird
39 Breathing organ of a fish
40 Large shop
41 Golf peg
42 Finish

# CROSSWORD

## ACROSS

**6** Revised hard for exams (7,2)

**7** Opponent, foe (5)

**8** Ostrich-like bird (3)

**9** Elephant's ivory fang (4)

**10** Make tunes with the voice (4)

**12** Sci-fi blood-suckers (8)

**15** Left without parents (8)

**17** Gripping, clutching (7,2)

**18** Aimed (at) (8)

**20** Well-schooled (8)

**23** As well (4)

**24** Land measurement (4)

**27** Glide across snow (3)

**28** Money, resources (5)

**29** Rented vegetable plot (9)

## DOWN

**1** Forcefully confident (9)

**2** Wanderers (6)

**3** Waits, remains (5)

**4** Likely to stick (8)

**5** Spend a lot of money (7)

**11** Tightrope performance (4-4,3)

**13** Alternative name for a seaman (7)

**14** Garden of ___, Adam and Eve's home (4)

**16** Lack of attention and care (7)

**17** Dislike intensely (4)

**19** Tough time, hardship (9)

**21** Follower of Jesus (8)

**22** Striker at cricket (7)

**25** Swiss house (6)

**26** Containing nothing, vacant (5)

# WORDSEARCH

The 30 musical terms have all been hidden in the diagram. They have been printed across (backwards or forwards), or up or down, or diagonally, but always in a straight line without letters being skipped. You can use the letters in the diagram more than once. You will probably find it helpful to mark the words in the diagram and cross them off the list as you find them.

```
B M G F Q U E M K W E G R B L L
S H A N T Y A P O L N S F D I E
S Z X H W D I L I O Q K B A L L
U T C E R I O H S N J D S L T E
D W R I K U E K T A I S T L Z G
D I G A N E L I T N A C C A V Y
N A T E I O C V H W V H I B H E
L O Y T F N I O N Y A G Y O N G
P N S A Y D T L D N M M R U N R
X Y C N B X N K T I E N T P J P
C N A E A P A S C A N Z O N E M
S I M K L H C L W F M R U L M L
A J R Q L N C I F N E E V Y O A
V J N Y U P O E M X L O H R K S
U B I M L Y T D M Z O F A T S P
P C B S U R O H C A D C E H N N
G E L A O S L W I T Y Z G Z B A
R R O P C S V R D J C A N T O Q
```

| | | |
|---|---|---|
| AIR | CHORUS | MELODY |
| ANTHEM | DITTY | NUMBER |
| BALLAD | ELEGY | PAEAN |
| CANTICLE | EPINICION | POEM |
| CANTILENA | FOLK SONG | PSALM |
| CANTO | HYMN | SHANTY |
| CANZONE | LILT | STRAIN |
| CAROL | LULLABY | TUNE |
| CHANSON | LYRIC | VOLKSLIED |
| CHANT | MADRIGAL | WASSAIL |

# ENGINUITY

Which lid will close and which will open when the engineer turns the handle?

bian

# TWO BY TWO

Each word in a clue can be preceded by the same two letters to spell out another word. For instance, INTER, LATE and TENT can be preceded by PA to make PAINTER, PALATE and PATENT. Can you solve the three clues below, then spell out the three pairs of letters to make a six-letter word?

- ASH, EASE, OWN

- IDLY, ERSE, ERRING

- TEND, TIRE, TEST

# TAKE FIVE

The three answers in this mini-crossword read the same across and down. We've clued the three answers, but not necessarily in the right order. See how quickly you can solve it.

1 **Pandemonium**

2 **Lustre**

3 **Plenteous**

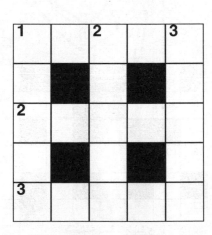

# CROSSWORD

## ACROSS

4 Cooking pot (3)
8 Rubbish bag (3-5)
9 Bring about (6)
10 Mounted (6)
11 Extra work for extra money (8)
13 Old Russian ruler (4)
15 Vulgar, gaudy (5)
16 Become outmoded (4)
18 Twanged instrument (4,4)
20 Island, capital Nicosia (6)
22 Writing-table with drawers (6)
23 Power of vision (8)
24 Cushion (3)

## DOWN

1 Zodiacal fishes (6)
2 Israeli airline (2,2)
3 Ms Blyton, creator of *The Famous Five* books (4)
4 Engrossed (11)
5 Five times eighteen (6)
6 Emended (6)
7 Film of impurities on a liquid (4)
12 Female sheep (3)
13 ___ Mahal, famous Indian mausoleum (3)
14 Schedule (6)
15 Drink container (6)
17 Easily offended (6)
19 One of the biblical Judges of Israel (4)
20 Prompted, reminded (4)
21 ___ Collins, rock singer/drummer (4)

# BOX WISE

Can you put these three-letter groups into the twelve numbered boxes to produce twelve six-letter words, each of which starts in one box and finishes in another as indicated by an arrow? For instance, 2 and 5 make a six-letter word, but not 5 and 9. One group of three letters has been filled in to start you off.

RET (CON) TED FER SUR ENT
VEY TIL SUL PAR ARD LEN

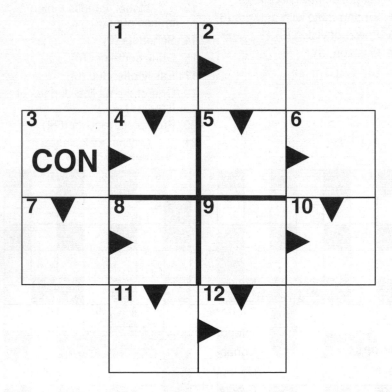

# JIG-WORD

No clues - just pattern and answers - but can you fit them in?

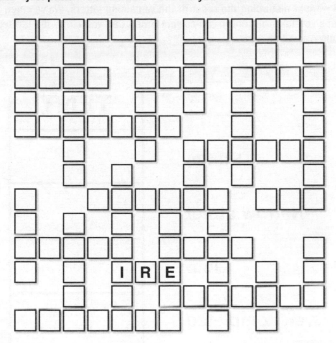

**3 letters**
Ego
Fib
Ire
Rid
Tip
Try
Wad

**4 letters**
Neat
Rode
Thee
Waft
Worn

**5 letters**
Faint
Miner
Raved
Silky
Whirr

**6 letters**
Attend
Canape
Daring
Evenly
Masked
Tariff

**7 letters**
Halting
Nullify
Raiding
Sniffed
Spacing
Voyaged

# STEP LADDER

Your task here is to climb from DOME to TENT changing just one letter at a time and without disturbing the order of the remaining letters. We've clued the seven steps you take, but not in the correct order. Can you climb the ladder successfully?

**TENT**

Status

Narrow street

Limp

Over, completed

Property revenue

Solitary

Tirade

**DOME**

# ARROWORD

The arrows show the direction in which the answer to each clue should be placed.

| Prisoner's release ▼ | | Animal foot ▼ | | Novel by Jane Austen ▼ | | *American* ___, talent show ▼ | |
|---|---|---|---|---|---|---|---|
| Worried, frightened ▶ | | | | | | | |
| Old Testament book | | Military brass instrument | | Unable to hear | | Strikes | |
| ▶ | | ▼ | Roald ___, children's author ▶ | ▼ | | ▼ | |
| Entice, bait ▶ | | | | | Put in order, set up again | | Give a better cutting edge |
| ▶ | | | Non-sci-ontific subjects ▶ | | ▼ | | ▼ |
| Washing-line fastener | Long time | | Trout, bream, for instance ▶ | | | | |
| Positive response ▶ | ▼ | | ▼ | Sets of clothes | | Emerald Isle | |
| Floor-length skirt | | Theatre attendant ▶ | | | | ▼ | |
| ▶ | | | | Gratuity ▶ | | | |
| Manipulates | | At that place ▶ | | | | | |
| ▶ | | | | Fox's lair ▶ | | | |

# PIECEWORD

With the help of the Across clues only, can you fit the 35 pieces into their correct positions in the empty grid (which, when completed, will exhibit a symmetrical pattern)?

## ACROSS

1 Plant with funnel-shaped flowers • Gather

2 African wildebeest

3 Wash lightly • Picture put into an album?

4 Nervous habit • Strongly scented herb

5 Details of location

6 Antlered creature • Force from a position of power

7 Minor bodywork knock • Belonging to us

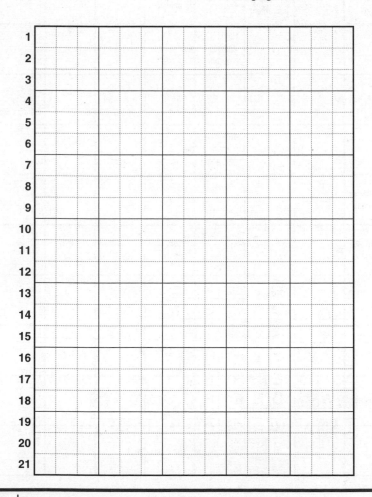

8 Place in a grave

9 Listen, pay attention • Nobleman ranking just below a marquess

10 Strengthening

11 Podium • Ceramic bathroom square

12 Excellent, fabulous

13 Small brown bird • European duck

14 Solution of salt and water

15 Offer for sale • Old land measure equivalent to a quarter of an acre

16 School boss • Pattern

17 Substance obtained from flax

18 Prohibition • Public transporter

19 Piquant • Simpler place or time

20 One's consciousness

21 Misbehaviour • Always on the move

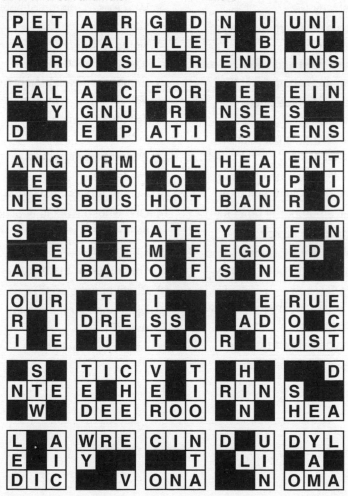

# TWO TIMER

Two sets of clues to the same answers. Cryptic clues below and straight clues beneath the grid.

## ACROSS

1 Lower record in clothing (7)
5 Cut tail off clever little animal (5)
8 Dodge nowadays taken in by first lady (5)
9 Completely virtuous young nuns? (7)
10 Think hard and resolve a dispute – about time! (8)
11 Obstinate type going on foot (4)
13 Castle that is used for raw recruit (6)
15 South American city man created a disturbance (6)
18 Nail a number of horses (4)
19 Innocuous advice to the sadist? (8)
22 Plunderer of outfit held by group (7)
23 One trapped in organ makes a racket (5)
24 Teacher filleted trout (5)
25 Revere ornate sceptre (7)

## DOWN

1 A fantasist? Yours truly in gloomy surroundings (7)
2 Quietly put on the checked material (5)
3 Vote Rex in charge of power supply (8)
4 Noted work from boy joining a reserve force (6)
5 Small prayer will protect from danger (4)
6 Tell about foreign nobleman (7)
7 A stew prepared but not wanted (5)
12 Suit for a girl's best friend (8)
14 One whose work is dealing with viewers' complaints (7)
16 Drop of French perfume (7)
17 Quick look at the bird (6)
18 Boast about clog (5)
20 Eject one learner into the river (5)
21 Just a loud melody (4)

## ACROSS

**1** Make miserable (7)
**5** Tiny long-snouted mammal (5)
**8** Avoid (5)
**9** Learners (7)
**10** Reflect deeply (8)
**11** Offspring of a horse and a donkey (4)
**13** Greenhorn (6)
**15** Ran amok (6)
**18** Metal fastener (4)
**19** Not likely to cause injury (8)
**22** Pirate (7)
**23** Sound (5)
**24** Educator (5)
**25** Admire (7)

## DOWN

**1** Vague, impractical person (7)
**2** Tartan (5)
**3** Exciting, tense (8)
**4** Piece of music for one instrument (6)
**5** Put money by (4)
**6** Relate in detail (7)
**7** Squander (5)
**12** Precious stones (8)
**14** Eye specialist (7)
**16** Act of moving down (7)
**17** Male goose (6)
**18** Wooden shoe (5)
**20** Banishment (5)
**21** Travelling show (4)

# CRYPTIC CROSSWORD

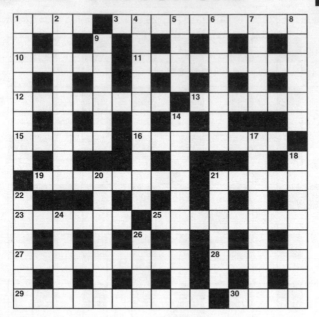

**ACROSS**

1 Terrible fellow, and kind of vain (4)
3 Uncle, with chess piece, damaged king (10)
10 Twitchy, later awake (5)
11 Person suing causes obvious row (9)
12 Domestic bird pinned by nail, unfortunately (8)
13 Quickly acquire from a lawn? (4,2)
15 New layer near the beginning (5)
16 Footballers who are not at work? (8)
19 Shocks, as nuts do, perhaps (8)
21 Rubbish tips – sad to be down in them (5)
23 Pressed one editor about Ron (6)
25 Holiday island is a drain, surprisingly (8)
27 Urgent demands certain to be admitted by reporters (9)
28 Letter from some gazette (5)
29 Offer head compassion (10)
30 Land in water is given to the French (4)

**DOWN**

1 Dreams popular game is arranged outside (8)
2 Broadcast set up rare openings (9)
4 Valuing a piano, uplifting (10)
5 Old shipbuilder coming from Hanoi I left (4)
6 Managed to fire rifle (7)
7 Stab Ken if troubled (5)
8 Blushing about enjoyment, though money back (6)
9 Tale about leader of militants, full of angry outbursts (6)
14 Enters unlawfully once father's broken locks (10)
17 Memos about babysitters (9)
18 Break free clutching notice – what a lark (8)
20 Supervise love poetry, emotionally at first (7)
21 Railway town acted with bed (6)
22 Inferior metal cooking vessel (6)
24 In which canoe could be wrecked (5)
26 Relation is mostly grand (4)

# SUDOKU

Place the numbers from 1 to 9 in each empty cell so that each row, each column and each 3 x 3 block contains all the numbers from 1 to 9 to solve this tricky Sudoku puzzle.

| | 7 | | | | | 1 | | |
|---|---|---|---|---|---|---|---|---|
| | | 5 | 1 | 7 | | | | |
| 8 | | 2 | | 5 | | | 6 | |
| 5 | | | | 1 | 4 | 2 | | |
| | 2 | | | 8 | | | | 4 |
| 1 | | | | 6 | 5 | 8 | | |
| 7 | | 4 | | 3 | | | 2 | |
| | | 6 | 9 | 4 | | | | |
| | 5 | | | | | 4 | | |

**EASY**

# KEYWORD

This puzzle has no clues in the conventional sense. Instead, every different number printed in the main grid represents a different letter (with the same number always representing the same letter, of course). For example, if 7 turns out to be a 'V', you can write in V wherever a square contains 7. We have completed a very small part of the puzzle to give you a start, but the rest is up to you.

| 5 | | 26 | | 8 | | | | 3 | | 10 | | 4 |
|---|---|---|---|---|---|---|---|---|---|---|---|---|
| 8 | 22 | 12 | 16 | 19 | 21 | 16 | | 5 | 25 | 19 | 20 | 9 |
| 15 | | 12 | | 16 | | 9 | | 24 | | 9 | | 12 |
| 19 | 16 | 19 | 20 | 1 | | 12 | 9 | 9 | 18 | 21 | 9 | 18 |
| 26 | | 9 | | | | 16 | | 21 | | | | 16 |
| 23 | 26 | 12 | | 9 | 13 | 9 | 1 | 26 | 9 | 8 | 9 | |
| 16 | | 18 | | 17 | | 21 | | 12 | | 5 | | 20 |
| | 4 | 22 | 12 | 17 | 20 | 9 | 21 | 16 | | 21 | 26 | 9 |
| 9 | | | | 16 | | 16 | | | | 10 | | 24 |
| 7 | 19 | 12 N | 8 | 2 | 9 | 16 | | 11 | 5 | 16 | 23 | 9 |
| 7 | | 5 A | | 9 | | 21 | | 26 | | 6 | | 12 |
| 9 | 14 | 1 P | 9 | 21 | | 13 | 5 | 1 | 1 | 26 | 12 | 17 |
| 18 | | 16 | | 21 | | | | 9 | | 12 | | 9 |

A ~~B~~ C D E F G H I J K L M ~~N~~ O ~~P~~ Q R S T U V W X Y Z

| 1 P | 2 | 3 | 4 | 5 A | 6 | 7 | 8 | 9 | 10 | 11 | 12 N | 13 |
|---|---|---|---|---|---|---|---|---|---|---|---|---|
| 14 | 15 | 16 | 17 | 18 | 19 | 20 | 21 | 22 | 23 | 24 | 25 | 26 |

# CROSSWORD

**ACROSS**

1 Two weeks (9)
6 Brushed (the floor) (5)
10 Member of a RC religious order (6)
11 North, Central and South America (3,5)
12 First Greek letter (5)
13 Eye flirtatiously (4)
15 Be jealous of (4)
17 Governed (5)
18 Junk email (4)
20 American inventor of the elevator (4)
21 Weighing machine (5)
24 Scandinavian capital city (8)
26 Wage-receiving time (3,3)
27 Site of the 1964 summer Olympic Games (5)
28 Anxiety (9)

**DOWN**

2 Lie partly upon (7)
3 Known facts (5)
4 Tiny amount (4)
5 Unpowered solo flight (4-7)
7 Used a pen (5)
8 Chum (3)
9 Had, possessed (5)
13 Away from home (3)
14 ___ *Misérables*, musical (3)
16 Vesuvius, for example (7)
17 Whole (number) (5)
19 Slightly foggy (5)
22 Tomb (5)
23 Narrow stretch of land running into the sea (4)
25 Sense of self (3)

# LINKWORD

For each of the word pairs listed find the four-letter word which can be placed after the first word and before the second word to make two new words or phrases. Enter your answers in the grid and unscramble the shaded letters to reveal the title of a novel (6,4).

SHELF _____ STYLE

PAPER _____ BENCHER

FUNNY _____ CHINA

DARK _____ SERVICE

APRIL _____ HARDY

CEASE _____ WORK

DEW _____ SCONE

NEVER _____ READER

RISING _____ SQUIB

ANISEED _____ BEARING

# ARROWORD

The arrows show the direction in which the answer to each clue should be placed.

| Havana's island | ▼ | Lyric poems | ▼ | __ Mother Brown, song (5-2) | ▼ | Requested | ▼ |
|---|---|---|---|---|---|---|---|
| ► | | | | | | | |
| Sweet courses | | Large tea dispenser | | Teaches, coaches | | __ Magritte, Surrealist painter | |
| Stark | ► | ▼ | | ▼ | | ▼ | |
| Be victorious | Neither here nor there (2,5) | | Second-hand | ► | | | |
| ► | ▼ | | 216 gallons of ale | ► | | | Nurse or nun |
| Viral cold | | Thick cords | ► | | | | ▼ |
| ► | | | Work-shy | | Big jump | Facilitate | |
| Within | Scilly __, group off Cornwall | ► ▼ | | | ▼ | ▼ | |
| ► | | | Take as food | ► | | | |
| __ Me Do, Beatles hit | Hire | ► | | | | | |
| ► | | | __ annum, yearly | | | | |

# NUMBER JIG

Just like a jig-word – but instead of letters, numbers.

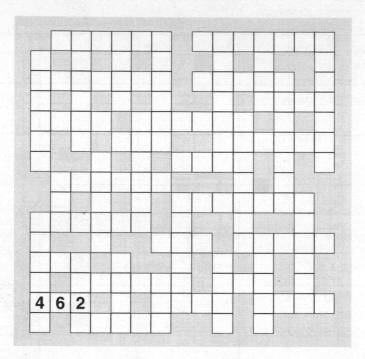

| 3-figures | 4715 | 6-figures | 7-figures |
|-----------|------|-----------|-----------|
| 102 | 5924 | 106878 | 2135609 |
| 285 | 6825 | 107842 | 4246537 |
| 370 | 7465 | 246570 | 4246590 |
| (462) | 9078 | 370785 | 6513107 |
| 560 | 9287 | 424646 | 7246560 |
| 786 | | 667475 | 8008942 |
| 997 | **5-figures** | 797072 | 9802827 |
| | 51517 | 805878 | |
| **4-figures** | 56567 | 824697 | |
| 1013 | 75801 | 831517 | |
| 1532 | 80789 | 870894 | |
| 2813 | 90814 | 980133 | |
| 3246 | | 980197 | |

# CROSSWORD

**ACROSS**

1 Nearest pub to home (5)
4 Glossy mac fabric (inits)(3)
6 Sudden surprising news (9)
7 Affiliated with one faction (8)
9 TV, radio, press etc (4,5)
10 Ballerina's skirt (4)
12 Black, murky (4)
14 London railway station (8)
17 Keep (a job) (4,4)
19 Female domestic servant (4)
21 Particular sort (4)
23 Discovering new lands (9)
25 Canine farm worker (8)
27 Condition helped by wearing glasses (3,6)
28 Lump (of butter) (3)
29 Wine residue (5)

**DOWN**

1 Fleshy part of the ear (4)
2 Clashing percussion instruments (7)
3 Become slow (clock) (4,4)
4 Kept going, stuck at it (7,2)
5 Period from January to December (8,4)
8 Granny ___, apple variety (5)
11 Judicial hearing (5)
13 Home office (5)
15 Unruly, noisy (5)
16 Soot remover! (7,5)
18 Piece of wood used as a doorstop (5)

20 Put into effect (9)
22 Calculated (8)
24 Set apart from others (7)
26 Duty, obligation (4)

# DATELINE

A number jig with a difference: with clues to figure out (with the help of a calculator if you wish!) to discover the date in the shaded line – in this case, an important date for London.

## ACROSS

1 Square root of 484
5 Add 2 to 1 Across
7 Divide 10 Down by 3
8 Subtract 1 from 7 Across
9 Add 202 to 18 Down
10 Subtract 1,402 from 13 Across
13 Subtract 1,000 from 23 Across
16 Cube 4 Down
20 Cube 3 Down
21 Subtract 1,991 from 23 Across
23 2 per cent of 272,300
25 Subtract 4 from 26 Down
27 Subtract 10 from 28 Across
28 Twice 7 Across
30 Add 30 to 5 Across
31 Subtract 1 from 30 Across

## DOWN

1 Subtract 2 from 29 Down
2 Multiply 1 Down by 100
3 Next in series 87, 96, 105, ...
4 Subtract 1 from 3 Down
5 Add 5 Across to 2 Down
6 Subtract 14 from 30 Across
10 Subtract 14,611 from 14 Down
11 Add 7,982 to 10 Down
12 Add 2,830 to 11 Down
13 Add 5,400 to 12 Down
14 8 per cent of 599,300
15 Twice 10 Down
17 Add 247 to 18 Down
18 Square root of 44,521
19 Add 427 to 17 Down
22 4 per cent of 103,100
24 Add 1 to 22 Down
25 Twice 3 Down
26 Twice 4 Down
27 Add 4 to 1 Down
29 Subtract 17 from 6 Down

# WORDSEARCH

The 30 types of hat have all been hidden in the diagram. They have been printed across (backwards or forwards), or up or down, or diagonally, but always in a straight line without letters being skipped. You can use the letters in the diagram more than once. You will probably find it helpful to mark the words in the diagram and cross them off the list as you find them.

```
M K O L P I K C O M G E L K T F
P U A R N V O T E R N N W N E E
A C S J U S P R U R E P B Z K D
C Y F H S A R B O M E R W Q C O
T D W A R Y M C T A R L B R U R
A Q C M W O I C D R E T W M B A
L K Z I H R O A S Q K H C O O Y
F M D V T Z P M R U L S E E B S
C O W B O Y U P N I A T O P A C
W T Y R O L E A N S T B W A N X
T P I F A O A I T Z S A F O B L
R J A Q K P O G B T R G S R H H
I T K N N I O N Y T E T D A E G
L R E T A O B R S E E R L E M T
B D W U H M C K K T D P I O F M
Y S I R S Y A V S P I L L B O X
C L S J U Z H N V N I J P F B X
E N R O C I B I E U Q E O X L G
```

| ALPINE | COWBOY | PANAMA |
|---|---|---|
| BERET | DEERSTALKER | PILL BOX |
| BICORNE | FEDORA | PORK PIE |
| BIRETTA | FEZ | SOMBRERO |
| BOATER | FLAT CAP | STETSON |
| BOWLER | HOMBURG | STRAW |
| BUCKET | KOLPIK | TRICORNE |
| CAMPAIGN | MARQUIS | TRILBY |
| CAPOTAIN | MERRY WIDOW | TYROLEAN |
| COSSACK | MUSHROOM | USHANKA |

# PIECEWORD

With the help of the Across clues only, can you fit the 35 pieces into their correct positions in the empty grid (which, when completed, will exhibit a symmetrical pattern)?

## ACROSS

1 Con trick • Chocolate/coffee mixture • Without the power of speech

2 Plural of 'is' • Meat baked in pastry

3 Smile broadly • Awry • Leak

4 Release • Join with heat

5 Travel permit • Port side of a boat

6 Stomach disorder • Soothed

7 Fruit of the dog rose

8 Lend approval to • Letter

9 Warm spot

10 Pencil eraser • Choose carefully

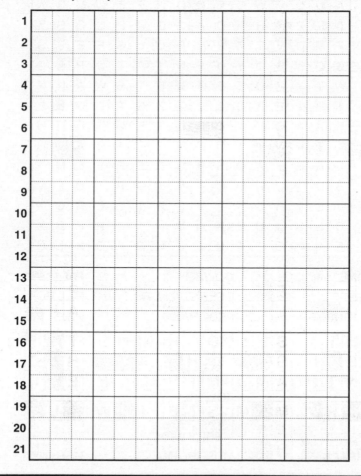

11 Window cover
12 Wife • Walker
13 Artwork made up of fragments
14 Dull • Go over again
15 Social insect
16 Nurse • Waster
17 Ballet skirt made from many layers of net • Noble gas element

18 Stallion's partner • Gave temporarily
19 Tread • With guns • Ninth Greek letter
20 Tall vase • The year ___, ages ago
21 Extra element • Stupid or drugged • Enclosed space near a building

# FISHY

Which two of the twelve fishes are perfectly identical?

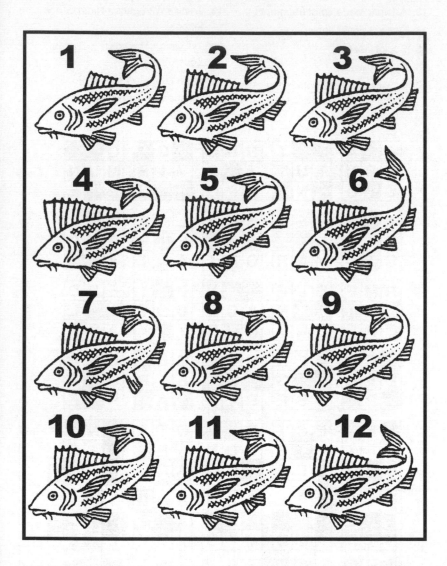

# CROSSWORD

## ACROSS

1 Indian or Chinese, eg (5)
4 Company's ongoing money position (4,4)
11 Piles of dried grass (9)
12 Bar of bullion (5)
13 Gulp down (4)
14 Butted (6)
16 Bare rocky outcrop (3)
18 Visual organ (3)
19 Scheme, plan (6)
22 Milky precious stone (4)
24 Elephant tusk (5)
26 Literary support? (9)
27 Pedestrian crossing symbol (5,3)
28 Curiously (5)

## DOWN

2 Vista of buildings? (7)
3 Pretentiously cultured (4)
5 Crime of lighting fires (5)
6 New style for the crowning glory (6)
7 Item kept by Captain Kirk aboard the *Enterprise* (3)
8 Fun swimming-pool apparatus (5,5)
9 Salutary (10)
10 Reflection of sound (4)
15 Decompose (3)
16 Uppermost canvas on the mast (7)
17 Decline to go out (4,2)
20 Highly venomous snake (5)
21 Laundry appliance (4)
23 Consumed (4)
25 Style of poem (3)

# RIDDLE ME REE

My first is in COMB but not in BRUSH,

My second's in LOUD but never in HUSH,

My third is in NANNY but not in GOAT,

My fourth's in OAR and also in BOAT,

My fifth is in SCARF and also in JACKET,

My sixth is in PARCEL but not in PACKET,

My seventh's in GEESE and also in HENS,

My whole is an elegant single lens.

---

# SILHOUETTE

Shade in every fragment that contains a dot and what have you got?

# KEYWORD

This puzzle has no clues in the conventional sense. Instead, every different number printed in the main grid represents a different letter (with the same number always representing the same letter, of course). For example, if 7 turns out to be a 'V', you can write in V wherever a square contains 7. We have completed a very small part of the puzzle to give you a start, but the rest is up to you.

| 19 |    | 19 |    | 24 |    | 1  |    | 10 |    | 18 |    | 24 |
|----|----|----|----|----|----|----|----|----|----|----|----|----|
| 24 | 13 | 24 A | 2 I | 21 L |    | 21 | 24 | 18 | 20 | 8  | 4  | 10 |
| 6  |    | 3  |    | 7  |    | 12 |    | 19 |    | 16 |    | 18 |
| 16 | 19 | 2  | 11 | 24 | 17 | 2  |    | 4  | 14 | 5  | 3  | 4  |
| 19 |    | 24 |    | 21 |    | 25 |    | 23 |    |    |    | 19 |
|    | 10 | 18 | 19 | 2  | 25 | 11 | 4  | 25 | 18 | 21 | 12 |    |
|    |    | 16 |    |    |    |    |    |    |    | 16 |    |    |
|    | 11 | 19 | 16 | 18 | 4  | 10 | 22 | 5  | 4  | 21 | 12 |    |
| 4  |    |    |    | 5  |    | 16 |    | 1  |    | 21 |    | 1  |
| 17 | 24 | 9  | 16 | 19 |    | 26 | 24 | 18 | 8  | 16 | 17 | 10 |
| 1  |    | 24 |    | 15 |    | 18 |    | 24 |    | 1  |    | 24 |
| 18 | 5  | 19 | 17 | 16 | 2  | 21 |    | 7  | 25 | 4  | 4  | 21 |
| 12 |    | 10 |    | 18 |    | 12 |    | 4  |    | 3  |    | 17 |

A̸ B C D E F G H̸ J K L̸ M N O P Q R S T U V W X Y Z

| 1    | 2 I  | 3    | 4    | 5    | 6    | 7    | 8    | 9    | 10   | 11   | 12   | 13   |
|------|------|------|------|------|------|------|------|------|------|------|------|------|
| 14   | 15   | 16   | 17   | 18   | 19   | 20   | 21 L | 22   | 23   | 24 A | 25   | 26   |

My friend Mary has a collection of teddy bears from all over the world. Last week she proudly showed me her latest acquisitions. From the clues given below, can you work out what colour fur each bear has, how it is dressed and where it was made?

## Clues

**1** The teddy with yellow fur wears a jockey's cap and silks.

**2** Cuthbert hails from Germany.

**3** Mayday, the rather garish orange bear from Europe, isn't the teddy dressed as an artist in beret and smock.

**4** Scramble, the pirate teddy, isn't pale brown in colour.

**5** The teddy dressed as a cowboy, which comes from the USA, isn't dark brown and Mary hasn't named it Bigly.

**6** The Swedish teddy has pale brown fur.

|  | Cream | Dark brown | Orange | Pale brown | Yellow | Artist | Cowboy | Jockey | Pirate | Soccer player | Germany | Hong Kong | Italy | Sweden | USA |
|---|---|---|---|---|---|---|---|---|---|---|---|---|---|---|---|
| Bigly |  |  |  |  |  |  |  |  |  |  |  |  |  |  |  |
| Cuthbert |  |  |  |  |  |  |  |  |  |  |  |  |  |  |  |
| Jersey |  |  |  |  |  |  |  |  |  |  |  |  |  |  |  |
| Mayday |  |  |  |  |  |  |  |  |  |  |  |  |  |  |  |
| Scramble |  |  |  |  |  |  |  |  |  |  |  |  |  |  |  |
| Germany |  |  |  |  |  |  |  |  |  |  |  |  |  |  |  |
| Hong Kong |  |  |  |  |  |  |  |  |  |  |  |  |  |  |  |
| Italy |  |  |  |  |  |  |  |  |  |  |  |  |  |  |  |
| Sweden |  |  |  |  |  |  |  |  |  |  |  |  |  |  |  |
| USA |  |  |  |  |  |  |  |  |  |  |  |  |  |  |  |
| Artist |  |  |  |  |  |  |  |  |  |  |  |  |  |  |  |
| Cowboy |  |  |  |  |  |  |  |  |  |  |  |  |  |  |  |
| Jockey |  |  |  |  |  |  |  |  |  |  |  |  |  |  |  |
| Pirate |  |  |  |  |  |  |  |  |  |  |  |  |  |  |  |
| Soccer player |  |  |  |  |  |  |  |  |  |  |  |  |  |  |  |

*Record in this grid all the information obtained from the clues, by using a cross to indicate a definite 'no' and a tick to show a definite 'yes'. Transfer these to all sections of the grid thus eliminating all but one possibility, which must be the correct one.*

| Bear | Fur | Costume | Country |
|---|---|---|---|
|  |  |  |  |
|  |  |  |  |
|  |  |  |  |
|  |  |  |  |
|  |  |  |  |

# JIG-WORD

No clues - just pattern and answers - but can you fit them in?

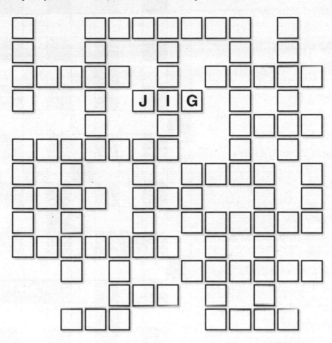

**3 letters**
Add
Cad
Fey
Hid
Jig
Sow

**4 letters**
Airs
Alms
Camp
Knew
Rosy
Soda

**5 letters**
Cinch
Epics
Mound
Niche
Skate

**6 letters**
Devoid
Dipped
Enmesh
Fanned
Loping
Sacked

**7 letters**
Drinker
Ensured
Faulted
Seeding
Stomped

# CROSSWORD

**ACROSS**

5  Cupboard under the dashboard (8)

7  Scrap of cloth (3)

8  Cooks bread (5)

9  Dried fruits used in cooking (8)

11  Bursts, like a balloon (4)

12  Fairy-tale giant (4)

14  Person looking after others (5)

15  Beer (3)

16  ___ pasty, West Country delicacy (7)

20  Metal in an unprocessed state (3)

21  Recreational activity (5)

23  Cook in bubbling liquid (4)

24  Knock momentarily senseless (4)

26  Brought into dishonour (8)

28  Ruffled lace trimming (5)

29  Pinch like a crab (3)

30  Tree surgeon's tool (8)

**DOWN**

1  Disruptive behaviour (5)

2  Athlete who leaps into sand (4,6)

3  Recently delivered baby (7)

4  Mirror (7-5)

6  Form of triangle (9)

10  Glasses, for short (5)

13  Noisy to chew (7)

17  Show's premiere (7,5)

18  Gave a weak excuse to (6,3)

19  Telling fibs (5)

22  Resentful feelings (10)

25  Newspaper in small format (7)

27  Frogs' eggs (5)

# COG-ITATE

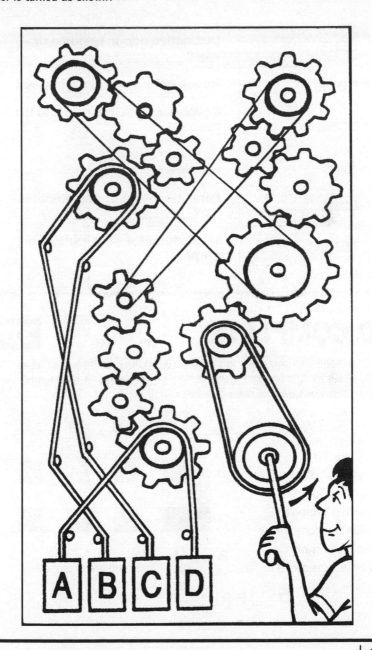

Can you work out which weights will rise and which weights will fall when the lever is turned as shown?

# ADD A LETTER

Insert or add a letter to these four-letter words to make five-letter words which fit the rhyming clues. The six added letters should spell out a word.

| Word | | Clue |
|------|---|------|
| SENT | | Distinctive odour, perfume or smell |
| BODE | | House or home, a place to dwell |
| BONE | | Colloquial term that refers to the head |
| ALAS | | He held the world on his shoulders, it's said |
| LOSE | | Parasitic insect or contemptible type |
| TEAL | | Take without paying, purloin or swipe |

# SO COMPLETE

KATHY, HENRIETTA, CAROLINE, KITTY and GERALDINE all like reading classic books, and each has her own favourite. Use all the letters in their names once each to fill in the names of these favourites.

W U _ _ E _ _ _ _    H _ _ G _ _ S

J _ _ E    _ _ _ E

_ _ I V _ _    _ W _ S _

B _ _ _ _    B _ _ U _ _

_ _ D _ _ P P _ _

# PATHFINDER

Starting from the letter in the box, move up or down or sideways (but NOT diagonally) using all the letters to find the path through the names of eighteen Spanish words.

| S | O | T | A | G | A | I | G | A | T | O |
|---|---|---|---|---|---|---|---|---|---|---|
| B | M | S | N | O | L | L | O | T | A | R |
| R | I | E | B | E | L | L | A | I | L | B |
| E | F | L | O | M | A | D | Q | U | N | I |
| R | O | E | A | R | M | A | S | O | O | G |
| N | I | R | O | S | U | O | O | M | E | U |
| G | M | F | G | T | A | M | S | E | R | R |
| O | A | L | N | A | V | O | G | R | L | I |
| C | I | G | U | A | N | A | B | A | L | A |
| O | O | I | T | A | A | N | O | C | O | E |
| R | R | A | L | P | N | Z | A | R | O | D |

| ALLIGATOR | ALBINO | FLAMINGO |
|---|---|---|
| CARGO | ARMADA | GALLEON |
| GUERRILLA | BOLERO | IGUANA |
| MUSTANG | BONANZA | MOSQUITO |
| PATIO | CORRAL | RODEO |
| VAMOOSE | FIESTA | SOMBRERO |

# MISSING LINKS

The answer to each clue is a word which has a link with each of the three words listed. This word may come at the end (eg HEAD linked with BEACH, BIG and HAMMER), at the beginning (eg BLACK linked with BEAUTY, BOARD and JACK) or a mixture of the two (eg STONE linked with HAIL, LIME and WALL).

**ACROSS**

1 BLUE, BUTTERFLY, FEATHER (7)
4 CUE, PLAYER, TABLE (7)
8 DISORDER, SPLIT, TRAIT (11)
11 BUSINESS, CASE, JUMPER (4)
12 BET, MEAT, PLAY (4)
13 AMERICA, LOVER, QUARTER (5)
15 DEAD, RASH, STINGING (6)
16 HORSE, JOY, SURF (5)
17 BLIND, CAT, SKITTLE (5)
18 PUBLIC, SHEPHERD'S, STRINGS (5)
20 MOVER, WORKS, WORM (5)
22 LIFT, STOLEN, TRAIN (5)
23 BLOOD, FOREVER, OFFENDER (5)
25 HALF, NIMBLE, QUICK (6)
27 CARPET, CASE, WELL (5)
29 BEARDED, DWARF, MURDOCH (4)
31 BENNETT, DAVIES, PARTRIDGE (4)
32 BODY, GAUGE, ROOM (11)
33 CHINESE, LIGHT, MAGIC (7)
34 BALL, LIQUID, PALACE (7)

**DOWN**

1 GAS, IVY, PEN (6)
2 CABIN, CUT, NECK (4)
3 FORE, KEEP, SAND (6)
5 BRUSHED, STOCKINGS, TWINE (5)
6 PORRIDGE, ROLLED, WILD (4)
7 MARKET, MEDICAL, SCIENTIST (8)
8 COLOURS, FOUR, PAINT (6)
9 BRAZIL, GINGER, MONKEY (3)
10 SCOTLAND, STICK, TIMBER (4)
14 BRITISH, CHANNEL, WESTERN (5)
16 BREAD, GRASS, WHISKY (3)
17 ROUND, RUN, TURN (5)
18 EXAMINATION, TRAINING, WORLD (8)
19 CUSTARD, EASTER, NEST (3)
21 FOOTBALL, SNAKE, TRAP (6)
24 FACTORY, KITCHEN, TRUST (4)
25 COPY, SCRIPT, SIGN (6)
26 PRACTICE, SURGEON, TREATMENT (6)
27 GRASS, MODEL, STORE (5)
28 AMBULANCE, FRESH, POCKET (3)
30 DRIVING, HOT, WINDOW (4)
31 FIRE, OPEN, TRADE (4)

# ARROWORD

The arrows show the direction in which the answer to each clue should be placed.

| Restaurant kitchen worker ▼ | | Mix ▼ | | Portal ▼ | | Brie and Edam, for example ▼ | |
|---|---|---|---|---|---|---|---|
| ▶ | | | | | | Came first (in a race) | |
| Slum district | | ___ Baba, *Arabian Nights* hero | | Be in debt ▶ | | ▼ | |
| Long way ▶ | | ▼ | | Fish-eggs ▶ | | | |
| Correct, check | Invent, imagine (5,2) | | Has ___ Fitzgerald, actress ▶ | | | | |
| ▶ | ▼ | | ▼ | Small variety of chicken | | Join (metal) | |
| Black and white striped animal | | Deep hole ▶ | | ▼ | | ▼ | |
| ▶ | | | | | ___ Lollobrigida, actress | | Slippery fishes |
| Unit of current | | Aspect, viewpoint ▶ | | | ▼ | | ▼ |
| ▶ | | | Water current ▶ | | | | |
| ___ for, select | | Group of experts ▶ | | | | | |
| ▶ | | | Roman god of war ▶ | | | | |

# WORDSEARCH

The 30 varieties of fruit have all been hidden in the diagram. They have been printed across (backwards or forwards), or up or down, or diagonally, but always in a straight line without letters being skipped. You can use the letters in the diagram more than once. You will probably find it helpful to mark the words in the diagram and cross them off the list as you find them.

```
L Q F E C B D E A W A P W A P O
F I U E R V T N I P O M Q M R R
G P W I A U P I H B R E E A N G
P L U M N V U R J L A I E L R E
Q J Y O B C A A J K N P C E O E
Y J C R E X E T S R G E E O E N
E O O G R N V C I H E N L H T B
C H F U R E I E P C G Z C P R Y
Y M R L Y C B N Z A A Y R A P L
K U M Q U A T W G E L N B S E A
T N A R R U C E A P U U A M I P
D A N K L G S O Y R H K O N A C
P Z G N I N S D R R T N D P A H
Q W O D M W I A R K W S A X B B
O T F U E X I C E T M Y L A M X
S A T S U M A O H T A G T O J V
B Z H Q C K A V C G M E D L A R
C G Z K C A V A U G H W F L Y R
```

| | | |
|---|---|---|
| APPLE | GUAVA | ORANGE |
| APRICOT | KIWI | PAPAYA |
| AVOCADO | KUMQUAT | PAWPAW |
| BANANA | LEMON | PEACH |
| CHERRY | LIME | PEAR |
| COCONUT | LYCHEE | PLUM |
| CRANBERRY | MANGO | QUINCE |
| CURRANT | MEDLAR | RHUBARB |
| FIG | MELON | SATSUMA |
| GREENGAGE | NECTARINE | STRAWBERRY |

# SUDOKU

Place the numbers from 1 to 9 in each empty cell so that each row, each column and each 3 x 3 block contains all the numbers from 1 to 9 to solve this tricky Sudoku puzzle.

| | | 6 | | | | | | |
|---|---|---|---|---|---|---|---|---|
| 2 | | | 8 | 3 | | | | |
| | 4 | | | | 7 | | | |
| | | | | | | 7 | | |
| 1 | 9 | 3 | | | | | 2 | |
| | 2 | 7 | | | | | 6 | |
| | | 4 | 6 | 1 | | | | 9 |
| 6 | | | 5 | 8 | | 3 | | |
| | 1 | | | 9 | | | 5 | |

**MEDIUM**

# PURPLE PASSAGE

In a Purple Passage, the grid of letters consists of an entertaining short story, reading across the rows from left to right and from top to bottom. However, 30 letters have been missed out. Not only that, but there are no spaces between words and no punctuation. Can you fill in the missing letters and work out where the word-breaks are to reveal the story?

| | | | | | | | | |
|---|---|---|---|---|---|---|---|---|
| T | H | E | P | ☐ | N | K | B | A |
| L | L | ☐ | W | E | R | ☐ | E | D |
| ☐ | O | U | N | ☐ | T | H | E | ☐ |
| L | U | ☐ | R | E | B | ☐ | U | N |
| D | E | D | O | ☐ | F | T | H | E |
| T | O | ☐ | C | U | S | ☐ | I | O |
| ☐ | A | N | D | ☐ | U | S | T | ☐ |
| I | S | ☐ | E | D | A | ☐ | E | D |
| B | E | F | O | ☐ | E | D | R | O |
| P | P | ☐ | N | G | I | ☐ | T | O |
| ☐ | C | O | R | ☐ | E | R | P | ☐ |
| C | K | ☐ | T | W | H | ☐ | T | A |
| S | H | A | M | ☐ | H | E | W | A |
| S | A | ☐ | M | I | N | ☐ | F | O |
| ☐ | T | H | E | ☐ | R | O | W | ☐ |

# CROSSWORD

## ACROSS

1 Thickening agent used in cooking (9)
9 Varied (7)
10 Antique (3)
11 Narrow passage (5)
12 Adjective often applied to Scotland (5)
14 Pack tightly (5)
16 Military cloth (5)
18 Large tropical root resembling the potato (3)
19 Fetch (3)
21 Person who prefers not to associate with others (5)
22 In a frosty manner (5)
23 Female adults (5)
25 Defendant's proof of not being at the scene of a crime (5)
26 Pair of musicians or comedy artistes (3)
27 Consumer of a product (3-4)
28 Tree which retains its leaves all year (9)

## DOWN

1 Particular! (6)
2 Element used in luminous paints (6)
3 Dread (11)
4 Waterproof cloth (7)
5 Shaft of light (3)
6 Regulating the balance of (11)
7 Smile broadly showing the teeth (4)
8 In a sluggish manner (4)
13 Christmas in France? (4)
15 Mexican snack (4)
17 Voucher redeemable against the cost of a flight (3,4)
19 Foundation garment (6)
20 Wealthy and powerful business person (6)
23 Plant friend of TV's Flowerpot Men (4)
24 South of France (4)
25 (We) exist (3)

# READY TO GO

Four of the six objects lined up at the top are hidden in the picture. Which are they and where are they hidden?

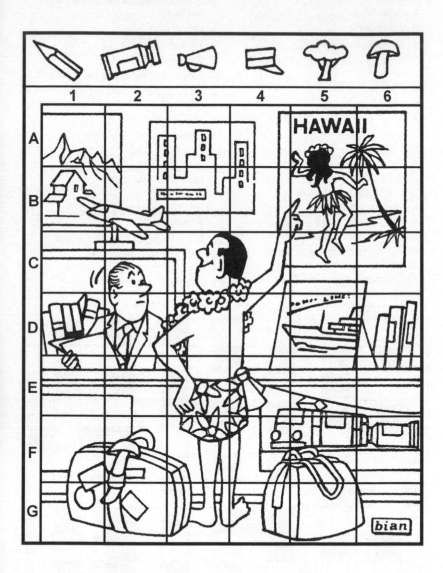

# SKELETON

Have double the fun with this puzzle: you've got to fill in the answers and the black squares! We've given you the bare bones to start and it will help you to know that the black squares in the finished grid form a symmetrical pattern, so that every black square has at least one other corresponding black square.

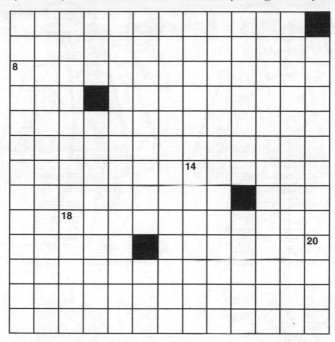

**ACROSS**

1 ___ Hill, area of London at Hyde Park Corner
8 Irate emotion
9 Podginess
10 Honesty and frankness
12 Carelessly
14 Radiator
17 Aggressive behaviour
21 Picture made from scraps
22 Blunder
23 Not on purpose

**DOWN**

1 Maul
2 Regularly, when dark
3 ___ firma, solid ground
4 Container from which pigs eat
5 Performance by actors for an audience
6 Small greasy cocktail fruit
7 Offensive sight
11 Act of revenge
13 Japanese creative art
15 Showing adroitness in dealing with people
16 Go back on a promise
18 Pale purple colour
19 Quarter of 32
20 Covered in moisture

Each clown features one detail that is not present in the other three. Can you spot all four extra details?

# CROSSWORD

## ACROSS

1 Seize (power) by force (5)
5 Grisly (4)
6 Horse's shelter (6)
7 African river (4)
8 Without purpose (6)
9 Thin rope attached to a sliding window pane (4,4)
12 Person whose name is on an envelope (9)
15 And so on (abbrev)(3)
16 Braid (5)
17 Rule of a monarch (5)
18 Costa del ___, holiday region (3)
19 Becoming more complex (of a mystery) (9)
21 Most self-respecting (8)
24 Chatterbox (6)
25 Fine net (4)
26 Mysteriously foreign (6)
27 Provide capital for (4)
28 ___ fatale, dangerously attractive woman (5)

## DOWN

2 Small variety of orange (7)
3 Trash, garbage (7)
4 With ruffled adornment (7)
5 Giving freely (8)
9 Buying and selling of humans (5,5)
10 Alluring, enticing (9)
11 Aircraft's trial run (4,6)
13 Wide area (7)
14 Faint lustre in the night sky (9)
20 Worked (the land) (8)
21 Edible conifer seed (4,3)
22 ___ of, throw away (7)
23 Large arena used for sporting events (7)

# KEYWORD

This puzzle has no clues in the conventional sense. Instead, every different number printed in the main grid represents a different letter (with the same number always representing the same letter, of course). For example, if 7 turns out to be a 'V', you can write in V wherever a square contains 7. We have completed a very small part of the puzzle to give you a start, but the rest is up to you.

| 15 | 25 | 15 E | 16 R | 3 C | 17 | 1 | 15 | ■ | 5 | 2 | 9 | 24 |
|----|----|----|----|----|----|----|----|----|----|----|----|----|
| 25 | ■ | 6 | ■ | 9 | ■ | 17 | ■ | 9 | ■ | 17 | ■ | 16 |
| 18 | 22 | 9 | 2 | 20 | ■ | 5 | 18 | 12 | 18 | 3 | 15 | 18 |
| 2 | ■ | 18 | ■ | 15 | ■ | 4 | ■ | 17 | ■ | 17 | ■ | 23 |
| 20 | 14 | 20 | 15 | ■ | 3 | 14 | 12 | 8 | 15 | 20 | 20 | 17 |
| ■ | ■ | 15 | ■ | 3 | ■ | 12 | ■ | 17 | ■ | ■ | ■ | 12 |
| 16 | 9 | 22 | 15 | 2 | 13 | ■ | 10 | 15 | 2 | 14 | 12 | 24 |
| 17 | ■ | ■ | 18 | ■ | 10 | ■ | 22 | ■ | 16 | ■ | ■ | ■ |
| 19 | 17 | 24 | 14 | 16 | 14 | 9 | 1 | ■ | 21 | 17 | 2 | 20 |
| 15 | ■ | 16 | ■ | 17 | ■ | 16 | ■ | 8 | ■ | 24 | ■ | 26 |
| 20 | 4 | 17 | 1 | 20 | 2 | 15 | ■ | 2 | 2 | 18 | 11 | 18 |
| 15 | ■ | 12 | ■ | 13 | ■ | 18 | ■ | 18 | ■ | 11 | ■ | 12 |
| 22 | 18 | 22 | 14 | ■ | 10 | 9 | 3 | 7 | 2 | 17 | 12 | 24 |

A B C̶ D E̶ F G H I J K L M N O P Q R̶ S T U V W X Y Z

| 1 | 2 | 3 C | 4 | 5 | 6 | 7 | 8 | 9 | 10 | 11 | 12 | 13 |
|----|----|----|----|----|----|----|----|----|----|----|----|----|
| 14 | 15 E | 16 R | 17 | 18 | 19 | 20 | 21 | 22 | 23 | 24 | 25 | 26 |

# JIG-WORD

No clues - just pattern and answers - but can you fit them in?

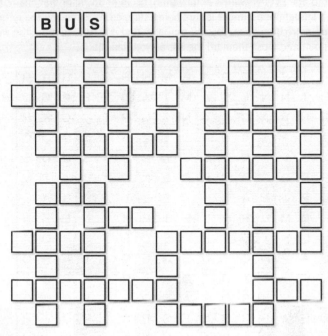

**3 letters**

Aft
Bus
Err
Fop
Fug
Irk
Jot
Oaf
Ply

**4 letters**

Abet
Fowl
Held

Judo
Spot
Stun

**5 letters**

Cloth
Colic
Oozed
Pilau
Piled

**6 letters**

Arcane
Attack
Bowled
Cueing

Dollop
Tingly

**7 letters**

Jogging
Lobelia
Scaring
Sculled

# WORDSEARCH

The 30 entertainers have all been hidden in the diagram. They have been printed across (backwards or forwards), or up or down, or diagonally, but always in a straight line without letters being skipped. You can use the letters in the diagram more than once. You will probably find it helpful to mark the words in the diagram and cross them off the list as you find them.

```
E  T  S  I  T  R  A  R  M  N  R  B  U  R  A  R
R  T  N  N  L  C  A  M  T  A  U  E  E  P  E  D
E  H  S  A  C  T  L  N  C  G  G  T  M  C  K  H
T  Y  I  I  S  O  A  O  L  Z  A  I  N  M  O  Q
S  G  P  P  N  I  M  E  W  E  O  A  C  U  U  S
E  P  O  S  D  O  R  P  E  N  D  J  J  I  T  M
J  P  T  E  A  N  I  R  E  L  L  A  B  U  A  L
K  N  M  H  R  D  I  S  I  R  X  R  N  E  B  N
V  O  K  T  O  F  J  R  S  D  E  T  S  P  O  A
C  A  V  W  C  T  U  E  G  E  M  T  I  F  R  C
M  R  I  S  K  R  G  D  X  A  R  P  E  R  C  T
Z  Y  S  B  G  O  G  A  N  O  E  P  F  C  A  O
W  E  W  L  R  U  L  E  S  R  S  B  M  U  Z  R
H  Q  T  N  O  P  E  L  M  U  S  I  C  I  A  N
U  O  C  Q  U  E  R  D  C  G  R  Z  N  T  O  E
L  M  R  W  P  C  O  N  J  U  R  O  R  G  F  S
S  H  O  W  M  A  N  A  J  A  P  V  H  X  E  B
R  E  K  S  U  B  Y  B  E  X  T  R  A  C  H  R
```

| | | |
|---|---|---|
| ACROBAT | COMPERE | MUMMER |
| ACTOR | CONJUROR | MUSICIAN |
| ARTISTE | DANCER | PIPER |
| BALLERINA | EXTRA | POP STAR |
| BANDLEADER | FIRE EATER | ROCK GROUP |
| BUGLER | IMPRESSIONIST | SHOWMAN |
| BUSKER | JESTER | SINGER |
| CHORUS | JUGGLER | STUNTMAN |
| CLOWN | MAESTRO | THESPIAN |
| COMEDIAN | MAGICIAN | TROUPE |

# STAIRCASE

When the seven modes of transport listed here in a mixed-up order are correctly placed along the horizontal rows, the letters in the diagonal 'staircase' will spell out an eighth vehicle.

### SLEIGH WHALER CORACLE CHOPPER
### TUGBOAT TRACTOR FERRY

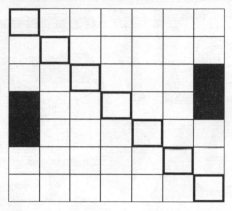

# IDENTIGRIDS

Which three squares are identical?

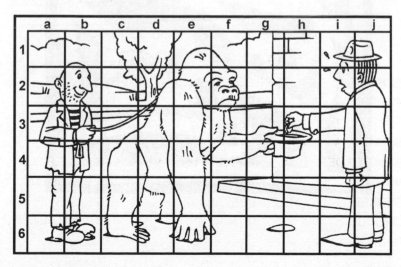

# PORTABLE

What route must each boat take to get to its respective port without crossing the path of the other three?

# KEYWORD

**335**

This puzzle has no clues in the conventional sense. Instead, every different number printed in the main grid represents a different letter (with the same number always representing the same letter, of course). For example, if 7 turns out to be a 'V', you can write in V wherever a square contains 7. We have completed a very small part of the puzzle to give you a start, but the rest is up to you.

| | | | | | | | | | | | | |
|---|---|---|---|---|---|---|---|---|---|---|---|---|
| 22 | 5 | 8 | 9 | 12 | 21 | 15 | 16 | ■ | 3 | 6 | 5 | 19 |
| 5 | ■ | 5 | ■ | 8 | ■ | 7 | ■ | 3 | ■ | 24 | ■ | 21 |
| 22 | 26 | 18 | 15 | 16 | ■ | 19 | 26 | 6 | 20 | 5 | 22 | 26 |
| 10 | ■ | 15 | ■ | 5 | ■ | 5 | ■ | 26 | ■ | 19 | ■ | 22 |
| 23 | 15 | 1 | 6 | ■ | 14 | 21 R | 5 O | 22 C | 22 | 5 | 1 | 20 |
| ■ | ■ | 19 | ■ | 12 | ■ | 19 | ■ | 20 | ■ | ■ | ■ | 8 |
| 26 | 8 | 23 | 5 | 8 | 15 | ■ | 12 | 8 | 3 | 12 | 8 | 11 |
| 17 | ■ | ■ | ■ | 12 | ■ | 2 | ■ | 11 | ■ | 8 | ■ | ■ |
| 12 | 8 | 13 | 26 | 3 | 24 | 15 | 16 | ■ | 3 | 22 | 26 | 19 |
| 26 | ■ | 20 | ■ | 12 | ■ | 16 | ■ | 19 | ■ | 5 | ■ | 13 |
| 19 | 5 | 21 | 8 | 26 | 16 | 5 | ■ | 26 | 25 | 12 | 21 | 15 |
| 20 | ■ | 15 | ■ | 1 | ■ | 21 | ■ | 7 | ■ | 19 | ■ | 15 |
| 22 | 5 | 16 | 15 | ■ | 2 | 26 | 4 | 20 | 3 | 24 | 15 | 16 |

A B ~~C~~ D E F G H I J K L M N ~~O~~ P Q ~~R~~ S T U V W X Y Z

| | | | | | | | | | | | | |
|---|---|---|---|---|---|---|---|---|---|---|---|---|
| 1 | 2 | 3 | 4 | 5 O | 6 | 7 | 8 | 9 | 10 | 11 | 12 | 13 |
| 14 | 15 | 16 | 17 | 18 | 19 | 20 | 21 R | 22 C | 23 | 24 | 25 | 26 |

# 4 SQUARE

Solve these four clues and then rearrange the solutions into a sixteen-letter phrase, for which a clue is given. The two diagonals also make four-letter words.

Yashmak

Anon

Christmas seaon

Valley

**Clue:**
**The Beatles didn't write this for tennis players! (3,3,4,2,4)**

---

# DOG SHOW

Starting from number 1, join all the black dogs with one continuous line; starting from letter A, join all the white ones with another line. The lines must not cross!

# PATHFINDER

Starting from the letter in the box, move up or down or sideways (but NOT diagonally) using all the letters to find the path through the names of nineteen precious stones.

```
P  P  O  P  A  L  E  J  A  S  P
A  H  L  E  P  J  N  I  R  T  E
S  I  R  A  Z  A  D  E  C  I  R
E  R  A  M  T  R  R  E  M  I  D
M  N  E  E  T  A  A  L  E  A  M
O  O  T  Y  H  U  Q  D  T  O  O
O  N  S  S  T  P  E  R  I  D  N
L  S  I  O  Z  O  T  A  G  A  D
A  A  P  N  A  P  E  T  R  R  U
Z  L  X  Y  R  Q  I  S  E  B  B
U  L  I  T  U  U  O  E  A  M  Y
```

| | | |
|---|---|---|
| EMERALD | JADE | DIAMOND |
| RUBY | MOONSTONE | JASPER |
| SAPPHIRE | AMBER | AMETHYST |
| OPAL | TURQUOISE | CITRINE |
| TOPAZ | AGATE | LAPIS LAZULI |
| PERIDOT | ONYX | |
| QUARTZ | PEARL | |

# CROSSWORD

## ACROSS

- **1** Harpooners' boat (6)
- **5** Entombment (6)
- **9** Wrath (3)
- **11** Roaring (7)
- **12** Tanned animal skin (7)
- **13** Computer information-storage device (4)
- **15** Source of ermine (5)
- **16** Clip into shape (4)
- **17** Naming part of speech (4)
- **19** Edition (of a publication) (5)
- **20** Village People classic (inits) (4)
- **24** Kitchen utensil (7)
- **25** Come across (3,4)
- **26** Frozen confection (3)
- **27** Round-trip ticket (6)
- **28** Big ___, fairground ride (6)

## DOWN

- **2** Trained hunting birds (5)
- **3** Pork joint (4)
- **4** Perfectly fit and well (5,2,4)
- **5** Persecuted (11)
- **6** Highway (4)
- **7** Find repugnant (5)
- **8** Underhand goings-on (9)
- **10** Leader of a marching band (4,5)
- **14** Person's relatives (3)
- **16** Give it a go (3)
- **18** Treatment, practice (5)
- **21** Chop finely (5)
- **22** Ballet skirt (4)
- **23** Small cut (4)

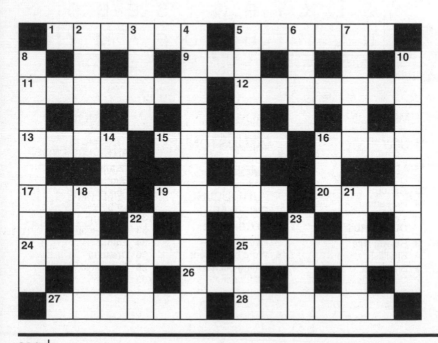

# ROUNDABOUT

Solutions to Radial clues (1 to 24) either start from the outer edge of the circle and read inwards, or start from the inner ring and read outwards to the edge (so they are all five-letter words). Solutions to Circular clues read in either a clockwise or an anti-clockwise direction round the circle.

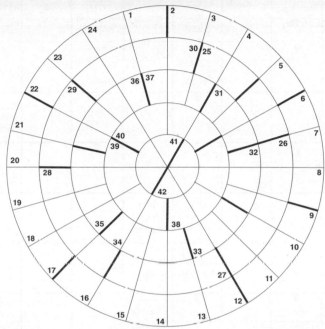

### RADIAL:
#### INWARDS

1 Bread maker
2 Long weapon
8 Dried cassia leaves
12 Drivers' stop-over
14 Spirit from *The Tempest*
15 Even
22 Hospital worker
23 Get up
24 Horseman

#### OUTWARDS

3 Rajah's wife
4 Shellfish
5 Snooped
6 Pear drink
7 Old fashioned pudding
9 Prank, caper

10 Sports site
11 Zodiacal ram
13 Shelf
16 Lawn plant
17 Cereal seed
18 Style of art
19 Wish fulfiller from *Aladdin*
20 Correct (a text)
21 Type of abrasive cloth

### CIRCULAR:
#### CLOCKWISE

2 Remit
6 Word of consent
12 Eating occasions
17 Very poor
25 Large jug
26 River of Paris
27 Monster

31 Atmosphere
32 Social insect
35 Princess Royal
37 ___ Livingstone, London mayor
40 Burn, scorch

#### ANTI-CLOCKWISE

1 Cereal roughage
11 Bag, pouch
28 Part of eye
29 Large vase
30 Duo
33 Equal score
34 Enthusiastic
36 Dreadful
38 Sea eagle
39 Pool, lake
41 ___ Varney, comedy actor
42 Circuit

# ARROWORD

The arrows show the direction in which the answer to each clue should be placed.

| Single figure | Slang word for 'food' | ▼ | Accidental loss of liquid | ▼ | *Simply the __*, Tina Turner hit | ▼ | Sultanate bordering Malaysia |
|---|---|---|---|---|---|---|---|
| ► | ▼ | | *Jane __*, Brontë novel ► / Hit gently | | | | |
| Porridge cereal ► | | | ▼ | | Take to mean | | __ Ivanisevic, tennis champion |
| Ice-rink sport ► | | | | | ▼ | | ▼ |
| ► | | | | Keanu Reeves' *The Matrix* role ► | | | |
| Bloke | Scoops (out) | | Large pink-fleshed fish | Evergreen tree ► | | | |
| ► | ▼ | | ▼ | Go to next page (inits) | | Temporarily shelved (2,3) | |
| A really long time | | Cook's pinny ► | | ▼ | | ▼ | |
| ► | | | | | Tit for __, revenge | | __ up, exasperated |
| Self-reproach | | Repeated design ► | | | ▼ | | ▼ |
| ► | | | | Winning tennis serve ► | | | |
| Brave fellow | | Jotted down ► | | | | | |

# HONEYCOMB

All the answers are six-letter words. Each answer is entered in a circle around its clue-number. The first letter of the answer is entered in the shaded triangle immediately above the clue-number. If the clue-number is even, enter the answer in a clockwise direction. If the clue-number is odd, enter the answer in an anti-clockwise direction.

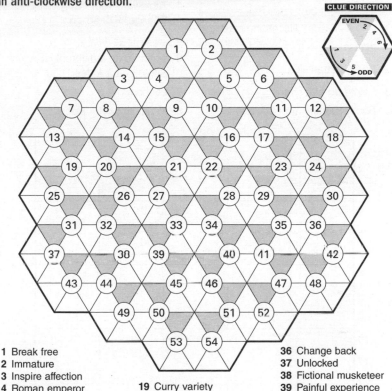

CLUE DIRECTION

1 Break free
2 Immature
3 Inspire affection
4 Roman emperor
5 District of Venice
6 Salad fruit
7 Instant
8 Pour from bottle
9 Companion
10 Victoria's consort
11 Cloak
12 Stick on a spike
13 ___ Butterfly, Puccini opera
14 Chirping insect
15 Roman orator and writer
16 Word of warning
17 Most modern
18 Central American country

19 Curry variety
20 Texan city
21 Redesignate
22 Elongated flower cluster
23 Confidential
24 Lodestone
25 More beloved
26 Sweet bay
27 Sickness
28 Mocha, perhaps
29 Money chest
30 Rule
31 Wore away
32 Rubbed out
33 Manorial lands
34 Decadent
35 Exertion

36 Change back
37 Unlocked
38 Fictional musketeer
39 Painful experience
40 Search for food
41 Relinquish
42 Sea journey
43 Don ceremonial garb
44 Drink
45 Dumbly
46 With spirit
47 ___ Cross, military decoration
48 Car port
49 Sour
50 Tie up
51 Household
52 Citrus fruit
53 Flourish
54 Inhabitant

# PIECEWORD

With the help of the Across clues only, can you fit the 35 pieces into their correct positions in the empty grid (which, when completed, will exhibit a symmetrical pattern)?

### ACROSS

1 Chaos, havoc • Recording race details

2 No ___, road sign

3 Front part of a ship • ___ in *Boots*, pantomime

4 Tableware item • Surplus • Change of direction

5 Simian creature

6 Teach to do a different job • Shrank back in fear

7 Feel poorly

8 Negative word • Edge

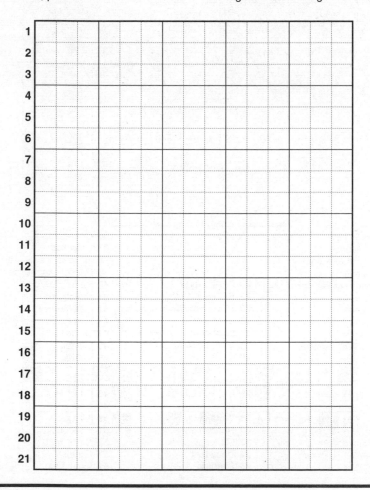

9 Very young frog • Poignancy

10 Frame for supporting a picture

11 Cried loudly • Shapeless mass (of soft food)

12 Show the way

13 Knock down • Angrily

14 Away from the wind • King

15 Item in an auction

16 Scrupulous • Worship

17 Nautically astern

18 Red-finned fish • Facial expression of scorn or contempt • ___ there, done that, motto of the jaded

19 Holler • Barren through lack of water

20 Church keyboard instrument

21 Bill of goods • Attic room

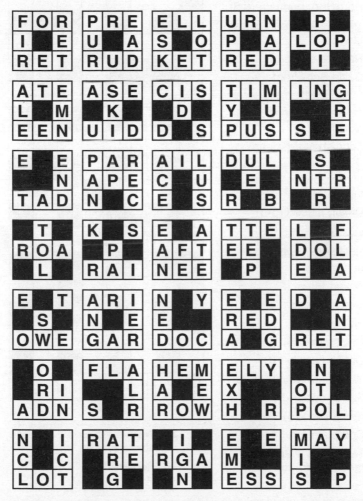

# CROSSWORD

## ACROSS

1 Assertive, domineering (8)
6 Gave up a throne (9)
7 Curve (3)
8 Fully grown (5)
9 Fleet's leading vessel (8)
12 Lose colour and brightness (4)
13 Tarzan's girlfriend (4)
16 Dormitory bedtime (6,3)
18 Tribal leader, or a British tank (9)
19 Require (4)
20 David Schwimmer's *Friends* role (4)
23 Went over (the limit) (8)
26 Not sharp (5)
27 Scottish word meaning 'small' (3)
28 Impromptu collection of money (4-5)
29 Unfair, biased (3-5)

## DOWN

1 Noisy disturbance, quarrel (6)
2 Poked fun at (9)
3 Switch, swap (8)
4 Fib, lie (7)
5 Revise text (4)
10 Girlish beauty (10)
11 Wine and beer shop (3-7)
14 Smell, odour (5)
15 Employees (5)
17 Complain, grumble (5)
21 Twisted (a watch mechanism) too much (9)
22 False teeth (8)
24 Warning given by a police officer (7)
25 Repaired (6)
26 Cry loudly (4)

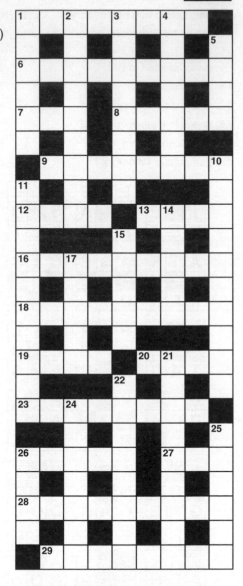

# TINKER, TAILOR...

To discover who this person is, unscramble the words in the verse, which hints at what the person does. Write these words into the boxes below, reading across, and, if you've placed them in the correct order, the arrowed column will spell out the occupation.

When ELEPOP UBDIL they need a LANP,

Which they MOOMSINSCI from this man.

He'll RECETA the STEB design,

For a ETUCRURST TTHA will NONFICTU fine.

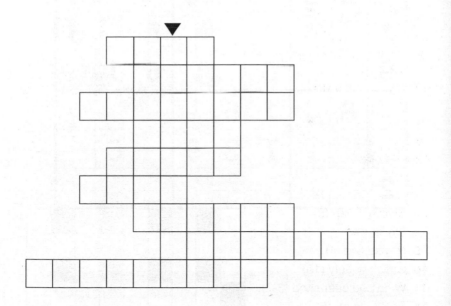

OCCUPATION: _____

# SUDOKU

Place the numbers from 1 to 9 in each empty cell so that each row, each column and each 3 x 3 block contains all the numbers from 1 to 9 to solve this tricky Sudoku puzzle.

| | | | | | | | | 1 |
|---|---|---|---|---|---|---|---|---|
| | 4 | | 9 | 5 | 1 | | | |
| | | | | 7 | 3 | | 4 | |
| | 3 | 5 | | | 6 | | | 4 |
| 1 | | 4 | | | | 8 | | 5 |
| 9 | | | 8 | | | 6 | 1 | |
| | 8 | | 1 | 6 | | | | |
| | | | 7 | 3 | 9 | | 6 | |
| 2 | | | | | | | | |

EASY

# WORDSEARCH

The 30 games have all been hidden in the diagram. They have been printed across (backwards or forwards), or up or down, or diagonally, but always in a straight line without letters being skipped. You can use the letters in the diagram more than once. You will probably find it helpful to mark the words in the diagram and cross them off the list as you find them.

```
Z S N O J V D A C S P J R C D M
W O T G D I H M F I B S K C A J
F T P H A N G T N S E C D W K S
O T B M G R E B U S Z T G R N Z
H O D I B U A K T E I P R I A R
O L D I F L A I U H Q Y P U F C
O M Q L L F T R V C U N L B M W
F B I L L I A R D S E S H Z E P
U O L R P H S E N T O G N I B T
A P R I U T W L O R A R C Z Q Z
C O T F R M Q O O A T S A N A C
E K N A E U M D T A S K V Y G T
X E D T K I X Y N P B E Q E O B
Y R I D O H T U O D R A V O E W
T O M B O L A S P V I T H E N H
O O Q U N S P O O F D S T S N I
X K S Y S Y I W L P G L H V B S
R E J B J M S N X P E X M K E T
```

| | | |
|---|---|---|
| BEETLE | FORFEITS | RUMMY |
| BEZIQUE | HOUSE | SEVENS |
| BILLIARDS | JACKS | SHOOT |
| BINGO | KENDO | SNOOKER |
| BRIDGE | LOTTO | SPOOF |
| CANASTA | OLD MAID | TENPINS |
| CARDS | PINBALL | TIP-IT |
| CHESS | POKER | TOMBOLA |
| DARTS | PONTOON | TRUMP |
| DRAUGHTS | REBUS | WHIST |

# FAKER'S DOZEN

The twelve proud collectors in the bottom picture have just bought the latest paintings by a famous artist. Unfortunately, five people have unwittingly bought fakes, which differ slightly from the originals in the top picture. Can you find the fakes?

# CROSSWORD

**ACROSS**

1 Members of the Queen's family (6)
5 Letter-writing friend (3,3)
9 Corn spike (3)
11 Cold infusion (4,3)
12 Constant (7)
13 Dash, flair (4)
15 Terrifying (5)
16 Baby sheep (4)
17 Be of assistance (4)
19 Act smugly (5)
20 Mexico's money unit (4)
24 Gliding on a rising current (7)
25 Signal to proceed (2-5)
26 Gardening tool (3)
27 Meal (6)
28 Cross through (6)

**DOWN**

2 Last Greek letter (5)
3 Busy insects (4)
4 Lamp and reflector for illuminating a target (11)
5 Planned (3-8)
6 Knot, swelling (4)
7 Ring or stadium (5)
8 Go in pursuit (4,5)
10 Whitish (hair) (3,6)
14 Quick bite (3)
16 Rim (of a vessel) (3)
18 Period of hire (5)
21 Straight-backed (5)
22 Spanish cry of acclaim (4)
23 Drop down (4)

# JIG-WORD

No clues - just pattern and answers - but can you fit them in?

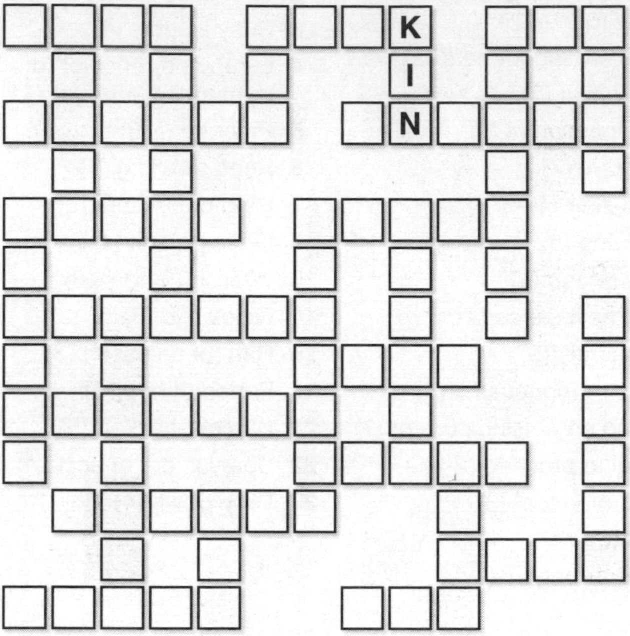

**3 letters**
Kin
Pad
Soy
Tot
Vex

**4 letters**
Dado
Emit
Grab
Icon
Oast
Seek

**5 letters**
Alder
Hared
Index
Mufti
Rumba

**6 letters**
Drivel
Fussed
Hijack
Sadden
Smutty
Snared

**7 letters**
Between
Conifer
Ignored
Joinery
Mayoral
Parting

# DATELINE

A number jig with a difference: with clues to figure out (with the help of a calculator if you wish!) to discover the date in the shaded line – in this case a significant day for West End musicals.

## ACROSS

1 Pounds in one hundredweight
3 Average of 594, 628 and 716
5 Subtract 195 from 33 Across
7 Divide 5 Across by 4
8 Three times 1 Across
9 Square root of 10,201
11 Subtract 233,767 from 2 Down
13 Double 1 Across
14 Add 59,760 to 15 Down
16 Add 20,743 to 2 Down
21 Subtract 150,923 from 16 Across
22 Square 1 Across
25 Double 9 Across
27 Subtract 416 from 30 Across
28 First three digits of 12 Down
30 2 per cent of 26,700
31 Half of 1 Across
32 Half of 30 Across
33 Half of 3 Across
34 Reverse digits of 1 Across

## DOWN

1 Multiply 33 Across by 4
2 Multiply 34 Across by 19 Down
4 Add 209 to 34 Across
5 Subtract 3,082 from 12 Down
6 Add 1 Down to 5 Down
9 Square 5 Down
10 Square 1 Down
12 Multiply 25 Across by 22
15 Add 40 to 12 Down
17 Add 5,000 to 18 Down
18 Add 13 to 9 Across
19 11 per cent of 10,100
20 Double 17 Down, then add 101,934
23 Pounds in 154 stones
24 Add 3,681 to 23 Down
26 Multiply 1 Across by 20, then add 21
29 Subtract 7 Across from 28 Across

# KEYWORD

This puzzle has no clues in the conventional sense. Instead, every different number printed in the main grid represents a different letter (with the same number always representing the same letter, of course). For example, if 7 turns out to be a 'V', you can write in V wherever a square contains 7. We have completed a very small part of the puzzle to give you a start, but the rest is up to you.

| 23 | 19 | 18 | 4 | 21 | 23 | | 11 | 18 | 1 | 25 | 16 | 4 |
|----|----|----|----|----|----|----|----|----|----|----|----|----|
| | 1 | | 3 | | 6 | | 16 | | 22 | | 5 | |
| 17 | 5 | 14 | 7 | 20 | 17 | 5 | 25 | | 1 | 7 | 15 | 23 |
| | 6 | | 26 | | 15 | | 12 | | 5 | | 12 | |
| 20 | 18 | 1 | 8 | | 15 | 18 | 4 | 5 | 4 | 6 | 17 | 19 |
| | 7 | | 12 | | 4 | | | | | 5 | |
| 23 | 19 C | 18 R | 4 E | 4 | 5 | | 11 | 18 | 4 | 7 | 19 | 9 |
| | 6 | | | | | | 4 | | 13 | | 9 | |
| 10 | 16 | 25 | 25 | 12 | 4 | 18 | 23 | | 16 | 5 | 17 | 6 |
| | 7 | | 16 | | 7 | | 8 | | 7 | | 5 | |
| 7 | 12 | 4 | 23 | | 23 | 9 | 1 | 18 | 6 | 7 | 25 | 4 |
| | 12 | | 6 | | 4 | | 2 | | 4 | | 12 | |
| 5 | 24 | 12 | 1 | 5 | 23 | | 4 | 23 | 23 | 7 | 24 | 23 |

A B C̶ D E̶ F G H I J K L M N O P Q R̶ S T U V W X Y Z

| 1 | 2 | 3 | 4 E | 5 | 6 | 7 | 8 | 9 | 10 | 11 | 12 | 13 |
|----|----|----|----|----|----|----|----|----|----|----|----|----|
| 14 | 15 | 16 | 17 | 18 R | 19 C | 20 | 21 | 22 | 23 | 24 | 25 | 26 |

# SKELETON

Have double the fun with this puzzle: you've got to fill in the answers and the black squares! We've given you the bare bones to start and it will help you to know that the black squares in the finished grid form a symmetrical pattern, so that every black square has at least one other corresponding black square.

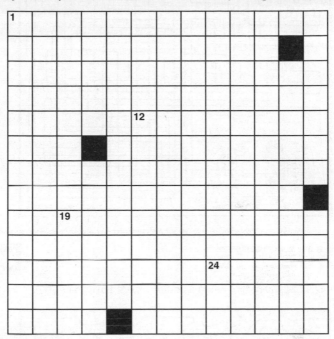

**ACROSS**

1 Large guard dog
5 Gusto, zest
9 Pungent vegetable
10 Druggist
11 Defraud
12 Sanatorium
14 Ennui
15 Congestion of events
18 Foreign
20 ___ of parliament, laws
23 Mrs ___, Cluedo character
24 Beard remover
25 Small lump of bread
26 Emitting water vapour

**DOWN**

1 So as to be heard
2 Dislocated (joint)
3 Portable shelter
4 Extremely cold northern area
6 Animal which wallows in mud
7 Ideal
8 Basic computer screen showing icons
13 US detective
14 Repertory player
16 Swirling bath
17 Punnet
19 Message
21 Gesture of indifference
22 Expressive song

# UNPLUGGED

Which of the plugs will connect the TV to the socket?

# SILHOUETTE

Shade in every fragment that contains a dot – what have you got?

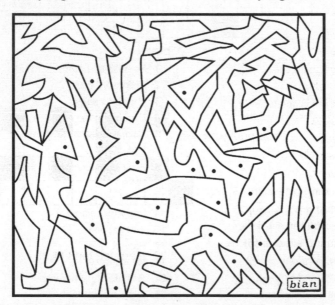

# CROSSWORD

## ACROSS

**1** Refer to in speech (7)

**7** Stamp book (5)

**8** One's inner self (3)

**9** Irish singer, famous for *Orinoco Flow* (4)

**10** Lash mark (4)

**12** Person for odd jobs (8)

**14** Lustful (9)

**15** Aircraft with three sets of wings (8)

**18** Allergic reaction to pollen (3,5)

**21** Arranged for a particular time (9)

**23** Thin slice of meat, coated and fried (8)

**25** Per person (4)

**26** Male red deer (4)

**28** Japanese carp (3)

**29** Provide food and drink (5)

**30** Serious investigation (7)

## DOWN

**2** Immature (9)

**3** Docile (4)

**4** Excessively detailed (4-9)

**5** Animals' drinking pool (9)

**6** Adolescence (5)

**11** Over-advertise (4,2)

**13** Wedding attendant (5)

**16** Part of a pop group that supplies the beat (6,7)

**17** Demand silence (5)

**19** Inspire affection (6)

**20** Thrilling or dangerous experience (9)

**22** Care for, tend (4,5)

**24** Sickly-looking (5)

**27** Biscuit colour (4)

The arrows show the direction in which the answer to each clue should be placed.

| Useless (2-4) | *La Traviata*, eg | Chinese cooking pan | ▼ | As a bit of a gamble (2,4) | Give out cards | This 24 hours | ▼ |
|---|---|---|---|---|---|---|---|
| ► | ▼ | | | ▼ | ▼ | Second time | |
| Church seat | | Massage, squeeze ► | | | | ▼ | |
| ► | | | *The Forsyte __*, TV series ► | | | | |
| Domestic heating fuel | | Turn outwards, spread out ► | | | | | |
| ► | | | ▼ | Move on snow | | Middle East language | Christian festival |
| Long story | Eskimo-style coat | | Bamboo stem | ► | ▼ | | ▼ |
| ► | ▼ | | | ▼ | Splutter | Singer of the 1964 hit *Shout* | |
| Official language of Pakistan | | Milky-white gems ► | | | | ▼ | |
| ► | | | | Nevertheless ► | | | |
| Ready money | | Cunning, craftiness ► | | | | | |
| ► | | | | Ill-bred dog ► | | | |

# MISSING LINKS

The answer to each clue is a word which has a link with each of the three words listed. This word may come at the end (e.g. HEAD linked with BEACH, BIG and HAMMER), at the beginning (e.g. BLACK linked with BEAUTY, BOARD and JACK) or a mixture of the two (e.g. STONE linked with HAIL, LIME and WALL).

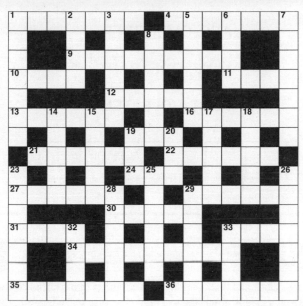

**ACROSS**

- **1** BULLDOG, ISLES, MUSEUM (7)
- **4** LOAN, NURSE, UNIVERSITY (7)
- **9** GENERAL, HOME, PERSONAL (9)
- **10** BELL, PEG, POLE (4)
- **11** ROUTE, SCREEN, WORM (4)
- **12** NIGHT, STAFF, WET (5)
- **13** BREAKER, HIT, WORLD (6)
- **16** LUGGAGE, RECORD, WINE (6)
- **19** PILL, TALK, UP (3)
- **21** BAR, LIZARD, SUIT (6)
- **22** BUSINESS, LINE, ROMAN (6)
- **24** FINE, MODERN, SCHOOL (3)
- **27** CHANNEL, MERSEY, VISION (6)
- **29** DOSE, INJECTION, WEAPON (6)
- **30** FILM, TERRESTRIAL, TIME (5)
- **31** DOOR, FLY, MOUSE (4)
- **33** FIT, LEFT, SAKE (4)
- **34** NAP, OFF, TEA (9)
- **35** RHYME, SCHOOL, SLOPES (7)
- **36** BIG, BLOOD, HOOD (7)

**DOWN**

- **1** FARM, HEN, RECHARGEABLE (7)
- **2** ACID, DRIVE, MATCH (4)
- **3** NATURE, SIGHT, THOUGHTS (6)
- **5** AGENT, AIR, SICKNESS (6)
- **6** DOG, SALAD, WEEK (4)
- **7** BATH, COFFEE, DELIGHT (7)
- **8** BEST, BUSH, CROSS (6)
- **14** COURT, DERBY, PRINCE (5)
- **15** CLOSE, FREE, MOUNTAIN (5)
- **17** CRAB, PIE, STEWED (5)
- **18** MOTHER, WORKS, WORM (5)
- **19** SHOOTER, SOUP, SWEET (3)
- **20** NAME, SHOP, TEACHER'S (3)
- **23** FIRE, POLICE, WAGON (7)
- **25** DAY, FARE, TAX (6)
- **26** BEDROOM, CARPET, GLASS (7)
- **28** BEGGING, CAPITAL, RACK (6)
- **29** HARD, PARTY, SAVING (6)
- **32** BUS, MOUNTAIN, WORD (4)
- **33** GARDEN, REEF, SLIP (4)

# TWO BY TWO

Each word in a clue can be preceded by the same two letters to spell out another word. For instance, AMBER, EAT and ILL can be preceded by CH to make CHAMBER, CHEAT and CHILL. Can you solve the three clues below, then spell out the three pairs of letters to make a six-letter word?

- APE, OUT, UTTER

- MINE, ODE, RANT

- RENT, ROLE, TENT

# 4 SQUARE

Solve these four clues and then rearrange the solutions into a sixteen-letter phrase, for which a clue is given. The two diagonals also make four-letter words.

**Way of walking**

**Miserly**

**Claret, for instance**

**Old instrument shaped like half a pear**

**Clue: goodbye for now (5,2,4,5)**

# KEYWORD

This puzzle has no clues in the conventional sense. Instead, every different number printed in the main grid represents a different letter (with the same number always representing the same letter, of course). For example, if 7 turns out to be a 'V', you can write in V wherever a square contains 7. We have completed a very small part of the puzzle to give you a start, but the rest is up to you.

| 16 | 2 | 7 | 18 | 10 | 11 |  | 3 | 4 | 18 | 1 | 6 | 19 |
|----|----|----|----|----|----|----|----|----|----|----|----|----|
|  | 20 |  | 10 |  | 2 |  | 25 |  | 10 |  | 8 |  |
| 22 | 8 | 12 | 2 |  | 15 | 24 | 1 | 1 | 2 | 12 | 25 | 24 |
|  | 3 |  | 7 |  | 12 |  |  |  | 5 |  | 10 |  |
| 3 | 17 | 5 | 3 | 14 | 3 |  | 17 | 19 | 12 | 18 | 19 | 10 |
|  |  |  | 14 |  | 12 |  | 3 |  |  |  | 8 |  |
| 9 | 8 | 10 | 12 |  | 18 | 19 | 10 |  | 11 | 3 | 12 | 2 |
|  | 10 |  |  |  | 19 |  | 13 |  | 17 |  |  |  |
| 15 | 18 | 17 | 4 | 2 | 10 |  | 15 | 9 | 3 | 25 | 2 | 13 |
|  | 12 |  | 10 |  |  |  | 14 |  | 26 |  | 7 |  |
| 5 | 3 | 10 | 19 | 25 | 3 | 1 | 3 |  | 18 | 19 | 12 | 3 |
|  | 25 |  | 21 |  | 23 |  | 5 |  | 2 |  | 19 |  |
| 14 | 24 | 11 | 10 | 2 | 12 |  | 2 | 2 | 25 | 18 | 17 | 24 |
|  |  |  |  |  |  |  |  |  | **E** | **R** | **I** |  |

A B C D E̸ F G H̸ J K L M N O P Q R̸ S T U V W X Y Z

| 1 | 2 | 3 | 4 | 5 | 6 | 7 | 8 | 9 | 10 | 11 | 12 | 13 |
|----|----|----|----|----|----|----|----|----|----|----|----|----|
|  | **E** |  |  |  |  |  |  |  |  |  |  |  |
| 14 | 15 | 16 | 17 | 18 | 19 | 20 | 21 | 22 | 23 | 24 | 25 | 26 |
|  |  |  |  | **I** |  |  |  |  |  |  | **R** |  |

# BLACKOUT

Can you identify which two models are shown in silhouette at the top?

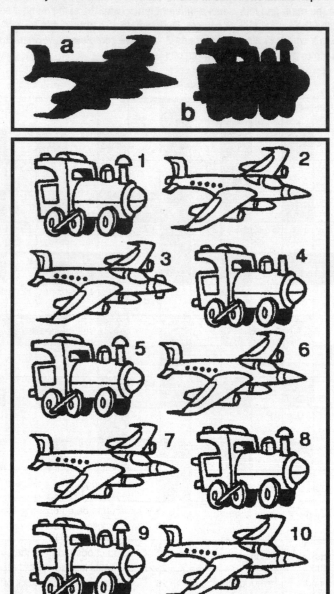

# CRYPTIC CROSSWORD

## ACROSS

7 Distributing Lagos car fuel (5,3)
8 Grab National Trust cash wildly (6)
11 Only doctor without a supply (3,2)
12 Dismiss acts in an outburst of bad temper (9)
13 First person to perform in international language (1,2)
14 The sovereign's hit on the head (5)
16 Inside, Steven Spielberg quits! (5)
17 Chaperone from foreign sector (6)
19 Up in space, circulate part of the frozen polar region (3,3)
21 They pile up as your assets fall! (5)
22 The awful old smoothie's introduction shows characteristic spirit (5)
24 Musical twosome returning during cloudburst (3)
25 Registering when long liner is at sea (9)
27 More underdone, though less common (5)
28 Wild dog shy with broken toe (6)
29 Hypocritical act few do, curiously (3-5)

## DOWN

1 A hundred demand applause (7)
2 Appear as fruit to act as chaperone (4,10)
3 Sarcastic, smooth and in charge (6)
4 One doubles it (4)
5 It's in no particular place when year changes (8)
6 Dissertation or article on Sabbath is (6)
9 Find the lady there, perhaps, with an eccentric fool (5-4,5)
10 Hold aloft a grain-based meal (8)
15 Another programme being broadcast when I come in (2,3,3)
18 Outdated to be off catching fish (8)
20 Russian fellow writes 'broken arm' in secret language (7)
21 Children choose to soak through (6)
23 Dodgy refits lead to conflict (6)
26 Good to possess posh frock (4)

# THAT BIT OF DIFFERENCE

There are eight differences between the two pictures. Can you spot them?

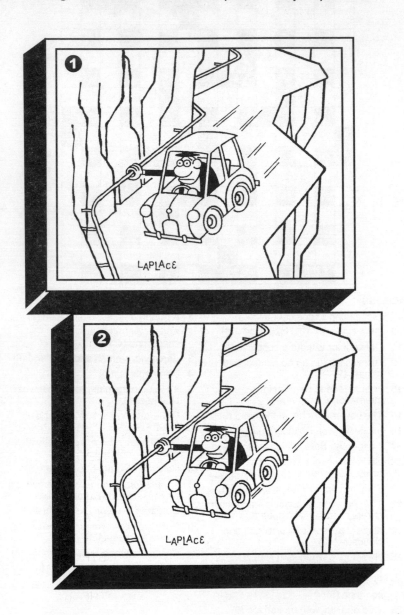

# WORDSEARCH

The 30 lochs have all been hidden in the diagram. They have been printed across (backwards or forwards), or up or down, or diagonally, but always in a straight line without letters being skipped. You can use the letters in the diagram more than once. You will probably find it helpful to mark the words in the diagram and cross them off the list as you find them.

```
M E X W A A C F N Z D O O N N L
T O Y V C T R A R O I M H E L N
C I R H N Y H S R V D K V O Y E
L T R L A C Y K N P W I B C P V
F A N N I C H A S S R I R A E I
Y R X O E C B L R T R N A R S S
C K U G N S H L S E R J Y R O E
B Q M S Y I S Y P A B D Z O G T
D O C H F O U R E O E C C N H F
N N J A J U V G I U N E V E L M
H C O N N A R S H O I S M D A T
O D Z M W L D B C F R T H R W H
L N U K O A J B O P T S E I A O
H A V N L L G Q L X A E Q E E M
O S E E G B L X R Q K Z M D L L
I R H Z U E Y G I A K R A D P F
W A T T E N O F A I U K Q G F T
L T T N X F U N G W O K R M H D
```

| | | |
|---|---|---|
| ACHRAY | FASKALLY | NEVIS |
| ARKAIG | FLEET | QUOICH |
| BOISDALE | FYNE | RANNOCH |
| CARRON | GAIRLOCH | RYAN |
| DOCHFOUR | KATRINE | SHIEL |
| DOON | LEVEN | STRIVEN |
| DUNGEON | LOMOND | TARSAN |
| EARN | MAREE | THOM |
| ERIBOLL | MORLICH | TORRIDON |
| FANNICH | NESS | WATTEN |

# CROSSWORD

**366**

## ACROSS

1 Reduce the price of (5,4)
6 Dirty mark (5)
10 Delete (3,3)
11 Frozen confection (3,5)
12 Rip up (5)
13 Carpet with a long rough pile (4)
15 Posing no difficulty (4)
17 Sudden rush or increase (5)
18 Wheel covering (4)
20 Quiet country road (4)
21 Fashion, form (5)
24 Popular spring bulb (8)
26 Of your clan (6)
27 Collective term for a group of foxes (5)
28 Job advancement (9)

## DOWN

2 Slightly wicked? (7)
3 Shut (5)
4 Responsibility (4)
5 Get ready for sailing (5,6)
7 Substitute for butter (abbrev)(5)
8 Turkish governor (3)
9 Pale neutral colour (5)
13 Health town (3)
14 Devoured (3)
16 Female singer (7)
17 Angle or incline (5)
19 Be better than (5)
22 Winch (5)
23 Flower support (4)
25 Himalayan ox (3)

# ROUNDABOUT

Solutions to Radial clues (1 to 24) either start from the outer edge of the circle and read inwards, or start from the inner ring and read outwards to the edge (so they are all five-letter words). Solutions to Circular clues read in either a clockwise or an anti-clockwise direction round the circle.

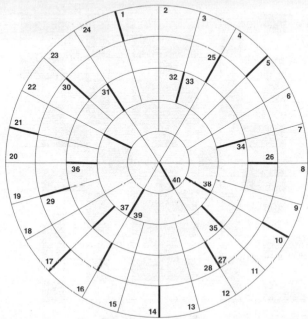

## RADIAL:
### INWARDS

2 Rough, rigorous
3 Flooded
8 Part of a school
9 From Geneva, for example
12 Singer, Miss Lennox
13 Spirit from Aladdin's lamp
14 Stop briefly
15 Rub out
17 Native American religious pole
18 Hot water vapour
20 Mediterranean island
21 Old castle mound
22 Reconcile, make up (for)

### OUTWARDS

1 Raise (a flag or sail)

4 Unit of weight for gems
5 Pile of stones on a mountain
6 Large evergreen coniferous tree
7 Stringed instrument
10 Leather for sharpening a razor
11 Attacks with a knife
16 Juicy gourd
19 Food miraculously provided for the Israelites
23 Go in
24 Cries like an owl

## CIRCULAR:
### CLOCKWISE

1 Which, who
14 Writing instrument
21 Roman god of war
28 Close by

33 Dry, barren
34 Animal's den
35 Happening every year
37 Take food

### ANTI-CLOCKWISE

9 Contempt
13 Catch one's breath
20 Actors in a play
25 Use unprofitably
26 *Dr Zhivago* heroine
27 Dish, basin
29 Also
30 Ripped
31 Carry
32 ___ de Janeiro, Brazilian city
36 Fishing mesh trap
38 Quarter of the year
39 Take a seat
40 Plan of proposed action

# MISSING LINKS

The answer to each clue is a word which has a link with each of the three words listed. This word may come at the end (e.g. HEAD linked with BEACH, BIG and HAMMER), at the beginning (e.g. BLACK linked with BEAUTY, BOARD and JACK) or a mixture of the two (e.g. STONE linked with HAIL, LIME and WALL).

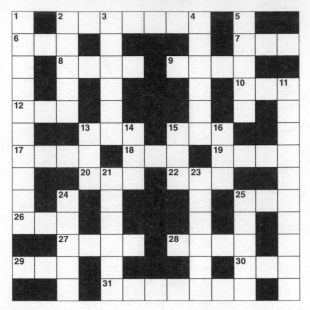

**ACROSS**

2 DUCK, PRETTY, ROOM (7)
6 BRAZIL, GINGER, WING (3)
7 BAG, DOLL, TRADE (3)
8 MODEL, OFFICER, REGULAR (4)
9 ABSOLUTE, HOUR, TOLERANCE (4)
10 CENTRE, HAND, LICENCE (3)
12 JET, PIECE, TELEVISION (3)
13 ART, CONCERT, STAR (3)
15 FLOWER, GUEST, WATER (3)
17 BUSH, HIP, PETAL (4)
18 AGE, BUCKET, CAP (3)
19 BOOK, HOUSE, SANDWICH (4)
20 CURTAIN, HAIR, PROFIT (3)
22 CUP, NEST, SHELL (3)
25 BREEZE, FRONT, HORSE (3)
26 GLOSS, READER, THICK (3)
27 DROP, INDIGESTION, RAIN (4)
28 BONE, CURIOSITY, GOSSIP (4)
29 CHOCOLATE, IRON, SALOON (3)
30 ALTER, BOOST, MANIAC (3)
31 FLAME, TRIANGLE, YOUTH (7)

**DOWN**

1 ACTION, ESPIONAGE, ESTATE (10)
2 FALSE, FRESH, STANDING (5)
3 BEEF, CHERRY, SAUCE (6)
4 ELBOW, GUN, PAINT (6)
5 LIVING, POSITIVE, SOUND (5)
11 COURSE, CREAM, GARMENT (10)
13 FOUNTAIN, FRIEND, KNIFE (3)
14 ORCHESTRA, PONY, SAND (3)
15 LINE, QUEEN, SPELLING (3)
16 COLLAR, GUARD, TOP (3)
21 FIRE, SEARCH, STEAM (6)
23 GATE, PARTY, SHED (6)
24 PART, TIME, TYRE (5)
25 BAND, STAINLESS, WOOL (5)

# ARROWORD

The arrows show the direction in which the answer to each clue should be placed.

| Casserole | Jewelled headwear | Saint whose day is July 15 ▼ | | Counting points ▼ | | Component | Illustrate, show |
|---|---|---|---|---|---|---|---|
| ► | ▼ | | | Chew the __, ruminate ► | | ▼ | ▼ |
| Ship's sail pole | Hole __, golf shot (2,3) ► | | | | | | |
| ► | | | | Slash or tear ► | | | |
| Vehicle available for hire | West Indies republic ► | | | | | | |
| ► | | | | Bitterly cold | | Obeyed, listened to | |
| Enquire | __ Jessica Parker, actress | Twelfth __, Shakespeare play ► | | ▼ | | ▼ | |
| ► | ▼ | | Throw a coin | | Wander at random | | Post, mail |
| Small musical group | Wheel surrounds ► | ▼ | | ▼ | | ▼ | |
| ► | | | Poem specifically addressed ► | | | | |
| The one over here | Number of deadly sins ► | | | | | | |
| ► | | | __ the Duck, TV puppet ► | | | | |

# SUDOKU

Place the numbers from 1 to 9 in each empty cell so that each row, each column and each 3 x 3 block contains all the numbers from 1 to 9 to solve this tricky Sudoku puzzle.

| 3 | 4 |   |   |   |   |   |   |   |
|---|---|---|---|---|---|---|---|---|
|   |   |   |   |   |   |   | 2 | 5 |
|   |   |   | 7 | 9 | 4 |   |   | 3 |
| 8 | 6 |   |   | 4 | 5 |   |   | 9 |
|   |   |   | 1 |   |   |   |   |   |
| 9 | 2 |   |   | 5 | 7 |   |   | 8 |
|   |   |   | 9 | 2 | 8 |   |   | 7 |
|   |   |   |   |   |   |   | 3 | 1 |
|   | 6 | 8 |   |   |   |   |   |   |

MEDIUM

# CROSSWORD

## ACROSS

**6** Confused (7,2)
**7** Flowed out (tide) (5)
**8** Tea-making vessel (3)
**9** Worry (4)
**10** Famous public school near Windsor (4)
**12** Bring to an end (8)
**15** Put one foot on either side of (8)
**17** Circus big cat controller (4-5)
**18** Financially took advantage (6,2)
**20** Recovering consciousness (6,2)
**23** Cylindrical hand warmer (4)
**24** Citric or sulphuric, for example (4)
**27** Acquired (3)
**28** Strawberries' topping (5)
**29** Club or disco (9)

## DOWN

**1** Flawed, faulty (9)
**2** Fit for eating (6)
**3** Brand-name air-freshener (5)
**4** Altered slightly (8)
**5** Aperture, gap (7)
**11** Settle misunderstandings (5,3,3)
**13** United ___, global peace-keeping body (7)
**14** Grizzly animal (4)
**16** Moistening (7)
**17** ___ Ness, deep lake (4)
**19** Maker of expensive jewellery? (9)
**21** In a theatre's wings (3-5)
**22** Picture in your mind (7)
**25** Weird, spooky (6)
**26** People living in the northern part of Britain (5)

# FRAME UP

Solve the clues and then fit the three nine-letter words around the outside of
the pyramid, two words starting from the top and one across the base. Do the
same with the three six-letter and three-letter words. The shaded letters will
spell out an occupation.

**3 letters**
Wager
Deep furrow
Pub counter

**6 letters**
Cherry brandy
Oration
Parrot's croaky call

**9 letters**
Disorderly, chaotic
Sociable, good
    company
Shaped like a globe

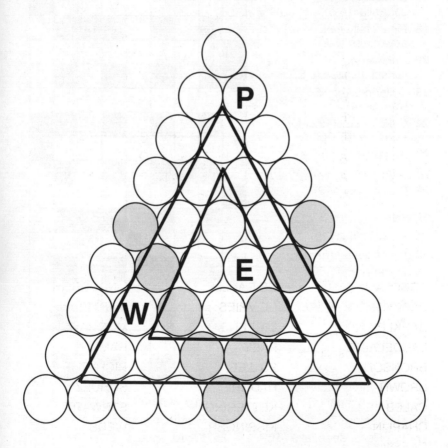

# WORDSEARCH

The 30 personalities below all have Charles as a first name and have been hidden in the diagram. They have been printed across (backwards or forwards), or up or down, or diagonally, but always in a straight line without letters being skipped. You can use the letters in the diagram more than once. You will probably find it helpful to mark the words in the diagram and cross them off the list as you find them.

```
M A R T E L H F G M M R C G V N
S B J W S A W N R Y G A O M O W
Q N E I U Z I R R E L M A D R O
M B E G Y R U E U P Y M K G A R
B C H K E F D G B A R K L E Y B
Z E G T C Z X N R E L L U F A Z
Y L T R L I E I N O T H G U A L
X E I U A G D S H J J A D D Q E
K E H N A W N S K M R E Y A D S
T C W B D B R I K C L G L R S N
S J B K E B P K O A E S G W T O
C A F L G Q E L I D E V R I E S
B H A T A A A R W T R U O N W N
I C A Y U R E L G E S E F V A O
H H P P L A M B H H B E I N R R
U B Y E L S E W V C Z V W V T B
W Q T I E I N C D I P U C A A T
E N F I O A N L B R X S C X D X
```

| | | |
|---|---|---|
| ARCOLA | DE GAULLE | LINDBERGH |
| BABBAGE | DE VRIES | MARTEL |
| BARKLEY | DICKENS | MCGRAW |
| BAUDELAIRE | FREY | RAMM |
| BRONSON | FULLER | RICHET |
| BROWN | HAUGHEY | SCHULZ |
| CALEB | KETTERING | STEWART |
| CHAPLIN | KISSINGER | WEBB |
| DARWIN | LAMB | WESLEY |
| DAWES | LAUGHTON | XAVIER |

# PIECEWORD

With the help of the Across clues only, can you fit the 35 pieces into their correct positions in the empty grid (which, when completed, will exhibit a symmetrical pattern)?

## ACROSS

1 Atoll substance • Fine-grained quartz

2 Past • Place with curative mineral springs

3 Informed on

4 Pure • Imprison pending trial

5 Carry out

6 Large jug • Weight of duty

7 Water excess

8 Guard duty • Allow

9 Break out suddenly like a volcano

10 Gain by merit • Fleshy parts around the mouth

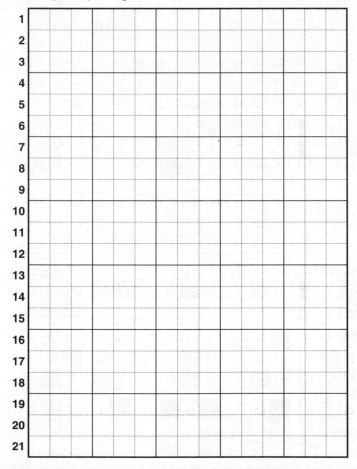

11 Smallest

12 Flower or part of the eye • Do nothing

13 Block of gold

14 Communicator with spirits • Moved ahead of

15 Walk through

16 Stern, severe • Make a brisk, sharp, cracking sound

17 Postage levy

18 On time • Hidden

19 Put back

20 Barn or tawny, for instance • Was in charge

21 Clutch • Make joyful

# RIDDLE ME REE

My first is in SIM CARD and CAMERA,

My second's in KEYPAD and CHARGER,

My third is in SELECT and RINGTONES,

My fourth is in CALLS and PHONES,

My fifth is in BATTERY and NAMES,

My sixth is in SIGNAL and GAMES,

My seventh's in NETWORK and MENU,

My whole is something texted to you.

---

# 4 SQUARE

Solve these four clues and then rearrange the solutions into a sixteen-letter phrase, for which a clue is given. The two diagonals also make four-letter words.

**Toothpaste flavour**

**Foot digits**

**Tilt**

**Leg bone**

**Clue: very quickly (2,4,4,2,4)**

# CROSSWORD

**ACROSS**

1 Lady customer's title? (5)
4 Early period in life (8)
9 Trying, making an effort (6,1,2)
10 Inner-city (area) (5)
11 Shun (6)
13 Opportunity (7)
16 Australian flightless bird (3)
17 Physical check-up (7)
19 Japanese car manufacturer (6)
22 Adherent of an Indian religion (5)
24 Vulgarity (9)
26 Furtively (2,3,3)
27 Sea currents (5)

**DOWN**

1 Main Seychelles island (4)
2 Planned (7)
3 Chew steadily (5)
4 Feathered scarf (3)
5 Erase (4,3)
6 Residential building (5)
7 Part of a monarch's regalia (3)
8 Forename of the architect Jones (5)
12 Waterproof boots (7)
14 Given a modulated pitch (7)
15 City on the River Missouri, USA (5)
18 Comfy piece of furniture (5)
20 Light sailing vessel (5)
21 Seed-buds of a potato (4)
23 Grandad's wife! (3)
25 24 hours (3)

# SUM UP

Using the totals given, can you calculate the price of the spool, hook, tin of shot and box of worms?

£ 27-50

£ 17-50

£ 32-50

£ 30-00

---

# PRESENT SUPRISE

Here's a quick wordsearch for you to enjoy. All these present ideas can be found in the grid. Look for them in the word search grid. They have been printed across (backwards or forwards), or up or down, or diagonally, but always in a straight line without letters being skipped.

BOARD GAME
BOOKS
CLOTHES
COMPUTER
DVDS
FOOTBALL
GAMEBOY
JEWELLERY
PUZZLES
TRAINERS
VOUCHERS

| S | E | H | T | O | L | C | V | F | Y |
|---|---|---|---|---|---|---|---|---|---|
| E | B | O | O | K | S | O | D | R | T |
| L | C | O | M | P | U | T | E | R | R |
| Z | L | G | A | C | D | L | T | Y | A |
| Z | S | A | H | R | L | V | O | P | I |
| U | X | E | B | E | D | B | D | N | N |
| P | R | O | W | T | E | G | I | S | E |
| S | M | E | L | M | O | Z | A | A | R |
| E | J | C | A | K | Q | O | B | M | S |
| H | V | G | U | R | W | Y | F | J | E |

# KEYWORD

This puzzle has no clues in the conventional sense. Instead, every different number printed in the main grid represents a different letter (with the same number always representing the same letter, of course). For example, if 7 turns out to be a 'V', you can write in V wherever a square contains 7. We have completed a very small part of the puzzle to give you a start, but the rest is up to you.

| 23 | 26 | 1 | 20 | 17 | | 1 | 23 | 3 | 18 | 21 | |
|----|----|----|----|----|----|----|----|----|----|----|----|
| 15 | | 8 | | 4 | | 17 | | 19 | | 11 | | 26 E |
| 17 | 6 | 12 | 21 | 13 | | 15 | 21 | 1 | 24 | 19 | 26 | 10 D |
| 1 | | 1 | | 4 | | 4 | | 16 | | 26 | | 4 I |
| 21 | 18 | 15 | | 20 | 12 | 9 | 15 | 4 | | 10 | 12 | 23 |
| | | 18 | | | | 9 | | 13 | | | | 19 |
| 12 | 13 | 21 | 4 | 6 | 26 | | 4 | 11 | 13 | 18 | 21 | 26 |
| 6 | | | | 26 | | 15 | | | | 2 | | |
| 25 | 26 | 13 | | 21 | 3 | 7 | 20 | 26 | | 26 | 19 | 9 |
| 26 | | 4 | | 5 | | 6 | | 22 | | 21 | | 12 |
| 26 | 22 | 26 | 14 | 12 | 15 | 26 | | 1 | 19 | 23 | 12 | 20 |
| 6 | | 14 | | 21 | | 10 | | 14 | | 4 | | 26 |
| | 23 | 26 | 21 | 7 | 19 | | 17 | 15 | 12 | 10 | 7 | |

A B C Ð Ɇ F G H Ɨ J K L M N O P Q R S T U V W X Y Z

| 1 | 2 | 3 | 4 I | 5 | 6 | 7 | 8 | 9 | 10 D | 11 | 12 | 13 |
|----|----|----|----|----|----|----|----|----|----|----|----|----|
| 14 | 15 | 16 | 17 | 18 | 19 | 20 | 21 | 22 | 23 | 24 | 25 | 26 E |

# TINKER, TAILOR...

To discover who this person is, unscramble the words in the verse, which hints at what the person does. Write these words into the boxes below, reading across, and, if you've placed them in the correct order, the arrowed column will spell out the occupation.

You've FALLYIN found a house you like and agree to buy,

You'll need this person's RICEVESS and here's the reason why:

They'll check the PMAD SURECO, FOOR STILE, SCRIBK and wood,

That there's no NICEBUSDES and the CUTERRUST is good.

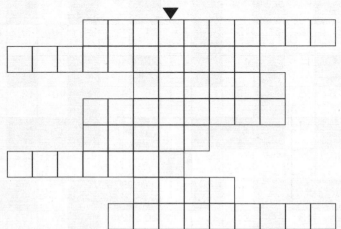

---

# 4 SQUARE

Solve these four clues and then rearrange the solutions into a sixteen-letter phrase, for which a clue is given. The two diagonals also make four-letter words.

**MISDEEDS**

**WORK, ESPECIALLY OF MUSIC**

**TWO-MASTED VESSEL**

**BIBLICAL GARDEN**

**clue: spanning structure (10,6)**

---

# JIG-WORD

**No clues - just pattern and answers - but can you fit them in?**

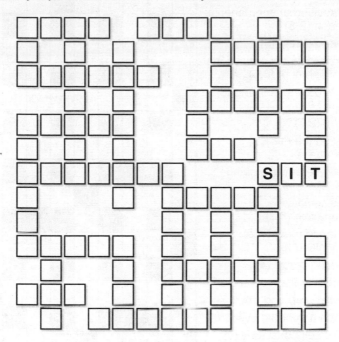

### 3 letters
Cob
Dug
Ill
Maw
Sit
Web

### 4 letters
Brig
Copy
Exam
Idly
Lull
Semi

### 5 letters
Drawl
Elude
Fumed
Irony
Taupe
Unfit

### 6 letters
Barbed
Farmed
Injure
Learnt
Myopia
Smiled

### 7 letters
Dutiful
Jumbled
Perform
Recycle
Studded

# CROSSWORD

## ACROSS

**1** Improvised or spontaneous speech (2-3)
**4** Striped insect (3)
**6** Non-residential educational establishment (3,6)
**7** (Of two cars) colliding (8)
**9** Available through pumps in a pub (2,7)
**10** City on the French Riviera (4)
**12** Distance between wing tips (4)
**14** Was socially compatible (6,2)
**17** Distance (people) from a risky place (8)
**19** Meeting of lips (4)
**21** Rubber wheel-covering (4)
**23** Shipping abroad (9)
**25** Watch a sporting event (8)
**27** Make self-conscious (9)
**28** Formal address to a gentleman (3)
**29** Administered medicine to (5)

## DOWN

**1** Presidential adviser (4)
**2** Tiered (7)
**3** ___ driver, car passenger who gives unwanted advice (4-4)
**4** Inflating (7,2)
**5** Imparting knowledge to (12)
**8** Open cut (5)
**11** Fine delicate pottery (5)
**13** Strong, dark, malty ale (5)
**15** Short simple song (5)
**16** Unthinking, irresponsible nature (12)
**18** Join (with another company) (5)
**20** Autumn month (9)
**22** Covered with shallow holes (8)
**24** Crying (2,5)
**26** Second-hand (4)

# BOX WISE

Can you put these three-letter groups into the twelve numbered boxes to produce twelve six-letter words, each of which starts in one box and finishes in another as indicated by an arrow? For instance, 2 and 5 make a six-letter word, but not 5 and 9. One group of three letters has been filled in to start you off.

### ACC ANT CAN DLE FIL FUL
### (HEM) MED ORD REC TER USE

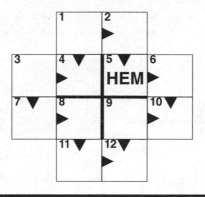

# SILHOUETTE

Shade in every fragment that contains a dot and what have you got?

# HONEYCOMB

All the answers are six-letter words. Each answer is entered in a circle around its clue-number. The first letter of the answer is entered in the shaded triangle immediately above the clue-number. If the clue-number is even, enter the answer in a clockwise direction. If the clue-number is odd, enter the answer in an anti-clockwise direction.

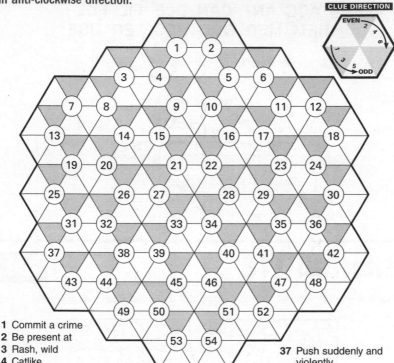

**CLUE DIRECTION**

1 Commit a crime
2 Be present at
3 Rash, wild
4 Catlike
5 Examined
6 Held the same opinion
7 Stiffly polite
8 Lightweight open shoe
9 Common finch
10 Public road
11 Buy back
12 Hymn of praise
13 Change for the better
14 Approached
15 Make smarter
16 Amend
17 Allocate, pledge
18 Separate grain by beating
19 Decomposed
20 Rubbed out
21 Engraved
22 Scorched
23 Thrown up into the air
24 Sitting down
25 Frugality
26 Distinctive smells
27 Squat
28 Specifying
29 Lively Brazilian dances
30 State firmly
31 Was appropriate for
32 Walked in a leisurely fashion
33 Attractively soft and plump
34 In a satisfactory way
35 Away
36 Not long past
37 Push suddenly and violently
38 Happen
39 Guard against attack
40 Shiny metal plating
41 Sacred place of worship
42 Section of a contract
43 Without doubt
44 These days
45 Nerve cell
46 Gesture, action
47 Blockhead
48 Give in
49 Leaseholder
50 Requiring immediate attention
51 Puts things away
52 Interweaves
53 Outstanding intellect
54 Athletic throwing event

# PATHFINDER

Starting from the letter in the box, move up or down or sideways (but NOT diagonally) using all the letters to find the path through the names of seventeen American States.

| | | | | | | | | | |
|---|---|---|---|---|---|---|---|---|---|
| E | R | O | L | O | D | A | C | O | L | O |
| G | T | A | F | R | I | R | E | D | A | R |
| O | O | S | E | N | O | M | V | O | O | R |
| N | A | M | I | N | N | T | C | I | F | N |
| L | N | A | A | L | O | Z | A | L | A | I |
| O | S | I | W | E | N | I | O | M | W | Y |
| U | I | R | A | D | A | R | N | G | N | O |
| N | A | E | A | L | O | A | T | A | I | M |
| S | K | A | M | A | I | H | O | N | A | I |
| A | E | V | A | B | A | W | A | N | A | N |
| S | N | A | D | A | H | A | I | I | I | D |

| | | |
|---|---|---|
| ALABAMA | INDIANA | VERMONT |
| ARIZONA | KANSAS | WYOMING |
| COLORADO | MINNESOTA | OHIO |
| CALIFORNIA | MONTANA | DELAWARE |
| FLORIDA | NEVADA | LOUISIANA |
| HAWAII | OREGON | |

# NUMBER JIG

Just like a jig-word – but instead of letters, numbers.

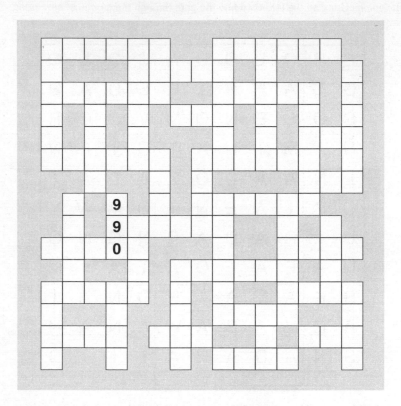

| 3-figure | | 5-figure | |
|---|---|---|---|
| 284 | 1592 | 30315 | 381814 |
| 292 | 2826 | 31305 | 424013 |
| 338 | 3104 | 38142 | 503922 |
| 556 | 3126 | 39146 | 524718 |
| 728 | 3128 | 60148 | 528426 |
| 802 | 4366 | 91234 | 534283 |
| 825 | 4923 | 92147 | 535164 |
| (990) | 4952 | | 621066 |
| | 6521 | | 683008 |
| | 9123 | **6-figure** | 914283 |
| **4-figure** | | 162551 | 926331 |
| 1362 | | 163554 | 932560 |
| 1587 | | 251966 | 983828 |

# ARROWORD

The arrows show the direction in which the answer to each clue should be placed.

| Decorative coatings ▼ | | Exercise hall ▼ | | Exclude ▼ | | Theatrical offering ▼ |
|---|---|---|---|---|---|---|
| Very bad ► | | | | | | |
| Small termite-like insect | | Unifying idea | | Hitch | | Surrounding glow |
| ► | | ▼ | | ▼ | | ▼ |
| Lean, narrow ► | | | Don't go! ► | Stipulations (in a contract, eg) | | Under-standing |
| ► | | | Measure of 4840 square yards ► | ▼ | | ▼ |
| Operate | Big __, fairground attraction | | __ up, dress attractively ► | | | |
| Spider's home | ▼ | | ▼ | Call My __, TV panel game | | Be at ease |
| Published list of meal options | | Daughter of the Duchess of Cornwall ► | | | ▼ | |
| ► | | | | Complete collection ► | | |
| Treble __, musical symbol | | Newly made or obtained ► | | | | |
| ► | | | | Pig's home ► | | |

# WORDSEARCH

The 30 varieties of butterfly have all been hidden in the diagram. They have been printed across (backwards or forwards), or up or down, or diagonally, but always in a straight line without letters being skipped. You can use the letters in the diagram more than once. You will probably find it helpful to mark the words in the diagram and cross them off the list as you find them.

```
A R B E Z Y J R B N O L L O P A
K A E R T S R I A H J U L I A S
C H A D M I R A L V A B R L W T
L L F D Y D G V L Q O I X A T Q
E G D C W P B N R L N H L E Y Y
O U I I R A G S I G I L P S C S
P U N C H I N E L L O T N R U N
A G S Y E N M E C W Y A I G O O
T T K D M T T S T A P A R R H M
R I I U I E W A O E R A R C F R
A M P J M D I M U N H D R G E O
C R P M N L M L P C R A I P K M
O E E U O A B P T E N O P N O E
M H R L M D W O Z O A O S A A U
M M F P M Y C H M Y C C W E D L
A L W U O S B R I M S T O N E B
S J Z P C I N R C T X P H C K T
P I T E G N A R O O E X K O K E
```

| | | |
|---|---|---|
| ADMIRAL | COPPER | PAINTED LADY |
| APOLLO | CRIMSON ROSE | PEACOCK |
| BIRDWING | FRITILLARY | PLUM JUDY |
| BLUE MORMON | GRAYLING | PUNCHINELLO |
| BLUE PANSY | HAIRSTREAK | RINGLET |
| BRIMSTONE | HERMIT | SCOTCH ARGUS |
| CARDINAL | JULIA | SKIPPER |
| CLEOPATRA | MONARCH | SWALLOWTAIL |
| COMMA | MORPHO | WHITE |
| COMMON MIME | ORANGE TIP | ZEBRA |

The popularity of out-of-town shopping centres has made life difficult for small shops all over the country, but five independent retailers in the small town of Vendingley are still thriving. From the clues given below, can you match each of these shops with its wares, its location and the year in which it opened for business?

**Clues**

1 The paint shop started trading in 1988, and Robinson's opened its doors to customers for the first time in 1994.

2 You can find the town's famous cheese shop in Hawking Way.

3 The retail establishment in Patter Street, which has been doing a roaring trade since it opened in 1997, does not sell confectionery.

4 By the time the shop in Commercial Lane started trading, Bertram's was already established in its current location.

5 Webster's, which is situated in Pitch Place, opened in the 1980s, as did the wool shop, Get Fleeced.

|  | Cheese | Confectionery | Paint | Stationery | Wool | Commercial Lane | Hawking Way | Patter Street | Pitch Place | Stock Road | 1985 | 1988 | 1994 | 1997 | 2002 |
|---|---|---|---|---|---|---|---|---|---|---|---|---|---|---|---|
| Bertram's | | | | | | | | | | | | | | | |
| Collin's | | | | | | | | | | | | | | | |
| Get Fleeced | | | | | | | | | | | | | | | |
| Robinson's | | | | | | | | | | | | | | | |
| Webster's | | | | | | | | | | | | | | | |
| 1985 | | | | | | | | | | | | | | | |
| 1988 | | | | | | | | | | | | | | | |
| 1994 | | | | | | | | | | | | | | | |
| 1997 | | | | | | | | | | | | | | | |
| 2002 | | | | | | | | | | | | | | | |
| Commercial Lane | | | | | | | | | | | | | | | |
| Hawking Way | | | | | | | | | | | | | | | |
| Patter Street | | | | | | | | | | | | | | | |
| Pitch Place | | | | | | | | | | | | | | | |
| Stock Road | | | | | | | | | | | | | | | |

*Record in this grid all the information obtained from the clues, by using a cross to indicate a definite 'no' and a tick to show a definite 'yes'. Transfer these to all sections of the grid thus eliminating all but one possibility, which must be the correct one.*

| Shop | Wares | Location | Year |
|---|---|---|---|
| | | | |
| | | | |
| | | | |
| | | | |
| | | | |

# BRACER

The first part of each clue gives a six-letter answer, five of whose letters make up the five-letter answer to the second part and four of which make up the four-letter answer to the third part. The unused letter from the first answer is entered in column A, and that from the second answer in column B. The two columns when completed, spell out two dogs.

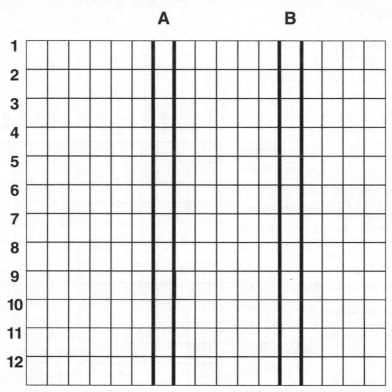

1 Roam; shoreline bird; take a risk

2 Humble, lower; called; curse

3 Linger; confuse; perished

4 Quicker; daisy-like flower; assess

5 Groups of fish; cut wildly; young girl

6 Chores; located; team

7 Land around a house; ranking; tow

8 Fly-catcher; interferes; pastry dishes

9 Visitor; transparent; delicate fabric

10 Was unsuccessful; put papers in order; ran away

11 Cause; got up; fly high

12 Extreme lack; core; warmth

# CROSSWORD

## ACROSS

1 Kind of lettuce (3)
8 Putting up (a building) (12)
9 Shopkeeper in *The Simpsons* (3)
11 Burglar (5)
12 Bloodsucking person with fangs! (7)
14 Parts of the body of interest to a podiatrist (4)
15 Number of days in June (6)
18 Any of two (6)
20 Place for drying hops (4)
23 Temperature scale (7)
25 Cowboy's home (5)
27 Japanese currency (3)
28 Not related, dissimilar (12)
29 UK river, in Devon (3)

## DOWN

1 Seafood snack (4,5)
2 Rabbit's tail (4)
3 Smear with oil (6)
4 Opposite of 'flexible' (5)
5 Bow (5)
6 Unit of matter (4)
7 Improve the quality of (6)
10 Organise differently (9)
13 Took food (3)
16 Style of roller skates (2-4)
17 *She Loves* ___, Beatles hit (3)
19 Burn (6)
21 Berkshire racecourse (5)
22 Characteristic (5)
24 ___ facto, by that very fact (4)
26 Dr Jekyll's alter ego (4)

# SUDOKU

Place the numbers from 1 to 9 in each empty cell so that each row, each column and each 3 x 3 block contains all the numbers from 1 to 9 to solve this tricky Sudoku puzzle.

| | | | | 4 | | 6 | | |
|---|---|---|---|---|---|---|---|---|
| | | 6 | | | 2 | | | |
| 2 | 4 | | | 5 | | | | 9 |
| | 5 | | | | | | 1 | |
| 3 | | | | 8 | | 4 | | 7 |
| 1 | 9 | 7 | | | | | | |
| 9 | | | 3 | | | | 5 | |
| 8 | | | 5 | | 1 | 9 | | |
| | 3 | 5 | 4 | 7 | | 2 | | |

**EASY**

# SKELETON

Have double the fun with this puzzle: you've got to fill in the answers and the black squares! We've given you the bare bones to start and it will help you to know that the black squares in the finished grid form a symmetrical pattern, so that every black square has at least one other corresponding black square.

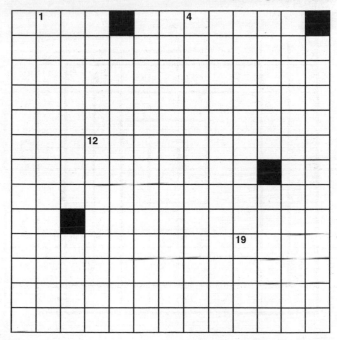

## ACROSS

7 Flame controller
8 For either gender
9 Chew away at
10 Paddling means of travel
11 Lacking distinction
14 Paying insufficient regard to danger
18 Difficult to grasp
19 Volume
20 ___ dancing, English tradition
21 Vindicate

## DOWN

1 Five-piece band
2 Be acquainted with
3 Seller of food
4 Small brook
5 Permitted seller of alcohol
6 Copper coin
12 Porcine feet
13 Miserly Dickens character
15 Gladden
16 In whatever case
17 Essential fluid
19 Small busy insects

# SPIRAL

Every answer (except the first) uses the last letter of the preceding answer as its initial letter, the chain thus formed following a spiral path to the centre of the grid. The diagonals spell two wines.

**START**

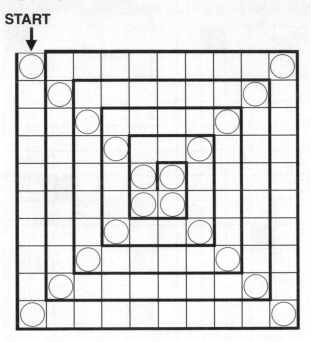

- Population survey (6)
- Got lost (7)
- Scandinavian country (7)
- Australian marsupial (8)
- Exile, reject (7)
- Long-range viewer (9)
- Aubergine (8)
- Boldness (8)
- Sailing boat (5)
- Finger protector (7)

- ___ Shackleton, Antarctica explorer (6)
- Summer sport (6)
- Book carrier (7)
- Scottish landowner (5)
- Circular plate (4)
- Happy (7)
- Small tower (6)
- Large frog-like amphibian (4)

# CROSSWORD

## ACROSS

5 Had bad posture (8)

7 Noah's ship (3)

8 Movements of the sea (5)

9 Short witty remark (3-5)

11 Timber (4)

12 Genesis garden (4)

14 Grumpy, irritable (5)

15 Needle-hole (3)

16 Decorate (a dish of food) (7)

20 Bone of the torso (3)

21 Not tipsy (5)

23 Join up with (friends) (4)

24 Part of a plant (4)

26 Early evening (8)

28 Chop (3,2)

29 ___ off, fall asleep (3)

30 Water off the east coast of England (5,3)

## DOWN

1 School composition (5)

2 Exercising in the gym (7,3)

3 Coal bucket (7)

4 Bridal gown (7,5)

6 Now living apart (husband and wife) (9)

10 Pirouette (5)

13 Acrobatic athlete (7)

17 Shortened form of a word (12)

18 Percussionist's tool (9)

19 US college dances (5)

22 Spiteful gossip (10)

25 Argument (7)

27 Just right (5)

# KEYWORD

This puzzle has no clues in the conventional sense. Instead, every different number printed in the main grid represents a different letter (with the same number always representing the same letter, of course). For example, if 7 turns out to be a 'V', you can write in V wherever a square contains 7. We have completed a very small part of the puzzle to give you a start, but the rest is up to you.

| 25 | ■ | 6 | ■ | 12 | ■ | 20 | ■ | 17 | ■ | 7 | ■ |
|----|----|----|----|----|----|----|----|----|----|----|----|
| 3 | 8 | 4 | 2 | 8 | 5 | 10 | 7 | 25 | 2 | 2 | 18 |
| 1 | ■ | 8 | ■ | 2 | ■ | 12 | ■ | 22 | ■ | 6 | 7 |
| 26 | 12 R | 9 I | 4 G | 6 | 23 | 9 | ■ | 8 | 12 | 12 | 26 | 12 |
| ■ | ■ | 20 | ■ | 24 | ■ | 16 | ■ | 13 | ■ | 8 | 8 |
| 17 | 6 | 23 | 13 | ■ | 13 | 8 | 21 | 26 | 2 | 1 | 8 | 3 |
| 6 | ■ | ■ | ■ | 25 | ■ | ■ | ■ | 24 | ■ | ■ | 14 |
| 5 | 12 | 8 | 8 | 11 | 9 | 3 | 4 | ■ | 19 | 25 | 6 | 18 |
| 22 | ■ | 3 | ■ | 7 | ■ | 26 | ■ | 13 | ■ | 3 | |
| 8 | 3 | 10 | 8 | 12 | ■ | 25 | 20 | 8 | 2 | 8 | 20 | 20 |
| 1 | ■ | 9 | ■ | 26 | ■ | 4 | ■ | 2 | ■ | 6 | 26 |
| ■ | 20 | 5 | 6 | 3 | 1 | 6 | 2 | 26 | 25 | 20 | 2 | 18 |
| ■ | 8 | ■ | 10 | ■ | 10 | ■ | 15 | ■ | 8 | 6 |

A B C D E F G̷ H̷ J̷ K L M N O P Q R̷ S T U V W X Y Z

| 1 | 2 | 3 | 4 G | 5 | 6 | 7 | 8 | 9 I | 10 | 11 | 12 R | 13 |
|----|----|----|----|----|----|----|----|----|----|----|----|----|
| 14 | 15 | 16 | 17 | 18 | 19 | 20 | 21 | 22 | 23 | 24 | 25 | 26 |

# JIG-WORD

No clues - just pattern and answers - but can you fit them in?

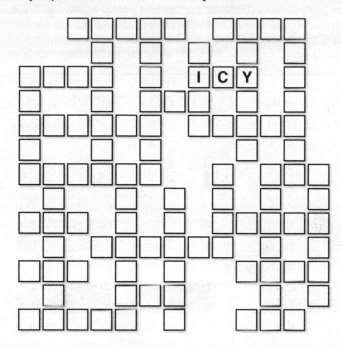

## 3 letters
Ago
Dye
Ewe
Icy
Ilk
Opt
Wit

## 4 letters
Boor
Gill
Hike
Sigh
Stub

## 5 letters
Added
Email
Ennui
Genus
Glint

## 6 letters
Dimmer
Neared
Outcry
Squall
Trying
Warmth

## 7 letters
Alimony
Banning
Infidel
Located
Malaria
Quipped

# WORDSEARCH

The 30 underground-related words have all been hidden in the diagram. They have been printed across (backwards or forwards), or up or down, or diagonally, but always in a straight line without letters being skipped. You can use the letters in the diagram more than once. You will probably find it helpful to mark the words in the diagram and cross them off the list as you find them.

```
J T U N N E L D B W V F E B A I
N U W H I S I U I Z A U T V R U
R H M R F M S N C E L L A R N B
B O N W F R C G E A B L S D T L
N U O X O P I E V L P N E M U U
T E N T C H O O C D O R M G B B
J S R K S W K N V I G M Y I E O
K X K R E L B A T R E T A W R P
C R O J A R C A O U E A Q E R U
G A G X M W D U L M O S F H Z F
D B T E Y N N C S A T J E Z N D
W U T A U D A T R E A S U R E N
K R E O C B L B A S T D T Y R Y
O R F Y L O Y Q V L O T O E A W
G O X E N I M Z R A P G V W C O
L W S V L H K B I O E A B S N R
T O R R A C Q B Q C C U C O R M
S M F E J L O P A V S D E F N T
```

| | | |
|---|---|---|
| BULB | CORM | ROOTS |
| BUNKER | DUNGEON | SETT |
| BURROW | FOUNDATIONS | SUBWAY |
| CABLES | LAVA | TREASURE |
| CARROT | METRO | TUBER |
| CATACOMB | MINE | TUNNEL |
| CAVERN | MOLE | UNDERGROUND |
| CELLAR | ORE | WARREN |
| COAL SEAM | POTATO | WATER TABLE |
| COFFIN | RESERVOIR | WORM |

# SO COMPLETE!

PENELOPE, STELLA, FERGUS, GERARD, BORIS, MIRIAM, NICKI and HUBERT were discussing nursery-rhyme characters. Use the letters of their names once each to reveal the list.

J _ _ K   S _ _ _ T

W I _ _ I _   W _ _ _ _ E

G _ O _ _ I _   P O _ _ _ _

M O _ _ _ _   H _ _ _ _ _ _

S _ _ _ _ E   _ I _ _ _

D _ K _   O F   Y _ _ K

M _ _ _   M U _ F _ _

---

# DOT TO DOT

Join the dots from 1 to 57 to reveal the hidden picture.

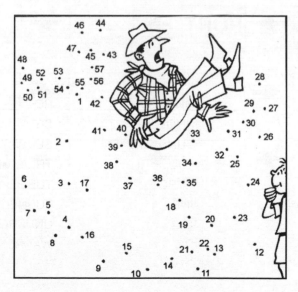

# WORD CHAIN

Place the groups of letters listed below into the boxes to form a chain of words, so that each box makes a word when paired up with the next box.

| | | | | |
|---|---|---|---|---|
| AK | AL | BA | EN | ENT |
| IN | ~~LAY~~ | ON | PLA | ~~PORT~~ |
| ~~QUE~~ | RAP | RAY | RUM | SIGN |
| SIL | SO | ST | TON | WARD |

```
┌──────┐     ┌──────┐     ┌──────┐     ┌──────┐
│      │ ──▶ │ QUE  │ ──▶ │      │ ──▶ │      │
└──────┘     └──────┘     └──────┘     └──────┘
                                            │
                                            ▼
┌──────┐     ┌──────┐     ┌──────┐     ┌──────┐
│      │ ◀── │      │ ◀── │      │ ◀── │      │
└──────┘     └──────┘     └──────┘     └──────┘
   │
   ▼
┌──────┐     ┌──────┐     ┌──────┐     ┌──────┐
│      │ ──▶ │ PORT │ ──▶ │      │ ──▶ │      │
└──────┘     └──────┘     └──────┘     └──────┘
                                            │
                                            ▼
┌──────┐     ┌──────┐     ┌──────┐     ┌──────┐
│      │ ◀── │      │ ◀── │      │ ◀── │      │
└──────┘     └──────┘     └──────┘     └──────┘
   │
   ▼
┌──────┐     ┌──────┐     ┌──────┐     ┌──────┐
│      │ ──▶ │      │ ──▶ │      │ ──▶ │ LAY  │
└──────┘     └──────┘     └──────┘     └──────┘
```

# KEYWORD

This puzzle has no clues in the conventional sense. Instead, every different number printed in the main grid represents a different letter (with the same number always representing the same letter, of course). For example, if 7 turns out to be a 'V', you can write in V wherever a square contains 7. We have completed a very small part of the puzzle to give you a start, but the rest is up to you.

| | 9 | | 4 | | 20 | | 3 | | 9 | | 1 | |
|---|---|---|---|---|---|---|---|---|---|---|---|---|
| 23 | 25 | 18 | 21 | 1 | 7 | 18 | 24 | | 13 | 8 | 3 | 6 |
| | 18 | | 9 **F** | | 3 | | 17 | | 3 | | 25 | |
| 9 | 18 | 25 | 25 **R** | 18 | 20 | | 8 | 25 | 5 | 3 | 21 | |
| | 10 | | 3 **A** | | 1 | | 4 | | | | 3 | |
| 12 | 18 | 3 | 25 | | 7 | 8 | 21 | 18 | 2 | 20 | 13 | 11 |
| | | | 18 | | | | | | 18 | | | |
| 7 | 18 | 3 | 24 | 26 | 3 | 21 | 24 | | 14 | 4 | 2 | 3 |
| | 15 | | | | 2 | | 18 | | 18 | | 16 | |
| | 12 | 4 | 14 | 8 | 20 | | 14 | 18 | 25 | 2 | 22 | 2 |
| | 3 | | 8 | | 22 | | 4 | | 18 | | 3 | |
| 19 | 21 | 8 | 20 | | 20 | 3 | 1 | 20 | 13 | 18 | 2 | 2 |
| | 24 | | 18 | | 18 | | 18 | | 11 | | 7 | |

A̶ B C D E F̶ G H I J K L M N O P Q R̶ S T U V W X Y Z

| 1 | 2 | 3 **A** | 4 | 5 | 6 | 7 | 8 | 9 **F** | 10 | 11 | 12 | 13 |
|---|---|---|---|---|---|---|---|---|---|---|---|---|
| 14 | 15 | 16 | 17 | 18 | 19 | 20 | 21 | 22 | 23 | 24 | 25 **R** | 26 |

# DROP OUT

In the top picture, the rocker is looking for his lost boot. In the bottom picture, he has found it. Which boot is the one he takes?

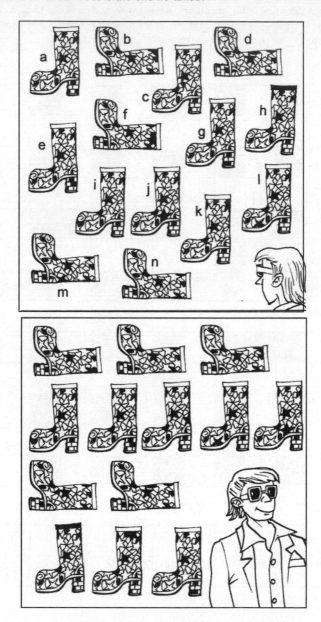

# PATHFINDER

Starting from the letter in the box, move up or down or sideways (but NOT diagonally) using all the letters to find the path through the names of seventeen Indian foods.

| | | | | | | | | | |
|---|---|---|---|---|---|---|---|---|---|
| R | Y | A | P | I | N | D | A | B | N | A |
| I | B | N | I | L | A | S | A | H | U | C |
| S | A | S | U | A | E | V | P | N | A | H |
| A | M | O | R | I | C | I | N | D | A | A |
| G | O | R | O | O | A | B | L | A | N | P |
| A | R | I | N | D | L | O | O | Z | I | A |
| N | D | O | A | T | T | A | L | E | I | T |
| J | H | P | I | A | I | J | F | R | B | H |
| O | S | Z | A | L | A | M | A | I | T | A |
| H | D | A | K | C | S | A | K | K | I | J |
| A | N | S | A | H | A | T | A | L | O | O |

| | | |
|---|---|---|
| BHAJI | BIRYANI | TIKKA MASALA |
| CHAPATI | DHANSAK | VINDALOO |
| SAMOSA | DOPIAZA | NAAN |
| TANDOORI | JALFREZI | CHAT ALOO |
| BALTI | PASANDA | PILAU RICE |
| BHUNA | ROGAN JOSH | |

# CROSSWORD

## ACROSS

1 Inconsistent figure of speech (5,8)
9 Old name for England (6)
10 Constructing again (8)
11 Hit (a fly) (4)
12 ___ Lords, *Blade* actress (5)
13 Parent's sister (4)
14 Umberto ___, Italian author (3)
15 *The World Is ___ Enough*, 1999 Bond movie (3)
16 *A Beautiful ___*, Russell Crowe film (4)
18 Fetch (5)
20 Soft part of the outer ear (4)
22 Bodily pain (8)
24 Taking food (6)
25 Beyond doubt (13)

## DOWN

2 Relative by marriage (2-3)
3 Threw out (7)
4 Adult males (3)
5 ___ firma, solid ground (5)
6 Trying to extract information from (7)
7 Tree bearing acorns (3)
8 Author unknown (4)
12 Source of nicotine (7)
13 Capital of Georgia, USA (7)
17 'Terrible' Russian ruler (4)
19 Lifeless, passive (5)
21 Vapid (5)
23 Barbie's ex-boyfriend (3)
24 ___ Moines, Iowa's capital (3)

# BACKWARDS

For this puzzle, we've filled in the answers, but there are letters in the grid, where the black squares should be. You need to black out the unwanted letters to make a symmetrical grid to match the clues, which are listed in random order.

| C | R | E | S | S | O | B | R | A | V | O |
|---|---|---|---|---|---|---|---|---|---|---|
| A | I | M | O | U | S | E | A | N | A | N |
| T | A | B | L | E | T | E | N | N | I | S |
| C | L | A | D | T | I | N | T | I | N | E |
| H | E | R | O | B | R | A | T | V | A | T |
| I | A | R | I | A | S | S | H | E | D | A |
| E | R | A | S | T | O | P | E | R | O | B |
| A | N | S | S | O | N | I | C | S | E | L |
| R | E | S | U | S | C | I | T | A | T | E |
| T | R | E | E | P | E | R | E | R | I | A |
| H | Y | D | R | A | R | K | A | Y | A | K |

## ACROSS

- Steal from
- Indoor sport played with bat and ball (5,6)
- Garden store
- That woman
- Inuit seal-skin canoe
- Spinning toy
- Quick-growing salad vegetable
- Historical period
- For each
- Barrel
- Many-headed mythological water monster
- Woman's undergarment
- Revive, bring back to consciousness
- Purpose
- Operatic solo
- Shout of approval

## DOWN

- On a single occasion
- Start
- Flying mammal
- Feeling shame
- Unsheltered, desolate
- Take to court
- Our planet
- Annoy, irritate
- Fuss, bother
- Mix with a spoon
- Viper, adder
- Trap, snare
- Health resort
- Yearly celebration
- Organ of hearing
- Honey-maker

# ARROWORD

The arrows show the direction in which the answer to each clue should be placed.

| Cut with scissors ▼ | | Japanese wrestling ▼ | | Flower of the iris family ▼ | | Showy daisy ▼ | |
|---|---|---|---|---|---|---|---|
| ► | | | | | | | |
| Asks (about) | | Beam of light | | Go to bed (4,2) | | Little __, lettuces | |
| Guided person, ward ► | | ▼ | | ▼ | | ▼ | |
| Snoop | Hermit, loner | Drug-dependent person ► | | | | | |
| ► | ▼ | | Edge of a glass ► | | | | German wartime leader |
| Section of a play | | Bite with a snap ► | | | | | ▼ |
| ► | | | Preserved | | Point of the compass | Mona __, Leonardo painting | |
| Ill-mannered | | Rested on bended legs ► | ▼ | | ▼ | ▼ | |
| ► | | | | Feel ill ► | | | |
| Food not eaten by vegetarians | | Outdated ► | | | | | |
| ► | | | | Bitu-minous substance ► | | | |

# JOLLY MIXTURES

In this puzzle, each clue is simply an anagram of the answer – but watch out! There might be more than one possible solution to each clue. For instance, the clue `TALE' might lead to the answer `LATE' or `TEAL'. You'll have to look at how the answers fit into the grid to find out which alternative is correct. None of the solutions are plurals or proper nouns.

**ACROSS**

1 ORBITS
4 OLD MAN
9 WED
10 LAMPS
11 MEL
12 SATE
14 READ
16 ALE
18 DEALT
19 RECAP
21 OPT
24 TRAY
25 LIED
28 SAG
30 TROVE
31 ART
32 TEA-URN
33 HEADER

**DOWN**

1 BARGED
2 WAS
3 PIER
5 MEAL
6 DOE
7 RAMPED
8 CLEAN
13 THESE
15 NAMED
16 PAL
17 CAT
20 ARMING
22 STONE
23 RECENT
26 ROUT
27 DUST
29 ITS
31 ORE

# GIANT CROSSWORD

**ACROSS**

1 One-off success (5,2,3,3)
10 Watch closely (7)
11 Electronic pager (7)
12 Job of producing boots, sandals etc (4-6)
14 Member of a Peruvian Indian people (4)
16 Neighbourhood (8)
18 ___ of Lebanon, large evergreen tree (5)
21 Taken (money) out of an account (9)
22 Surface gloss (5)
23 Ring the same number again (6)
25 Stupefy (8)
28 Magic trick or false impression (8)
29 Salt and ___, condiments (6)
31 Firearm with a long barrel (5)
33 Strangely (9)
35 Fourteen divided by two (5)
36 Passed through the eye of (a needle) (8)
40 Bird of prey (4)
41 Nickname for a dachshund (7,3)
44 Come before in history (3-4)
45 Amount of film shot (7)
46 Catching up, gaining ground (7,3,3)

**DOWN**

2 Cattle-catching rope (5)
3 ___ eggs, simple meal with toast (9)
4 Drink cooler (3)
5 Plastic piping (6)
6 Always (4)
7 Thing added to something larger or more important (9)
8 Either of two small organs in the throat (6)
9 ___ Tuck, one of Robin Hood's band (5)
13 Sports-gear holding sack (3-3)
15 Precious or semi-precious jewel (8)
17 Fortress protecting a town (7)
19 Grind your teeth together (5)
20 Rushing (2,1,5)
21 Fighting men (8)
24 Replied (8)
26 Applied without consent (restrictions, eg) (7)
27 Slouch about (5)
30 Curves (6)
32 Ride a bike without pedalling (9)
34 Protection against hot dishes (4,5)
37 Short sword (6)
38 Fried pieces of potato (5)
39 Be dressed in (4,2)
42 Theatre art (5)
43 Roman god of war (4)
45 Overweight (3)

# CROSSWORD

## ACROSS

4 Iron block used by smiths (5)
9 Admitted to office (5,2)
10 Without contents (5)
11 Contribution exacted by the state (3)
12 Mum's partner (3)
13 River on which Ripon stands (3)
14 Sculled (7)
15 Showing off by strutting (5,2,1,7)
19 Boundless (7)
20 Name shared by actors Brooks and Gibson (3)
21 Entertaining (3)
22 Former Portuguese enclave in W India (3)
23 Beauty treatment shop (5)
24 Country, capital Zagreb (7)
25 Furze (5)

## DOWN

1 (Of resources) consumed, exhausted (4,2)
2 Strong link (4)
3 Relieving of distress (11)
4 Card player's stake (4)
5 Informal statements from members of the public (3,3)
6 Go down like a ___, be a complete flop (4,7)
7 Greek sun-god (6)
8 Tinted (4)
16 Alloy of copper, zinc and tin (6)
17 Pete ___, US protest singer (6)
18 State north of Oklahoma (6)
19 Bergman's *Casablanca* character (4)
20 Medieval weapon and modern protective spray (4)
21 Nickname of Thomas Waller, jazz musician (4)

# WHO'S WHO?

Using the descriptions given, can you match each chef to his assistant?

# 4 SQUARE

Solve these four clues and then rearrange the solutions into a sixteen-letter phrase, for which a clue is given. The two diagonals also make four-letter words.

Quick swims

Compassion

Ringlet

Liver secretion

Clue: with care for the community? (6-10)

---

# TWO BY TWO

Each word in a clue can be preceded by the same two letters to spell out another word. For instance, INTER, LATE and TENT can be preceded by PA to make PAINTER, PALATE and PATENT. Can you solve the three clues below, then spell out the three pairs of letters to make a six-letter word?

- AMP, ART, INK

- EON, IOUS, OUR

- LIGNITE, ODE, STATE

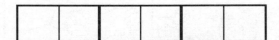

# WORDSEARCH

The 30 words all associated with the word heart have been hidden in the diagram. They have been printed across (backwards or forwards), or up or down, or diagonally, but always in a straight line without letters being skipped. You can use the letters in the diagram more than once. You will probably find it helpful to mark the words in the diagram and cross them off the list as you find them.

```
N  I  F  Y  S  K  G  G  D  N  Y  L  W  W  H  S
M  O  J  H  K  T  O  G  O  B  T  W  Q  H  B  P
C  E  I  E  M  O  T  I  O  N  I  C  O  R  E  I
S  L  T  T  F  S  T  Q  E  L  N  N  Y  D  K  R
N  T  X  C  C  U  G  Y  L  C  A  I  E  W  R  I
A  T  D  G  L  E  R  L  M  O  M  Z  E  R  Q  T
I  E  S  O  U  X  F  M  U  M  U  P  V  T  V  T
C  M  S  Q  U  T  A  F  Z  P  H  V  O  T  I  E
L  E  N  R  E  K  S  P  A  A  W  E  L  C  Z  K
R  N  C  W  Z  C  A  F  A  S  S  O  K  H  C  N
E  D  U  T  I  T  R  O  F  S  N  E  R  U  O  E
F  N  L  V  Z  L  J  Y  E  I  R  P  L  R  G  P
H  E  U  J  D  D  U  N  F  O  E  P  B  A  A  V
E  C  E  C  B  X  C  O  R  N  C  M  R  X  U  M
A  E  K  L  L  E  O  L  S  U  N  U  T  O  O  R
R  U  J  E  I  E  P  U  R  P  O  S  E  N  L  H
T  X  J  V  P  N  U  A  E  C  C  S  U  I  T  U
M  I  D  D  L  E  G  S  E  Q  R  B  O  B  N  B
```

| | | |
|---|---|---|
| AFFECTION | GUTS | NUB |
| COMPASSION | HEART | NUCLEUS |
| CONCERN | HUB | PLUCK |
| CORE | HUMANITY | PURPOSE |
| COURAGE | KERNEL | RESOLUTION |
| CRUX | LOVE | ROOT |
| EMOTION | MARROW | SOUL |
| ESSENCE | METTLE | SPIRIT |
| FEELING | MIDDLE | TICKER |
| FORTITUDE | NERVE | WILL |

# SUDOKU

Place the numbers from 1 to 9 in each empty cell so that each row, each column and each 3 x 3 block contains all the numbers from 1 to 9 to solve this tricky Sudoku puzzle.

| | 6 | | | | | | | |
|---|---|---|---|---|---|---|---|---|
| 9 | 3 | | 6 | 8 | | | | |
| | | 8 | | | 5 | 6 | | |
| | | 1 | | | | | 7 | 2 |
| | | | 2 | | 7 | 4 | 5 | |
| | | 5 | | | | | 8 | 9 |
| | | 6 | | | 4 | 7 | | |
| 8 | 7 | | 9 | 2 | | | | |
| | 5 | | | | | | | |

**MEDIUM**

# CROSSWORD

## ACROSS

1 Guitar-like instrument (5)
5 Let fall (4)
6 Chinese exercise system (3,3)
7 Flower jar (4)
8 Dog's mouth cover (6)
9 Musical interval (8)
12 Large Arctic mammal (5,4)
15 ___ Rum, famous racehorse (3)
16 Rock fragment (5)
17 Brown or rainbow fish (5)
18 Grease (3)
19 Getting smaller (9)
21 Connective tissue (8)
24 Overlook, omit (4,2)
25 Word said to frighten away an animal (4)
26 Ruins, wrecks (6)
27 Small mosquito (4)
28 Girl's clothing (5)

## DOWN

2 Usually (2,1,4)
3 Spa, hot tub (7)
4 Lean cut of beef (7)
5 Attack from a plummeting aircraft (4-4)
9 Individually (10)
10 Tuneful (9)
11 Path of an untethered glider (4,6)
13 Showjumping winner's ribbon badge (7)
14 Cut down on costs (9)
20 Roadside pointer to places (8)
21 Flogging, whipping (7)
22 Thought wrongly about (7)
23 Cloudy, hazy (7)

# JIG-WORD

No clues - just pattern and answers - but can you fit them in?

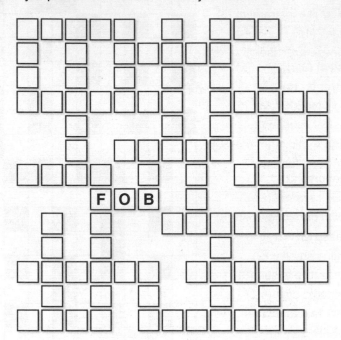

| 3 letters | 5 letters | 7 letters |
|---|---|---|
| Bib | Bonus | Affixed |
| Dun | Crock | Anxious |
| Fob | Horde | Bruised |
| Nor | Parka | Nurture |
| Orb | Unlit | Paraded |
| | Vista | Sharpen |
| **4 letters** | | |
| Aped | **6 letters** | |
| Bomb | Babble | |
| Doer | Blanch | |
| Skid | Coaxed | |
| Tuna | Cruder | |
| Vamp | Subbed | |

# VISIVASE

Which three vases are identical?

# RIDDLE ME REE

My first is in SISTER and also in BROTHER,

My second's in FATHER as well as in MOTHER,

My third's not in FOLKS but is found in KIN.

My fourth is in NEPHEW but never in TWIN,

My fifth is in GIRL but never in GRANNY,

My sixth is in NIECE but isn't in NANNY,

My seventh's in PARENT but not in a SPOUSE,

My whole's not the only child in the house.

---

# STEP LADDER

Your task here is to climb from BACK to DOOR changing just one letter at a time and without disturbing the order of the remaining letters. We've clued the five steps you take, but not in the correct order. Can you climb the ladder successfully?

**DOOR**

chess piece

toast holder

reading matter

ill-mannered person

sway

**BACK**

# SKELETON

Have double the fun with this puzzle: you've got to fill in the answers and the black squares! We've given you the bare bones to start and it will help you to know that the black squares in the finished grid form a symmetrical pattern, so that every black square has at least one other corresponding black square.

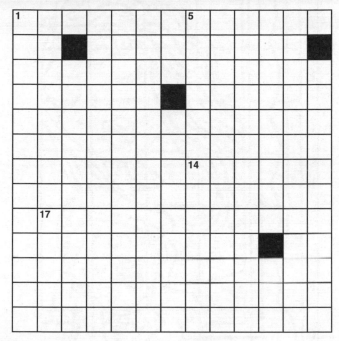

**ACROSS**

1 Creamy rich cake from France
5 Construct new buildings between (existing ones)
8 Old second person singular pronoun
9 Earnest prayer
10 Call to mind
11 Pubs
12 Female bovine animal
14 Long-haired goat
16 Render momentarily unconscious
18 Cruel or violent act
20 Particularly delicious food
21 Instrument read-out
22 Muddled, confused
23 Increase in length

**DOWN**

2 Realise
3 Shun
4 Showing no discomfiture
5 Wedlock between people of different groups
6 Perception
7 Classical language
13 Ceremony for the deceased
15 Learn to do a different job
17 Coy
19 Trainee soldier or policeman

# IDENTIGRIDS

Which three squares are identical?

# CROSSWORD

**ACROSS**

1  Tear into small pieces (3,2)
4  Copies, models (8)
9  Red food colouring obtained from insects (9)
10  Concreted garden area (5)
11  Northernmost Irish province (6)
13  Physical disorder (7)
16  Soufflé ingredient (3)
17  Quite a bit of money (4,3)
19  Inspire affection (6)
22  Secret organisation headed by a 'don' (5)
24  Gave a sign (9)
26  Pledged (8)
27  Lure into danger (5)

**DOWN**

1  Speed competition (4)
2  Preserved in vinegar (7)
3  Tapered end (5)
4  Species of deer (3)
5  Loot (7)
6  Drive (5)
7  Creative work (3)
8  Writers of verse (5)
12  Stays put (7)
14  Stretchy (7)
15  Part of a wicket (5)
18  Teem (5)
20  Cubed (5)
21  Apprehensive (4)
23  Animal's coat (3)
25  Common computer peripheral (inits)(3)

# ARROWORD

The arrows show the direction in which the answer to each clue should be placed.

| Slang word for one pound ▼ | | Curds and __, Miss Muffet's food ▼ | | Shake-spearean tragedy ▼ | | Echoes | ▼ |
| | | | | | | __ up, confess | |
| Beach headgear item (3,3) | | Skating surface | | Move on one leg ▶ | | ▼ | |
| Home improve-ments (inits) ▶ | | ▼ | | Lamb's mother ▶ | | | |
| Botanical project near St Austell | Inundates | | Arm-bone ▶ / TV's Mrs Batty | | | | |
| ▶ | ▼ | | ▼ | Strikes | | Slowly develop | |
| Plant life | Double-reeded wind instruments ▶ | | | ▼ | | ▼ | |
| ▶ | | | | | __ Porter, US composer | | Adolescent |
| In days gone by | Royal race meeting ▶ | | | ▼ | | ▼ | |
| ▶ | | | Orifice ▶ | | | | |
| Deciduous tree | Dig ▶ | | | | | | |
| ▶ | | | Noticed ▶ | | | | |

406

# CRISS-CROSS

Every solution is entered diagonally, either to the left or to the right, from the square indicating its clue-number.

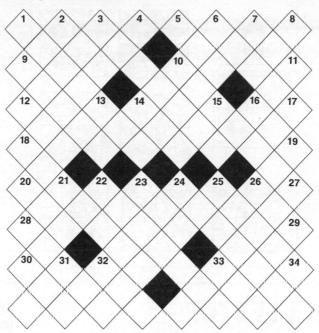

## TO THE RIGHT

1 Exhibit
2 Hill
3 Fugitive
5 Drinks counter
6 Christmas song
7 Feline
9 Large fruit
10 Muslim month of fasting
12 Earth's star
14 Purchase tax (inits)
16 Gentle touch
18 Discussion group
20 Steal
22 Under, below
23 Buzzing insect

24 Body-building drug
25 Leather razor sharpener
26 Used a chair
28 Body fluid
30 Make a mistake
32 Decimal number
33 Consumed

## TO THE LEFT

2 ___ Rice, lyricist
3 Thorny flower-bearing shrubs
4 Excess, remainder
6 Mobile home
7 Aromatic seed used in cooking

8 Distant
11 The present time
13 Solitary person
15 Small rug
17 Boy
19 Spoon fat over
21 Unruly crowd
22 Holy book
23 Big ___, Parliament's bell
24 US politician
25 Guided
27 Tell a story
29 Molar, eg
31 Mineral rock
34 Pastry dish

# IMPRINT

Can you work out which one of the seven prints was created by the stamp?

---

# ADD A LETTER

Insert or add a letter to these four-letter words to make five-letter words which fit the rhyming clues. The six added letters should spell out a word.

| | | |
|---|---|---|
| **LUKE** | | Any accidental success |
| **CLAM** | | Request, assert or profess |
| **ALOE** | | Unaccompanied, on one's own |
| **SPIN** | | Vertebral column, the backbone |
| **GAZE** | | Scrape the surface or shave |
| **EARN** | | Long for, desire deeply, crave |

# KEYWORD

This puzzle has no clues in the conventional sense. Instead, every different number printed in the main grid represents a different letter (with the same number always representing the same letter, of course). For example, if 7 turns out to be a 'V', you can write in V wherever a square contains 7. We have completed a very small part of the puzzle to give you a start, but the rest is up to you.

| 25 |    | 10 |    | 9  |    | 4  |    | 2  |    | 14 |    | 9  |
|----|----|----|----|----|----|----|----|----|----|----|----|----|
| 10 | 8  | 6  | 18 | 19 | 11 | 12 | 26 | 10 |    | 19 | 11 | 10 |
| 10 |    | 15 |    | 18 |    | 7  |    | 13 |    | 13 |    | 24 |
| 9  | 22 | 22 | 2  | 18 | 10 | 21 |    | 2  | 24 | 5  | 11 | 2  |
| 18 |    |    |    | 3  |    | 18 |    |    |    | 11 |    | 15 |
| 10 | 18 | 25 |    | 22 | 26 | 10 | 24 | 1  | 13 | 12 | 3  |    |
|    |    | 22 |    | 23 |    |    |    | 13 |    | 3  |    |    |
|    | 19 | 18 | 2  | 10 | 24 | 12 | 22 | 24 |    | 10 | 9  | 9  |
| 9  |    | 17 |    |    |    | 20 |    | 13 |    |    |    | 24 |
| 13 | 18 | 18 (L) | 22 | 16 |    | 1  | 13 | 7  | 6  | 13 | 17 | 10 |
| 18 |    | 22 (O) |    | 13 |    | 22 |    | 22 |    | 21 |    | 13 |
| 20 | 13 | 24 (R) |    | 25 | 12 | 11 | 15 | 12 | 7  | 10 | 11 | 11 |
| 5  |    | 10 |    | 2  |    | 10 |    | 3  |    | 3  |    | 2  |

A B C D E F G H I J K L̸ M N Ø P Q R̸ S T U V W X Y Z

| 1  | 2  | 3  | 4  | 5  | 6  | 7  | 8  | 9  | 10 | 11 | 12 | 13 |
|----|----|----|----|----|----|----|----|----|----|----|----|----|
| 14 | 15 | 16 | 17 | 18 (L) | 19 | 20 | 21 | 22 (O) | 23 | 24 (R) | 25 | 26 |

# ROUNDABOUT

Solutions to Radial clues (1 to 24) either start from the outer edge of the circle and read inwards, or start from the inner ring and read outwards to the edge (so they are all five-letter words). Solutions to Circular clues read in either a clockwise direction or anti-clockwise around the circle.

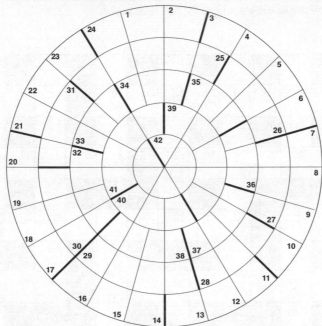

## RADIAL:
### INWARDS

1 Basketry willow
2 Stopwatch
3 Long waxed spill
4 Love deeply
5 Measure of liquid volume
6 Curved sword
10 Spiral movement
11 Oyster's gem
12 Master of ceremonies
13 Conical tent
14 Tool for smoothing wood
16 Incendiary crime
17 Ben ___, comedy writer
18 Acquire knowledge
19 Embellish
20 Deduct from an account
21 Encircle
22 Sunday joint
23 Animal
24 Senior person

### OUTWARDS

7 Gradually diminish
8 ____ Doone, novel
9 Solitary type
15 Follow

## CIRCULAR:
### CLOCKWISE

7 Hearing organs
11 Favourite
14 Part of a whistle
21 Ornamental sphere
30 Conducted
33 Bleat
34 Gloomy
35 Cooking utensil
38 Elapse
39 Blunder
41 Ascend
42 Soften

### ANTI-CLOCKWISE

2 Foot feature
6 Wooden lath
20 ___ Winton, TV presenter
25 Church passageway
26 Assist
27 Finale
28 Cat's cry
29 Regulation
31 Useful mineral
32 Sailing vessel
36 Steal
37 Abel's brother
40 Individual

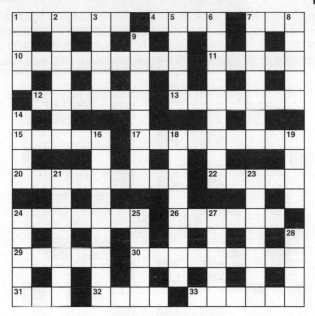

## ACROSS

1 Backbone-related pains terrible over fifty (6)
4 Reading up part of Plato's *Republic*, I perceive that it's a long narrative poem (4)
7 Low heathland appears endless (3)
10 Diverting feature in fringe publication (4,5)
11 Declare void some pieces of Schumann – ultra-modern! (5)
12 Up in the garden I plant one in the rockery? (6)
13 Initially dead rough having been given narcotics (7)
15 Female, a female with a bundle (5)
17 Great Dane destroyed refreshment area outdoors (3,6)
20 One's in an eastern country – an eastern republic (9)
22 Church official with two European articles (5)
24 Erased, we read? It's allowed, indeed! (7)
26 Entry made by expert about prow of container ship (6)
29 Profit about right for cereal (5)
30 Took bones out with pads (9)
31 A ship's donkey (3)
32 Missile to fly quickly (4)
33 Before crown of the Queen, prohibit teasing remarks (6)

## DOWN

1 Average, thus doubled (2-2)
2 Cooked ling due to spoil (7)
3 Bail organised, one having provided legal defence (5)
5 Quietly go ahead and appeal (5)
6 Clot replaced catalogue (9)
7 Chap matured and coped (7)
8 Drunk cooked without a top on (5)
9 Basset so confused by fireproof material (8)
14 Firstly, all should try Italian wine (4)
16 Discover hidden eastern song when tweaked (4-5)
18 As on the menu, a real cat recipe (1,2,5)
19 Geek appears during dinner date (4)
21 Everybody held back by Diana's money (7)
23 Diana's wrong to twist the facts (7)
24 Fixed opinion of hound by mother (5)
25 Person eating at home wearing red, retired (5)
27 Snake and horse painter (5)
28 Selfish person contrived ruse (4)

# MISSING LINKS

The answer to each clue is a word which has a link with each of the three words listed. This word may come at the end (eg HEAD linked with BEACH, BIG and HAMMER), at the beginning (eg BLACK linked with BEAUTY, BOARD and JACK) or a mixture of the two (eg STONE linked with HAIL, LIME and WALL).

## ACROSS

1 BLOCK, GENTLE, SEA (6)
4 IN, SOUND, SPECIAL (6)
7 BIN, CARDINAL, DEADLY (3)
8 FISH, GUIDING, MORNING (4)
10 ACID, BOW, DROP (4)
12 AFTER, POLICE, PROCESS (7)
13 EYE, OUT, TOGETHER (4)
15 LESS, PAY, TAKE (4)
18 MOUNTAINS, ROAD, WORLD (5)
21 PAMPAS, ROOTS, SKIRT (5)
22 BOX, ROW, SPARROW (5)
23 BIRTHDAY, MEDIUM, SLAP (5)
26 ARMY, FALL, MASS (4)
29 DEATH, REAPER, TRUTH (4)
31 MOTH, PENGUIN, ROMAN (7)
32 BRIGHT, NO, ORIGINAL (4)
33 AFTER, OUT, QUESTIONS (4)
35 RESULT, SOUTH, STICKY (3)
36 ARABIAN, LONG, STAG (6)
37 ATOMIC, GAP, KINETIC (6)

## DOWN

1 COMPANY, CONDUCTOR, STOP (3)
2 MOTHER, SCORCHED, WORM (5)
3 AGENCY, ARMED, FORD (6)
4 CODE, COMPLETE, VARIATIONS (6)
5 BRIDGE, COMING, RIGHT (5)
6 CAN, FOIL, SOLDIER (3)
9 CUP, LEMON, STRAINER (3)
11 CREAM, CUBE, PACK (3)
13 EAGLE, PROCESS, TENDER (5)
14 BLOOD, COFFEE, REMOVER (5)
16 BERRY, BROTHER, STATESMAN (5)
17 BOAT, DAY, SEQUENCE (5)
18 POT, TRAY, TREE (3)
19 SALVE, SERVICE, UPPER (3)
20 COCONUT, LOCK, WORK (3)
24 COOKING, CRAB, OAK (6)
25 EASTER, GROUND, HIT (6)
27 BAND, FIRST, HEARING (3)
28 MASK, RATTLE, VALLEY (5)
29 NOTE, SAVING, YOUR (5)
30 RED, SPOT, WELL (3)
32 COACHING, JAMAICA, KEEPER (3)
34 BLUE, DIVING, SCRAPER (3)

# WORDSEARCH

The 30 words that contain the word BED have all been hidden in the diagram. They have been printed across (backwards or forwards), or up or down, or diagonally, but always in a straight line without letters being skipped. You can use the letters in the diagram more than once. You will probably find it helpful to mark the words in the diagram and cross them off the list as you find them.

```
D  E  B  M  I  L  C  B  V  M  D  N  P  Q  A  Z
E  P  P  S  R  E  E  W  T  E  N  B  J  B  H  J
B  Q  L  F  P  D  V  D  D  N  D  G  E  O  G  O
B  K  Z  U  S  E  E  D  E  B  E  D  O  U  I  N
A  A  E  O  M  B  E  S  S  B  B  I  E  N  K  Z
T  U  C  W  M  B  L  C  U  J  B  B  D  O  U  Z
S  K  I  U  M  O  E  D  B  M  A  I  T  E  E  A
S  I  N  E  Q  M  L  D  E  F  R  U  R  B  B  F
D  E  B  B  O  R  H  T  D  B  G  U  E  C  H  O
B  W  P  R  O  B  E  D  I  Y  B  D  B  F  X  C
D  I  S  R  O  B  E  D  T  A  E  O  K  B  L  B
B  E  B  M  S  M  B  Y  O  E  M  G  L  I  E  E
S  E  E  C  X  R  H  E  R  I  I  W  V  B  D  D
O  D  D  U  Y  B  X  S  D  M  T  E  E  L  E  A
B  Q  S  R  J  W  E  B  B  E  D  D  C  B  J  U
B  T  I  G  O  O  D  T  S  E  E  I  B  R  A  B
E  T  D  U  V  O  X  P  B  C  B  A  C  R  H  K
D  V  E  Y  Z  N  M  L  K  D  D  E  B  B  I  J
```

| | | |
|---|---|---|
| ABED | CLIMBED | OBEDIENT |
| BEDAUB | CRIBBED | PLUMBED |
| BEDECK | DABBED | PROBED |
| BEDEVIL | DISROBED | RUBBED |
| BEDOUIN | EMBEDDED | SOBBED |
| BEDROOM | GRABBED | STABBED |
| BEDSIDE | JIBBED | SUBEDITOR |
| BEDSOCKS | LOBBED | THROBBED |
| BEDTIME | MOBBED | WEBBED |
| BOBBED | NUMBED | ZEBEDEE |

# CROSSWORD

**436**

## ACROSS

1 Oppressive leader (8)
6 Raised objections (9)
7 Large deer (3)
8 Slobber (5)
9 Lazy behaviour (8)
12 Parent's sister (4)
13 Paddington Bear's country of origin (4)
16 Name for Australia (4,5)
18 One who pays extravagant compliments (9)
19 Trees with acorns (4)
20 Petrol company with a tiger as its emblem (4)
23 Relating to an operation (8)
26 ___ of a river, wide entrance (5)
27 Friend, mate (3)
28 Occurred at the same time (9)
29 Throwing a tantrum (2,1,5)

## DOWN

1 Big ___, fairground ride (6)
2 Registered the start of the working day (7,2)
3 ___ Angus, breed of cattle (8)
4 Result of an action (7)
5 Hero, object of worship (4)
10 Number often multiplied by itself in maths lessons (6,4)
11 Fluffy spun sugar on a stick (10)
14 Senior tribe member (5)
15 Chip or bacon sandwich (5)
17 Strike hard (5)
21 Rushed away in mass panic (9)
22 Drink taken at bedtime (8)
24 Get-together of old friends (7)
25 Wet and covered in mud (6)
26 Filth (4)

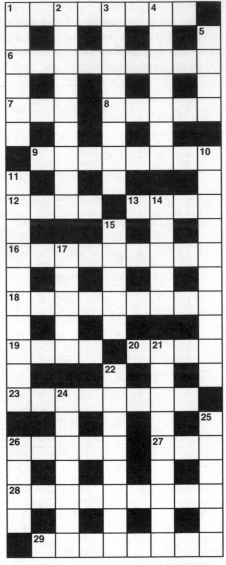

# HONEYCOMB

All the answers are six-letter words. Each answer is entered in a circle around its clue-number. The first letter of the answer is entered in the shaded triangle immediately above the clue-number. If the clue-number is even, enter the answer in a clockwise direction. If the clue-number is odd, enter the answer in an anti-clockwise direction.

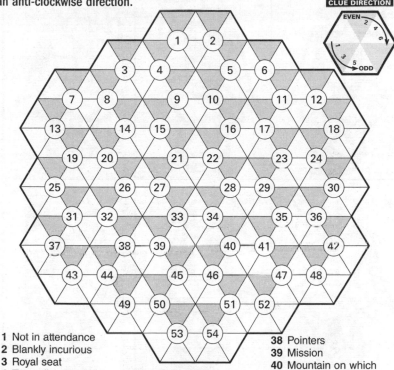

CLUE DIRECTION

EVEN

ODD

1 Not in attendance
2 Blankly incurious
3 Royal seat
4 Tranquil
5 Vocation
6 Rot and stagnate
7 Straight
8 Gnawing animal
9 Modern
10 Soften
11 Thoroughfare
12 Group of seven performers
13 Develop into
14 Mock
15 Cherry red
16 Papal ambassador
17 Strict plan
18 Powerful
19 Unassuming
20 Assimilate food

21 Artist's model
22 Wine sampler
23 Male title
24 Tidier
25 Lower in rank
26 In abundance
27 Natural skill
28 Underlease
29 Give in
30 Queen Victoria's consort
31 Browns bread
32 Bakes in the oven
33 Required
34 Joyful
35 Hinder
36 Slope backwards
37 Authority to enter

38 Pointers
39 Mission
40 Mountain on which Noah's Ark came to rest
41 Laud
42 Small savoury
43 Respectable
44 Fleecy
45 That is to say
46 Dryly
47 Senior nurse
48 Sales talk
49 Musical based on a Dickens novel
50 Less generous
51 Standards of perfection
52 Pilfers
53 Reply
54 Religious festival

# MIRROR IMAGES

There are four pairs of mirror images below. Can you identify the pairs and find the odd one out?

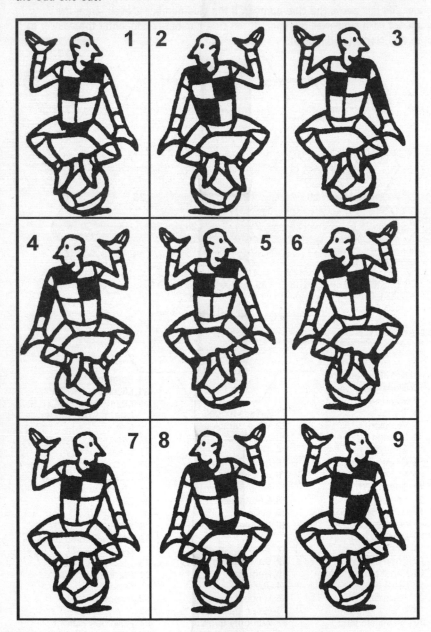

# ARROWORD

The arrows show the direction in which the answer to each clue should be placed.

| One's inner self | Opening in a fence | ▼ Mirthful | | ▼ Only or fair | | ▼ ___ Lansbury, actress |
|---|---|---|---|---|---|---|
| ▶ | ▼ | Large tea dispensers ▶ | | | | |
| | | Notable age | | | | |
| Expert drivers ▶ | | ▼ | | Compare | | More cunning |
| Amphibious animals with hard shells ▶ | | | | ▼ | | ▼ |
| ▶ | | | Adverse, harmful ▶ | | | |
| ___ Bartok, Hungarian composer | Mistreats | | Vests, pants etc | Peter ___, *Phoenix Nights* star ▶ | | |
| ▶ | ▼ | | ▼ | Extreme annoyance | Black or green cocktail fruit | |
| Armed conflicts | Of little importance ▶ | | | ▼ | ▼ | |
| ▶ | | | | Two times five | | Fresh, unused |
| Sir Alan ___, businessman | | Grant admission to (3,2) ▶ | | ▼ | | ▼ |
| ▶ | | | Bible's first woman ▶ | | | |
| Breakfast, dinner etc | Tissue that joins muscle to bone ▶ | | | | | |

# WIRED UP

Which of the four plugs is connected to the electric guitar?

---

# ADD A LETTER

Insert or add a letter to these four-letter words to make five-letter words which fit the rhyming clues. The six added letters should spell out a word.

| SANK | | Be a show-off, brag and boast; |
|------|---|------|
| SORE | | The beach beside the sea, the coast; |
| VICE | | Speak up, opine, talk and chat; |
| DROP | | Sag, look weary, limp and flat; |
| SILT | | Describes a liquid that's slopped over; |
| HIPS | | Big boats found in ports like Dover |

# CROSSWORD

## ACROSS

1 Cut the top off (3)
8 Network of interconnecting burrows (6,6)
9 Latin word meaning 'by way of' (3)
11 Water supply (5)
12 Get rid of, eliminate (4,3)
14 Incline (to) (4)
15 Bicycle made for two! (6)
18 Small variety of plum (6)
20 One of the official languages of India (4)
23 Eat away (7)
25 Notches (5)
27 Take advantage of (3)
28 Instruction to a financial institution (7,5)
29 Cooking grease (3)

## DOWN

1 Domestic animals on a farm (9)
2 Four-wheeled carriage for a baby (4)
3 Gratify (6)
4 Before all others (5)
5 (Had) pledged (5)
6 Zest (4)
7 Brave men (6)
10 Act of reparation (9)
13 Mismatched (3)
16 Unexceptional (6)
17 Soft wet earth (3)
19 Covered walkway (6)
21 Update weapons (5)
22 Joining together (5)
24 Trees with acorns (4)
26 Ride the waves (4)

# SUDOKU

Place the numbers from 1 to 9 in each empty cell so that each row, each column and each 3 x 3 block contains all the numbers from 1 to 9 to solve this tricky Sudoku puzzle.

| | | | | 1 | | 7 | | 5 |
|---|---|---|---|---|---|---|---|---|
| 2 | | | 9 | 7 | | | | 6 |
| 1 | | | 5 | | | | | 8 |
| | 9 | 2 | | | 8 | | 3 | |
| | | | | | | | | |
| | 3 | 5 | | | 1 | | 8 | |
| 5 | | | 1 | | | | | 2 |
| 6 | | | 3 | 9 | | | | 7 |
| | | | | 6 | | 8 | | 3 |

**EASY**

# WORDSEARCH

The 30 colours have all been hidden in the diagram. They have been printed across (backwards or forwards), or up or down, or diagonally, but always in a straight line without letters being skipped. You can use the letters in the diagram more than once. You will probably find it helpful to mark the words in the diagram and cross them off the list as you find them.

```
C  L  A  R  E  T  S  C  T  A  O  E  N  N  W  E
M  P  H  P  Q  C  U  H  M  S  K  R  O  M  K  V
B  A  I  C  A  G  T  A  T  G  Y  O  A  D  L  I
X  S  G  R  A  E  D  M  T  Z  R  H  I  N  W  L
U  T  L  E  S  E  W  P  Q  A  O  B  T  P  G  O
U  E  V  S  N  M  P  A  M  V  N  R  L  E  J  E
T  L  U  H  N  T  H  G  K  Z  E  O  O  A  M  C
R  R  C  J  O  H  A  N  J  E  E  N  E  I  C  A
E  L  A  V  E  N  D  E  R  F  R  Z  J  Y  N  K
C  O  R  A  L  L  V  X  T  N  G  E  X  J  F  L
E  U  L  B  Y  V  A  N  O  E  E  S  I  R  E  C
C  S  W  G  A  E  D  S  P  F  L  X  N  M  Y  C
E  O  K  M  T  Q  M  O  Z  L  T  O  O  L  A  M
L  S  B  I  B  I  Y  G  Z  R  T  N  I  N  H  A
P  E  H  A  R  A  C  I  N  T  O  G  A  V  P  U
R  W  R  C  L  O  V  D  B  A  B  R  F  L  I  V
U  Y  S  D  C  T  R  N  T  S  Y  Q  P  B  U  E
P  S  A  L  M  O  N  I  A  M  W  O  L  L  E  Y
```

| | | |
|---|---|---|
| AMBER | CORAL | ORANGE |
| AMETHYST | CRIMSON | PASTEL |
| BLACK | INDIGO | PEACH |
| BOTTLE GREEN | LAVENDER | PURPLE |
| BRONZE | LEMON | RUSSET |
| CANARY | MAGENTA | SALMON |
| CERISE | MAROON | SCARLET |
| CHAMPAGNE | MAUVE | VIOLET |
| CLARET | NAVY BLUE | WHITE |
| COBALT | OLIVE | YELLOW |

# PIECEWORD

With the help of the Across clues only, can you fit the 35 pieces into their correct positions in the empty grid (which, when completed, will exhibit a symmetrical pattern)?

## ACROSS

1 Calmed (a situation) • Look after a child for a short time

2 Drink cooler

3 Vaccine • Old-fashioned sleeveless knee-length garment

4 Inform • Butt

5 With speed

6 Silence • Intertwining of rope, string etc

7 Pack down firmly • Band

8 Given help

9 Point of land running into the sea • Movement of air

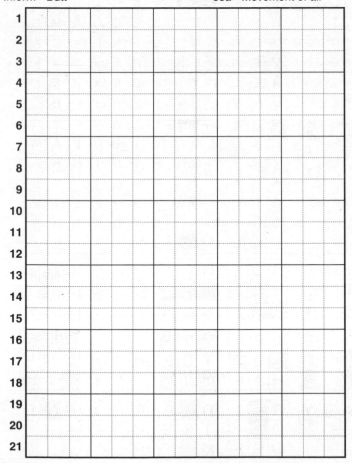

10 Jeopardising

11 Crimson • In tennis, a service obstructed by the net

12 Island group

13 Single-handed • Advance

14 S American dance

15 Set up, establish • Limited period of time

16 Base • Continental currency unit

17 Beau

18 Fluffy mat • Hive insect

19 Lounged • One who opposes authority

20 Clamour

21 Excited • Parched and needing a drink

# TWIN SET

Two of the pictures below are identical. Can you spot which two, and identify what is different in the remaining pictures?

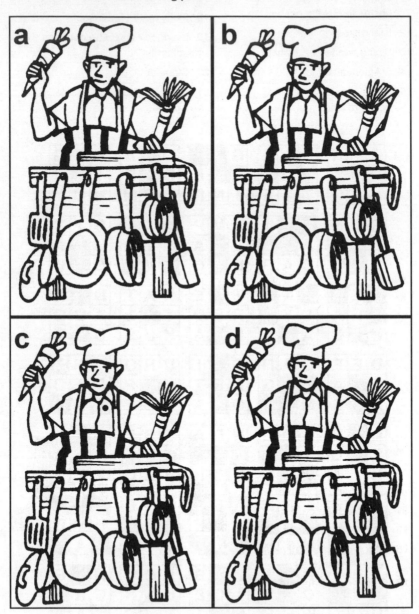

# CROSSWORD

**ACROSS**

1 Chilled first-aid accessory (3,4)
7 Theatre performer (5)
8 Central (3)
9 *Licence to ___*, 1989 Bond film (4)
10 Group of thugs (4)
12 Most zany (8)
14 Inappropriately amusing (9)
15 Ceremonially burn (8)
18 Feeble old person (8)
21 Continued (7,2)
23 Powerfully built (8)
25 Endanger (4)
26 Wealthy (4)
28 *Dr ___*, sci-fi show (3)
29 Sleep late (3,2)
30 Long-established royal family (7)

**DOWN**

2 ___ converter, engine emission-control device (9)
3 Go separate ways (4)
4 Showing concern for others (13)
5 Double up (of a truck) (4-5)
6 Old saying or proverb (5)
11 French-style cafe (6)
13 Beneficial possession (5)
16 Study of the relatively recent past (6,7)
17 Official proclamation (5)
19 Prove beyond doubt (6)
20 Grabbing (9)
22 Anti-government campaigner (9)
24 Knit your brow (5)
27 Jumping biting insect (4)

**448**

Just like a jig-word – but instead of letters, numbers.

| **3-figures** | 2515 | **5-figures** | 89592 |
|---|---|---|---|
| 187 | 3291 | 14511 | 90017 |
| 201 | 4691 | 16529 | 92710 |
| 310 | 4897 | 21192 | |
| 455 | 5014 | 21321 | **6-figures** |
| 529 | 5224 | 31529 | 490315 |
| 691 | 6152 | 43241 | 524515 |
| 726 | 6506 | 44368 | 652661 |
| 890 | 7601 | 44401 | 684480 |
| | 7890 | 51687 | 801589 |
| **4-figures** | 8280 | 59094 | 957764 |
| 1074 | 8918 | 64595 | |
| 1129 | 9591 | 72561 | |
| 1300 | | 78951 | |
| 2013 | | 80097 | |

# KEYWORD

This puzzle has no clues in the conventional sense. Instead, every different number printed in the main grid represents a different letter (with the same number always representing the same letter, of course). For example, if 7 turns out to be a 'V', you can write in V wherever a square contains 7. We have completed a very small part of the puzzle to give you a start, but the rest is up to you.

| 6 | 24 | 15 | 24 | 13 | 13 | 24 | 18 | 9 | | 7 | | 24 |
|---|----|----|----|----|----|----|----|---|---|---|---|----|
|   | 19 |    | 11 |    | 4  |    | 5  |   | 15 | 5 | 25 | 8 |
| 21 | 1 | 3 | 23 | 24 | 18 | 12 | 1 | 26 |   | 25 |   | 10 |
|   | 12 |   | 9 |   | 24 |   | 3 |   | 14 | 18 | 1 | 14 |
| 17 |   | 14 |   |   | 11 | 25 | 25 | 8 |   | 12 |   | 12 |
| 4 | 3 | 21 | 1 | 12 |   | 16 |   | 1 | 3 | 13 | 24 | 12 |
| 1 |   | 21 |   | 25 | 20 | 24 | 18 | 12 |   | 1 |   | 13 |
| 16 | 4 | 18 | 1 | 25 |   | 14 |   | 12 | 14 | 7 | 12 | 24 |
| 22 |   | 25 |   | 13 | 1 | 3 | 22 |   |   | 12 |   | 11 |
| 7 | 1 | 3 | 22 |   | 23 G |   | 3 |   | 25 |   | 7 |   |
| 12 |   | 12 |   | 21 | 13 L | 25 | 25 | 11 | 23 | 14 | 12 | 24 |
| 24 | 9 | 24 | 11 |   | 25 O |   | 16 |   | 13 |   | 9 |   |
| 26 |   | 11 |   | 2 | 25 | 25 | 22 | 24 | 24 | 26 | 24 | 18 |

A B C D E F Ǧ H I J K Ɫ M N Ø P Q R S T U V W X Y Z

| 1 | 2 | 3 | 4 | 5 | 6 | 7 | 8 | 9 | 10 | 11 | 12 | 13 L |
|---|---|---|---|---|---|---|---|---|----|----|----|------|
| 14 | 15 | 16 | 17 | 18 | 19 | 20 | 21 | 22 | 23 G | 24 | 25 O | 26 |

# BOXWISE

Can you put these three-letter groups into the twelve numbered boxes to produce twelve six-letter words, each of which starts in one box and finishes in another as indicated by an arrow? For instance, 2 and 5 make a six-letter word, but not 5 and 9. One group of three letters has been filled in to start you off.

NCH IDE (TRE) SEL AIN VER
CLE MOR STR MIN DOM DER

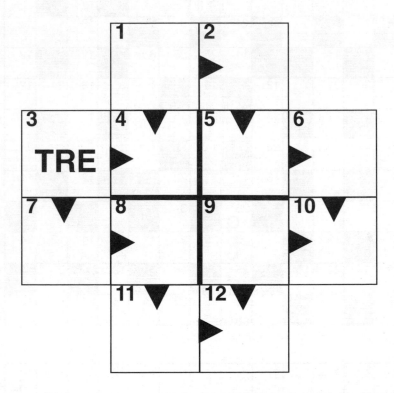

428

# JIG-WORD

No clues - just pattern and answers - but can you fit them in?

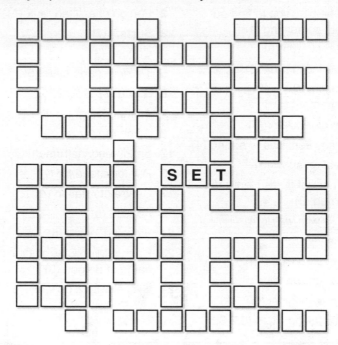

**3 letters**
Fin
Hog
Jut
Nub
Set
Yam

**4 letters**
Afar
Demo
Dour
Hush
Meek
Prep
Puny

**5 letters**
Hunch
Livid
Muggy
Often
Ogled
Pouch

**6 letters**
Adjoin
Eschew
Felled
Fought
Grubby
Logjam

**7 letters**
Jolting
Staging
Towpath
Vaulted

## ACROSS

1 Not helping you to find out about something (13)
9 Make off with (6)
10 Lowering in rank (8)
11 Penultimate match in a tournament (4)
12 Item of crockery (5)
13 Organs sensitive to sound (4)
14 Travel on snow (3)
15 Number of times Henry VIII married (3)
16 Clean with water (4)
18 Deceiver (5)
20 Gas compressor (4)
22 Make known (8)
24 Railway engines (6)
25 Avoid taking sides (3,2,3,5)

## DOWN

2 Person of exalted rank (5)
3 Sustain (7)
4 Choose (3)
5 TV, newspapers etc (5)
6 Storm (7)
7 Animal doctor (3)
8 Climb rapidly (4)
12 Small wind instrument (7)
13 Pay for, atone for (7)
17 Centre of rotation (4)
19 Appoint (5)
21 Frenzied, crazy (5)
23 Ho ___ Minh City, official name of Saigon (3)
24 Secure with a bow (3)

# TRIO

The man would like to buy three identical ornaments. Which design will he choose?

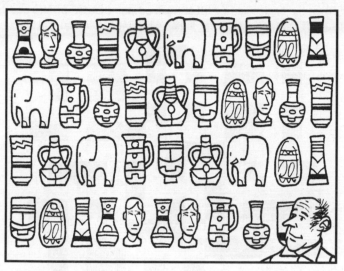

# STAIRCASE

When the seven holes listed here in a mixed-up order are correctly placed along the horizontal rows, the letters in the diagonal 'staircase' will spell out another type of hole.

### RAVINE  MORTISE  CONCAVE  TRENCH
### CRANNY  FISSURE  OPENING

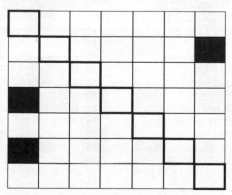

# MISSING LINKS

The answer to each clue is a word which has a link with each of the three words listed. This word may come at the end (e.g. HEAD linked with BEACH, BIG and HAMMER), at the beginning (e.g. BLACK linked with BEAUTY, BOARD and JACK) or a mixture of the two (e.g. STONE linked with HAIL, LIME and WALL).

## ACROSS

1 EVIL, HIGH, LOW (7)
4 BED, COUNTRYMAN, TRAVELLER (6)
8 FLOWERS, INTELLIGENCE, SWEETENER (10)
9 HOME, LIBRARY, PHONE (6)
10 END, FREEZE, WATER (4)
12 HIGH, STILETTO, WEDGE (5)
14 DRIVING, OFF, POETIC (7)
17 ROAD, WASH, WHOLE (3)
19 BLUE, PAN, PRINCIPLE (5)
20 FLYING, HILL, SOLDIER (3)
21 BIG, CART, CRAB (5)
23 PLUGS, TRUMPET, WIG (3)
24 BACK, SHOOTER, SPOT (7)
26 BIKE, BLAZER, NATURE (5)
28 LANE, PUNCTURE, WORM (4)
31 FOWL, NEW, PIG (6)
33 FRENCH, INDUSTRIAL, RUSSIAN (10)
34 DANCING, MINOR, OXFORD (6)
35 BURN, GOOSEBERRY, LANTERN (7)

## DOWN

1 ENGINE, LIGHTS, PARTY (6)
2 COMMON, COMPOUND, RATES (8)
3 DEGREE, PARTY, WORLD (5)
4 CLING, SET, STUDIO (4)
5 BABY, BODY, SETTING (6)
6 MINIMUM, PACKET, SLAVE (4)
7 BIG, PIECE, SHARE (4)
11 DINNER, GLASS, NUMBER (5)
13 BORDER, CLIMBING, ROSE (5)
15 ROOM, SEA, TOPPER (5)
16 LINER, PRIVATE, WASH (3)
18 BILL, FLOOD, PEARLY (5)
19 BOILER, LUCK, SHOT (3)
22 GENERAL, SHARP, TARGET (8)
25 BATH, REED, TWIST (6)
27 BAR, DEPARTURE, SUIT (6)
29 CUPBOARD, NEST, PUPPY (4)
30 CAKE, DRESSER, RAREBIT (5)
31 CELL, WARFARE, WHEAT (4)
32 BLACK, FINE, MARTIAL (4)

# PATHFINDER

Starting from the letter in the box, move up or down or sideways (but NOT diagonally) using all the letters to find the path through fourteen types of sweets.

| J | E | N | S | B | R | D | P | S | F | U |
|---|---|---|---|---|---|---|---|---|---|---|
| L | L | A | A | L | A | R | O | O | G | D |
| Y | B | E | C | K | E | P | S | B | E | G |
| I | W | S | K | J | B | S | T | A | R | M |
| N | E | G | C | A | A | D | O | G | C | I |
| S | T | U | L | L | I | P | P | U | E | F |
| B | R | M | A | S | D | E | P | S | S | L |
| O | A | S | B | D | L | R | A | C | E | U |
| N | E | L | O | E | I | Q | L | U | B | M |
| B | H | E | V | E | S | U | O | C | E | P |
| O | N | S | A | N | I | O | R | I | C | S |

COLA CUBES

PEAR DROPS

JELLY BEANS

LOVE HEARTS

WINE GUMS

BONBONS

BLACK JACKS

FUDGE

DIP DABS

GOBSTOPPER

ANISEED BALLS

FLUMPS

SUGAR MICE

LIQUORICE

# LOGISTICAL

Local historian Barry Stone has been digging out the facts about some of the worthy citizens of his town in Victorian times – and has come to the conclusion that they weren't all that worthy. From the clues below, can you work out each person's full name, how he or she is remembered today and the little failing that Barry dug out?

## Clues

**1** It wasn't the poetess who had a weakness for stealing small, valuable objects from friends and neighbours.

**2** Sebastian's surname was Somerfield; Millicent wasn't the highly respected headmistress of the local girls' school.

**3** The philanthropist turned out to have amassed wealth by lending money at extortionate rates of interest.

**4** Neither of the women turned out to be an embezzler; Mrs Rowlandson wasn't a bigamist.

**5** Harcourt wasn't the philanthropist or the naval officer.

**6** Benjamin's surname wasn't Bracegirdle and neither Benjamin nor Bracegirdle proved to be a bigamist.

**7** Mrs Horsley-Jones was helplessly addicted to opium.

| | Bracegirdle | Harcourt | Horsley-Jones | Rowlandson | Somerfield | Headmistress | Missionary | Naval officer | Philanthropist | Poetess | Bigamist | Embezzler | Moneylender | Opium addict | Thief |
|---|---|---|---|---|---|---|---|---|---|---|---|---|---|---|---|
| Benjamin | | | | | | | | | | | | | | | |
| Jonathan | | | | | | | | | | | | | | | |
| Lucy | | | | | | | | | | | | | | | |
| Millicent | | | | | | | | | | | | | | | |
| Sebastian | | | | | | | | | | | | | | | |
| Bigamist | | | | | | | | | | | | | | | |
| Embezzler | | | | | | | | | | | | | | | |
| Moneylender | | | | | | | | | | | | | | | |
| Opium addict | | | | | | | | | | | | | | | |
| Thief | | | | | | | | | | | | | | | |
| Headmistress | | | | | | | | | | | | | | | |
| Missionary | | | | | | | | | | | | | | | |
| Naval officer | | | | | | | | | | | | | | | |
| Philanthropist | | | | | | | | | | | | | | | |
| Poetess | | | | | | | | | | | | | | | |

*Record in this grid all the information obtained from the clues, by using a cross to indicate a definite 'no' and a tick to show a definite 'yes'. Transfer these to all sections of the grid thus eliminating all but one possibility, which must be the correct one.*

| First name | Surname | Achievement | Failing |
|---|---|---|---|
| | | | |
| | | | |
| | | | |
| | | | |
| | | | |

# ARROWORD

The arrows show the direction in which the answer to each clue should be placed.

| Get back (losses) | Mischievous fairies | Island in the Aegean Sea ▼ | | Not fashionable | Equal, fellow | Quips | ▼ |
|---|---|---|---|---|---|---|---|
| ► | ▼ | | | ▼ | ▼ | Manage-ment, for short | |
| Parasitic climbing plant | | Go furtively ► | | | | ▼ | |
| ► | | | Yield (to another) ► | | | | |
| Canada's neighbour (inits) | | Documents you have to fill in ► | | | | | |
| ► | | | ▼ | Beast of burden or fool | Lure | | Water-ice dessert |
| Circular token | Frivolous waster of time! | | Part of a camera ► | | ▼ | | ▼ |
| ► | ▼ | | | ▼ | __ along, glide | Continental currency unit | |
| Lioness in *Born Free* | | Fish-eating mammal ► | | | | ▼ | |
| ► | | | | Apply friction ► | | | |
| Court summons | | Divide between all ► | | | | | |
| ► | | | | Sink (a snooker ball) | | | |

# WORDSEARCH

The 30 types of dog have all been hidden in the diagram. They have been printed across (backwards or forwards), or up or down, or diagonally, but always in a straight line without letters being skipped. You can use the letters in the diagram more than once. You will probably find it helpful to mark the words in the diagram and cross them off the list as you find them.

```
L D M A S T I F F B R M P B N I
I A Z R O D N O M O K E O C Q J
I L T R M E E Q T R K R W T V N
B M I S E S V T P E Z N U Z A E
T A P T E I W C H O W C H O W S
P T S T E E R D I U L G O L U A
S I L S I W C R S A L U K I X B
J A Z L E R E V E I R T E R D E
M N E O E T L S H T R W K J N K
D R A I R B H W P F X G X A U B
S T B E R N A R D A F O D M H N
P P Y Y U O S K G W N T F U S O
B O P H D D A E H O A I Z A H L
E O I H H R A I I E D T E M C L
A D R N E U P F R L H L Q L A I
G L J X T P S G S I L B L V D P
L E O A E E O K H L I O Y U X A
E B H T P G R S Y D C N C Z B P
```

| | | |
|---|---|---|
| BASENJI | DALMATIAN | POINTER |
| BASSET | FOX TERRIER | POODLE |
| BEAGLE | GREAT DANE | RETRIEVER |
| BORZOI | HUSKY | ROTTWEILER |
| BOXER | KOMONDOR | SALUKI |
| BRIARD | LHASA APSO | SHIH TZU |
| BULLDOG | MALTESE | SPANIEL |
| CHOW CHOW | MASTIFF | SPITZ |
| COLLIE | PAPILLON | ST BERNARD |
| DACHSHUND | PEKE | WHIPPET |

# PLUG IN

Which of the four plugs has to be inserted in the socket before the writer can switch on the light?

# SILHOUETTE

Shade in every fragment that contains a dot and what have you got?

# DATELINE

A number jig with a difference: with clues to figure out (with the help of a calculator if you wish!) to discover the date in the shaded line – in this case an important date in lexicography.

## ACROSS

**1** Add 28 to 5 Across

**5** Square root of 169

**7** Add 20,719 to 2 Down

**8** Add 2 to 7 Across

**9** Subtract 20 from 4 Down

**10** Add 1,020 to 3 Down

**13** Subtract 40 from 5 Down

**16** Square 2 Down

**20** Square 5 Down

**21** Add 29 to 10 Across

**23** Add 4,361 to 21 Across

**25** Add 10 to 3 Down

**27** Add 34,104 to 28 Across

**28** Add 87 to 7 Across

**30** Subtract 6 Down from 27 Down

**31** Add 10 to 27 Down

## DOWN

**1** Add 1 to 1 Across

**2** Next in series 921, 1,011, 1,101,…

**3** Add 1 to 9 Across

**4** Add 68 to 27 Down

**5** Add 4 to 2 Down

**6** Add 19 to 5 Across

**10** Add 10,000 to 2 Down

**11** Add 6,775 to 12 Down

**12** 5 per cent of 286,800

**13** Add 3,885 to 12 Down

**14** Subtract 6,370 from 13 Down

**15** Add 40,000 to 10 Down

**17** Square root of 20,164

**18** Add 338 to 19 Down

**19** Add 338 to 17 Down

**22** Add 10 to 21 Across

**24** Add 1 to 5 Down

**25** Add 2 to 25 Across

**26** Add 10 to 25 Down

**27** Add 10 to 1 Down

**29** Add 20 to 27 Down

# CROSSWORD

## ACROSS

6 Diced or minced (food) (7,2)
7 Garden plant with flowers on long spikes (5)
8 Poorly, unwell (3)
9 Sharp pull (4)
10 Clever and competent (4)
12 Giant South American water-snake (8)
15 Transport up a mountainside (5-3)
17 Cloth put on the floor when decorating (4,5)
18 Neat order (8)
20 Mull over in order to make an informed decision (8)
23 Sentimentally cute (4)
24 ___ bomb, nuclear weapon (4)
27 Solid fuel cooker (3)
28 Gain knowledge (5)
29 Film-making capital of the world (9)

## DOWN

1 Rogue, rascal (9)
2 Money-off voucher (6)
3 Playfully smack (5)
4 Spoke off the cuff (2-6)
5 Read out letter by letter (7)
11 Lack of good sense (11)
13 Accumulated (7)
14 Crushed stone (4)
16 Wrinkled (of clothes) (7)
17 Palm tree's sweet brown fruit (4)
19 Walkway on a seafront (9)
21 One-piece garment for messy work (8)
22 ___ case, document file (7)
25 Vessel for brewing a cuppa (6)
26 Ruses, tactics (5)

# LINKWORD

For each of the word pairs listed, find the five-letter word which can be placed after the first word and before the second word to make two new words or phrases. Enter your answers in the grid and unscramble the shaded letters to reveal a mode of transport.

UNITED _____ RUNNER

FOOT _____ CHANGE

STRIP _____ FACED

TECHNICAL _____ HIKE

ARM _____ PERSON

SWEET _____ STRING

WRITER'S _____ CAPITALS

SNOW _____ WOOD

BOWLING _____ CAT

SCARLET _____ PITCH

# SKELETON

Have double the fun with this puzzle: you've got to fill in the answers and the black squares! We've given you the bare bones to start and it will help you to know that the black squares in the finished grid form a symmetrical pattern, so that every black square has at least one other corresponding black square.

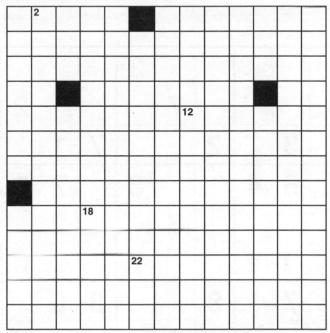

## ACROSS

1 Foot movements in a dance
4 Nauseate
9 Adjournment
10 Over
11 Zodiac sign, the Twins
12 Field entrances
13 Argument
15 Creative work
16 Deciding committee
17 Welsh canine
19 Chilled creamy dessert
21 Resonant metal disc
22 Planned
23 Ta-ta!
24 Beautiful girl

## DOWN

2 Plural of 'this'
3 Forecast
5 Born out of wedlock
6 Lean, haggard
7 Financial backer
8 Impatience
14 Very small wind instrument
16 Expedition
18 Unbending
20 Extend in a long arch

# SUDOKU

Place the numbers from 1 to 9 in each empty cell so that each row, each column and each 3 x 3 block contains all the numbers from 1 to 9 to solve this tricky Sudoku puzzle.

| | | | | | 3 | | | |
|---|---|---|---|---|---|---|---|---|
| | | | | 7 | | | | 2 |
| | 8 | | 2 | | | 7 | 1 | |
| | 6 | 4 | | | 8 | | 7 | 1 |
| | | | | 3 | | | 2 | |
| | 3 | 2 | | | 7 | | 9 | 6 |
| | 7 | | 8 | | | 5 | 6 | |
| | | | | 4 | | | | 8 |
| | | | | | 6 | | | |

**MEDIUM**

# CROSSWORD

## ACROSS

1 Physical game (5)
4 Legendary ladies' man (8)
11 Be realistic (4,5)
12 Pole tossed by Highland athletes (5)
13 Border, lean upon (4)
14 Link (4,2)
16 Debt note (inits)(3)
18 Wrath (3)
19 Claim (6)
22 Viva voce (4)
24 Conclude (from evidence) (5)
26 Money owing to the bank (9)
27 Emphatic personal pronoun (8)
28 Break to bits (5)

## DOWN

2 Image (7)
3 Teeming (4)
5 Crime of fire-raising (5)
6 Agree with (6)
7 Small ornamental sphere (3)
8 Standard of the surrounding atmosphere (3,7)
9 Geniality, good humour (10)
10 Greek nymph who faded away to become only a voice (4)
15 Solidified water (3)
16 Progress (7)
17 Port in SE India, capital of Tamil Nadu (6)
20 Bobbin (5)
21 Riverside grass (4)
23 First man in Genesis (4)
25 Viral infection (3)

# KEYWORD

This puzzle has no clues in the conventional sense. Instead, every different number printed in the main grid represents a different letter (with the same number always representing the same letter, of course). For example, if 7 turns out to be a 'V', you can write in V wherever a square contains 7. We have completed a very small part of the puzzle to give you a start, but the rest is up to you.

| | 6 | 14 | 10 | 2 O | 5 | 22 | 2 | 21 | 15 | |
|---|---|---|---|---|---|---|---|---|---|---|
| | 22 | | 24 | | 24 F | | 14 | | 17 | | 19 |
| 26 | 15 | 12 | 2 | 2 | 13 T | | 18 | 2 | 3 | 12 | 11 | 15 |
| | 26 | | 2 | | 15 | | 15 | | 5 | | 23 | |
| 8 | 2 | 14 | 13 | 11 | 21 | 4 | | 13 | 22 | 26 | 2 | 16 |
| 14 | | 21 | | 26 | | 26 | | | | 14 | | 26 |
| 5 | 9 | 4 | | 15 | 7 | 9 | 14 | 23 | | 12 | 2 | 2 |
| 15 | | 15 | | | | 21 | | 11 | | 12 | | 21 |
| 1 | 2 | 23 | 23 | 17 | | 13 | 14 | 13 | 13 | 11 | 21 | 4 |
| | 25 | | 11 | | 23 | | 6 | | 14 | | 2 | |
| 20 | 14 | 9 | 21 | 13 | 17 | | 13 | 11 | 23 | 11 | 21 | 4 |
| | 23 | | 15 | | 26 | | 15 | | 2 | | 15 | |
| | 15 | 21 | 1 | 15 | 14 | 26 | 11 | 21 | 4 | | |

A B C D E F̶ G H I J K L M N Ø̶ P Q R S T̶ U V W X Y Z

| 1 | 2 O | 3 | 4 | 5 | 6 | 7 | 8 | 9 | 10 | 11 | 12 | 13 T |
|---|---|---|---|---|---|---|---|---|---|---|---|---|
| 14 | 15 | 16 | 17 | 18 | 19 | 20 | 21 | 22 | 23 | 24 F | 25 | 26 |

# JIG-WORD

No clues - just pattern and answers - but can you fit them in?

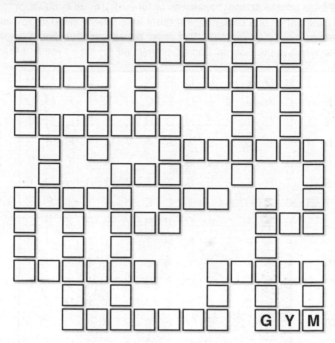

**3 letters**

Apt

But

Eye

Fab

Gym

Hem

Lag

Lop

Sag

**4 letters**

Earn

Fact

Iota

Less

Tint

**5 letters**

Crept

Crush

Fable

Sable

Slosh

Taper

**6 letters**

Arrest

Belief

Oblong

Sentry

Series

Triple

**7 letters**

Amongst

Feebler

Forcing

Reprint

Tigress

# WORDSEARCH

The 30 words below each have two Ts and have all been hidden in the diagram. They have been printed across (backwards or forwards), or up or down, or diagonally, but always in a straight line without letters being skipped. You can use the letters in the diagram more than once. You will probably find it helpful to mark the words in the diagram and cross them off the list as you find them.

```
Z  T  N  O  T  T  O  C  B  X  A  O  D  T  N  M
E  I  C  W  T  U  E  U  E  C  R  T  I  F  M  U
B  L  S  E  T  R  T  H  C  H  R  E  S  E  R  T
N  T  T  L  S  T  U  X  A  A  V  C  T  H  Z  A
K  V  A  T  E  R  I  S  T  T  I  M  O  T  J  T
S  S  T  R  I  E  E  S  T  T  C  Q  R  W  O  E
T  T  C  Z  H  H  H  T  E  E  H  H  T  T  F  E
U  U  R  T  A  C  W  M  N  R  Y  Q  E  X  L  H
P  J  E  A  P  T  H  N  P  I  P  U  T  T  Y  S
D  E  X  B  T  T  P  I  R  O  U  E  T  T  E  T
T  U  C  N  I  E  V  B  D  D  Y  I  W  C  T  R
I  L  L  R  C  U  G  K  E  J  R  I  Y  M  L  K
D  L  A  A  I  A  H  Y  L  B  E  Y  U  O  J  B
T  P  M  E  T  N  O  C  T  A  T  T  A  G  E  R
P  P  Y  T  A  E  Q  T  I  W  T  P  Z  O  G  I
F  L  A  T  T  E  N  F  T  L  A  F  R  F  A  N
E  C  Y  S  S  G  G  T  N  R  B  O  A  Q  I  M
H  D  E  K  A  S  C  V  E  G  K  I  T  T  E  N
```

| ARITHMETIC | FLATTEN | REGATTA |
| ATTACH | HATCHET | START |
| BATTERY | INTERSECT | STATIC |
| BRITTLE | KITTEN | STRATEGY |
| BUTTERCUP | LATENT | TEETHE |
| CHATTER | MUTATE | THEFT |
| CONTEMPT | OTTER | TILT |
| COTTON | OUTLAST | TOTE |
| DISTORT | PIROUETTE | TRUST |
| ENTITLED | PUTTY | WHITTLE |

# LOGISTICAL

During the worst blizzards for fifty years five residents of Gentle Snoring were driving home from work. They had to abandon their cars at the village green and struggle the rest of the way home on foot. From the clues can you work out their full names and the colour and make of each car? (Thankfully, they all arrived home safely.)

## Clues

**1** Mr Hunt and the owner of the silver car shared the same first name initial. Colin and the Ford driver shared the same surname initial. These are four different men.

**2** Fangio drove the Renault which wasn't black.

**3** None of the motorists had the same intial for both first name and surname and none of the cars shared an initial with its colour.

**4** George Senna wasn't the owner of the green Vauxhall.

**5** Neither Frank nor Mansell owned the BMW.

|          | Fangio | Hunt | Mansell | Schumacher | Senna | Black | Green | Red | Silver | White | BMW | Ford | Jaguar | Renault | Vauxhall |
|----------|--------|------|---------|------------|-------|-------|-------|-----|--------|-------|-----|------|--------|---------|----------|
| Brian    |        |      |         |            |       |       |       |     |        |       |     |      |        |         |          |
| Colin    |        |      |         |            |       |       |       |     |        |       |     |      |        |         |          |
| Frank    |        |      |         |            |       |       |       |     |        |       |     |      |        |         |          |
| Fred     |        |      |         |            |       |       |       |     |        |       |     |      |        |         |          |
| George   |        |      |         |            |       |       |       |     |        |       |     |      |        |         |          |
| BMW      |        |      |         |            |       |       |       |     |        |       |
| Ford     |        |      |         |            |       |       |       |     |        |       |
| Jaguar   |        |      |         |            |       |       |       |     |        |       |
| Renault  |        |      |         |            |       |       |       |     |        |       |
| Vauxhall |        |      |         |            |       |       |       |     |        |       |
| Black    |        |      |         |            |       |       |
| Green    |        |      |         |            |       |       |
| Red      |        |      |         |            |       |       |
| Silver   |        |      |         |            |       |       |
| White    |        |      |         |            |       |       |

*Record in this grid all the information obtained from the clues, by using a cross to indicate a definite 'no' and a tick to show a definite 'yes'. Transfer these to all sections of the grid thus eliminating all but one possibility, which must be the correct one.*

| First name | Surname | Colour | Car |
|------------|---------|--------|-----|
|            |         |        |     |
|            |         |        |     |
|            |         |        |     |
|            |         |        |     |
|            |         |        |     |

# WORDMAZE

Find your way through the maze by answering each clue in turn. The dots mark the start of each answer, and the last letter of one word is the first letter of the next. All the squares will be used. The letters and guidelines already in position should keep you on the right track, and the first answer has been inserted to start you off.

| P | | M | • C | | • O | N | | • |
|---|---|---|---|---|---|---|---|---|
| | • | H | | T | G | | | M | |
| M | | • R | • | • | • | • | | | P |
| | • | | L | | X | G | | N | H | T | • |
| B | | | • | U | | • | | • | • | | R | |
| | G | C | | | H | | T | L | R | N | • |
| | L | • | | • | Y | • | | | | | L | C |
| C | | D | | | | • | H | | N | | R | • |
| ← | | | T | | G | | • | | • | | • | Q |
| X | | • | U | B | B | | P | | • | | O |
| | • | | M | | | N | | | D | N | • |
| V | | | | G | | • | |
| P | O | O• | | C | U | | F | | G | | • | M | P |
| M | A | | • | | • | | | M | • | | T | | • |
| → S | H | D | | | T | | • | | | P | | S |

## CLUES

Hair-washing preparation (7)

US film award (5)

Central heating element (8)

Give money back (6)

Underground prison (7)

Bad dream (9)

Small strong coffee (8)

Positive, looking on the bright side (10)

Health centre (6)

Ball-and-mallet lawn game (7)

Long journey on foot (4)

Sales booth (5)

Abductor (9)

Money paid for release of a hostage (6)

Small passenger coach (7)

*The Taming of the* ___, play (5)

Wellington's victory of 1815 (8)

The East (6)

Scottish emblem (7)

To do with votes and voters (9)

Satire, skit (7)

Proposal for an award, perhaps (10)

Lump of precious metal (6)

Later today (7)

Hackney carriage (4)

Ancient Peruvian (4)

Board administering the Navy (9)

Colour of custard (6)

Racing-dog (7)

Entice, attract (5)

Type of sledge (8)

Nothing, zero (6)

Characteristic, predictable (7)

Line connecting the Poles (9)

Worked by battery, perhaps (8)

Unwieldy, awkward (10)

Cricket-team number (6)

Following in place or time (4)

This puzzle has no clues in the conventional sense. Instead, every different number printed in the main grid represents a different letter (with the same number always representing the same letter, of course). For example, if 7 turns out to be a 'V', you can write in V wherever a square contains 7. We have completed a very small part of the puzzle to give you a start, but the rest is up to you.

| 14 | 8 | 9 | 20 | 3 | 19 | 19 | 1 | | 4 | 8 | 15 | 18 |
|---|---|---|---|---|---|---|---|---|---|---|---|---|
| 19 | | 11 | | 23 | | 14 | | 7 | | 21 | | 3 |
| 14 | 12 | 24 | 1 | 4 | | 7 | 8 | 9 | 15 | 12 | 3 | 9 |
| 12 | | 13 | | 12 | | 15 | | 12 | | 12 | | 2 |
| 1 | 15 | 12 | 26 | | 18 | 12 | 23 | 21 | 19 | 4 | 4 | 24 |
| | | 14 | | 6 | | 16 | | 8 | | | | 23 |
| 4 | 11 H | 19 E | 14 M | 19 | 1 | | 3 | 23 | 18 | 15 | 12 | 6 |
| 24 | | | | 9 | | 8 | | 19 | | 3 | | |
| 7 | 15 | 3 | 14 | 5 | 19 | 9 | 1 | | 8 | 6 | 8 | 9 |
| 7 | | 14 | | 24 | | 14 | | 10 | | 26 | | 8 |
| 15 | 12 | 5 | 19 | 15 | 24 | 8 | | 19 | 7 | 12 | 22 | 16 |
| 19 | | 9 | | 1 | | 17 | | 9 | | 9 | | 12 |
| 17 | 24 | 8 | 15 | | 14 | 8 | 9 | 25 | 1 | 14 | 19 | 23 |

A B C D E̷ F G H̷ I J K L M̷ N O P Q R S T U V W X Y Z

| 1 | 2 | 3 | 4 | 5 | 6 | 7 | 8 | 9 | 10 | 11 H | 12 | 13 |
|---|---|---|---|---|---|---|---|---|---|---|---|---|
| 14 M | 15 | 16 | 17 | 18 | 19 E | 20 | 21 | 22 | 23 | 24 | 25 | 26 |

# TWO BY TWO

Each word in a clue can be preceded by the same two letters to spell out another word. For instance, INTER, LATE and TENT can be preceded by PA to make PAINTER, PALATE and PATENT. Can you solve the three clues below, then spell out the three pairs of letters to make a six-letter word?

- ART, PLY, PROVE

- ACE, EVE, RUSE

- ARM, COVE, WAYS

---

# DOT TO DOT

Join the dots from 1 to 47 to reveal the hidden picture.

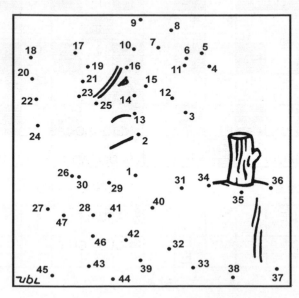

---

# PATHFINDER

Starting from the letter in the box, move up or down or sideways (but NOT diagonally) using all the letters to find the path through twelve TV soaps.

| C | O | R | A | D | O | N | G | H | B | O |
|---|---|---|---|---|---|---|---|---|---|---|
| I | T | O | R | O | D | E | I | A | D | U |
| O | A | N | T | H | L | E | E | L | R | R |
| N | R | E | Y | E | S | U | L | L | E | S |
| S | T | E | T | U | S | A | V | I | M | F |
| O | D | T | L | A | A | N | S | E | M | A |
| C | C | I | T | Y | C | R | E | L | I | M |
| T | Y | B | L | O | H | S | D | Y | A | F |
| O | R | S | O | O | K | S | N | E | T | F |
| O | R | C | R | B | S | I | E | A | S | A |
| S | S | R | O | A | D | D | E | S | R | I |

EASTENDERS

CORONATION STREET

CROSSROADS

EMMERDALE

BROOKSIDE

DOCTORS

FAMILY AFFAIRS

NEIGHBOURS

ELDORADO

THE SULLIVANS

CASUALTY

HOLBY CITY

# CROSSWORD

## ACROSS

**5** Fruitful, abundant (8)

**7** Long slippery fish (3)

**8** Passageway between pews (5)

**9** Sent in a different direction (8)

**11** Triangle's peak (4)

**12** Capital of Norway (4)

**14** Defeated player (5)

**15** Old coaching house (3)

**16** Knights' protective plates (7)

**20** Freddy's nightmare street (3)

**21** Titter, giggle (5)

**23** Pepper and ___, seasoning (4)

**24** Unwrap (a present) (4)

**26** Expensive woollen fabric (8)

**28** Latin-American dance (5)

**29** Shortened name for a glamorous Brazilian city (3)

**30** Hired killer (8)

## DOWN

**1** Secret agents (5)

**2** Men who work down the pits (10)

**3** Buccaneers (7)

**4** Fed up, unhappy (12)

**6** Tally of those present (4,5)

**10** Round objects used in tennis (5)

**13** Brutally, savagely (7)

**17** Lack of a fixed address (12)

**18** Victimise (9)

**19** Use your brain (5)

**22** Posh, top-drawer (5-5)

**25** Failing to adhere to ethical principles (7)

**27** Urban communities (5)

# THAT BIT OF DIFFERENCE

There are eight differences between the two pictures. Can you spot them?

# SOLUTIONS

## No 1

RADIAL: 1 Prial 2 Petty 3 Pesky 4 India 5 Inapt 6 Capri 7 Irish 8 Rache 9 Altar 10 Poser 11 Gazer 12 Aside 13 Aspen 14 Apart 15 Appal 16 Taste 17 Sweat 18 Treat 19 Smart 20 Haste 21 Arete 22 Eater 23 Eared 24 Prams

CIRCULAR: 5 Tay 6 Cheap 11 Gentlest 19 Shard 24 Sly 25 Tame 26 Kip 27 Ash 28 Load 29 Tare 30 Maw 31 Era 32 Ads 33 Picts 34 Zip 35 Apse 36 Ease 37 Trait 38 Earner 39 Sparta 40 Pirate

## No 2

ACROSS: 1 Picnic 4 Pit 7 Auto 8 Protection 9 King 10 Soldier 14 Key 15 Sperm 17 Dry 18 Instant 23 Food 25 Engagement 26 Cane 27 Pet 28 Washer
DOWN: 1 Paper 2 Cross 3 Ideal 4 Prize 5 Tank 6 Standard 11 Dip 12 Rum 13 Personal 15 Ski 16 Rat 19 Night 20 Arena 21 Teeth 22 Water 24 Deep

## No 3

## No 4

ACROSS: 1 Strum 5 Strap 8 Egret 9 Iliad 10 Eager 11 Ankle 12 Shell 15 Latch 18 Grandchildren 19 Adore 22 Cress 25 April 26 Oscar 27 Alice 28 Leeds 29 Ferry 30 Petal
DOWN: 1 Swiss 2 Raise 3 Medal 4 Broken-hearted 5 Steel 6 Right 7 Parch 13 Herod 14 Liner 16 Alder 17 Chess 19 Aloof 20 Occur 21 Early 22 Clasp 23 Edict 24 Spell

## ACROSS: 1 Cross 5 Cages 8 Choir

9 Miner 10 Abate 11 Aspic 12 Cheap 15 Kayak 18 Helter-skelter 19 Farce 22 Sweat 25 Monet 26 Diana 27 Angel 28 Inter 29 Sisal 30 Trend
DOWN: 1 Comic 2 Ounce 3 Scrap 4 Compassionate 5 Crack 6 Gravy 7 Sleek 13 Hyena 14 Attic 16 Allow 17 Arena 19 Fades 20 Reams 21 E-mail 22 Start 23 Eagle 24 Tiled

## No 5

## No 6

## No 7

Tin of peas – £1.00; bag of sweets – £1.50; box of cornflakes – £1.75; bottle of milk – £1.25

# SOLUTIONS

## No 8
Tact, mare, hilt, mine. The phrase is:
MENTAL ARITHMETIC

## No 9
ACROSS: 1 Abominable snowman
2 Donate; tail; tile; ore 3 Hospital; veal;
dense 4 Eternal; lecture; top 5 Rather;
oast; elevens 6 Expire; odd; ounce; can
7 Dean; answer; narrate 8 Camera;
erect; secret 9 Apply; seer; oil; allot
10 Spear; annoy; lotions 11 Person;
Derby; tingle 12 Inestimable; fog; rye
13 Add; gate; rioting; arm 14 Nicely;
natter; penal 15 Scan; enact; also; Eire
16 Eerie; Achilles; sten 17 Aster; peep;
bat; heart
DOWN: 1 Adhered; Caspian Sea 2 Boot;
axe; appendices 3 Onset; pampered;
cart 4 Map; Rhine; lass; genie
5 Itinerary; rota; leer 6 Net; arena;
sanity; nap 7 At a loose end; menace
8 Ballad; wren; earache 9 Lives; deer;
orbit; tip 10 Elector; coy; blot; alb
11 State; until; yet; Ella 12 Nil; ulna;
slot; fir; set 13 Old; recreation; Posh
14 Wee; ever; cling; geese 15 Monte
Carlo; granita 16 Arson; ate; only; rarer
17 Neeps; nett; seem; Lent

## No 10
BEDTIME

## No 11

| | | | | | | | | | | | |
|---|---|---|---|---|---|---|---|---|---|---|---|
| D | Y | N | A | S | T | | J | A | R | G | O | N |
| E | | I | | H | A | Z | E | L | | O | | U |
| F | A | C | T | O | R | | T | I | N | P | O | T |
| E | | E | | W | | | G | | H | | | M |
| C | A | L | M | E | R | | T | H | I | E | V | E |
| T | R | Y | | D | E | P | O | T | | R | A | G |
| | S | | | V | | Q | | | | L | | |
| B | O | A | | N | E | X | U | S | | S | U | B |
| U | N | R | E | A | L | | E | A | S | I | E | R |
| L | | B | | T | | | M | | G | | | E |
| G | N | O | M | I | C | | S | P | O | N | G | E |
| E | | U | | V | O | W | E | L | | E | | Z |
| D | A | R | K | E | N | | G | E | N | T | L | Y |

## No 12
ACROSS: 1 Bovine 5 Clammy 9 Ago
11 Seducer 12 Run into 13 Airy
15 Sheet 16 Walk 17 Lock 19 Brush
20 Opal 24 Sarcasm 25 Old hand
26 Own 27 Sensor 28 Eleven
DOWN: 2 Order 3 Inch 4 Earth tremor
5 Cornerstone 6 Aunt 7 Mania
8 Establish 10 Rockslide 14 Yak
16 Woo 18 Carve 21 Plate 22 Jags
23 Edge

## No 13
ACROSS: 1 Communist 7 Marine
8 Earned 9 Rank 10 Seem 12 The
15 Died 16 Born 17 Set 18 Each
19 Done 21 Active 22 Return
23 Alienated
DOWN: 1 Committee 2 More
3 Unnerved 4 Speak 5 Concerns
6 Had 11 Mentioned 13 Educated
14 Foreseen 19 Dwell 20 Just 21 Any
The person described is:
JOSEPH McCARTHY

## No 14
1 Wea 2 Pon 3 Sil 4 Ken 5 Cho 6 Sen
7 Ver 8 Bal 9 Gen 10 Try 11 Lad 12 Der

## No 15
The words in their correct order,
are: araBesque, dAncer, Leap, soLo,
entrEchat, piRouette, posItion,
audieNce, performAnce.
The occupation is: BALLERINA

## No 16

# SOLUTIONS

## No 17

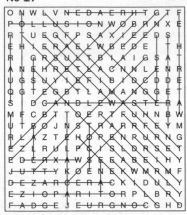

## No 18

```
2 3 1 3 6   1   9   8 3 1 4 6
5   0   5   5 2 6 1 7   2     5
0   9   0   9   2   1   0     0
0   9   5 1 1   0   1   7     5
7 0 2 3 4   8 6 3   1 3 4 1 2
    9         9         9   0
7 0 9 1 3     1 7 1 0 2     1
4     3 4 2 6 1   0   6 2 5
5 1 3 0 8 4       3       4 0 7
  6       6 2 4 3 9 7   3
4 3 1 6 2   1 1 4   1 9 0 6 6
3     3   6 0 7   1         1
9 1 0 6 0   3   2   6 1 1 3 4
1     9 1 4   8 3 4         0
5 2 2 8 9   5 0 8   2 3 3 6 8
```

## No 19

1 Rodent, drone, node 2 Impair, prima, prim 3 Cradle, clear, real 4 Stride, resit, rest 5 Stolen, stone, toes 6 Gyrate, grate, tear 7 Waddle, addle, lead 8 Caries, cares, cars 9 Mantle, metal, late 10 Choker, chore, Cher 11 Strung, grunt, trug.
The two games are: TIDDLYWINKS and RACING DEMON

## No 20

Courteous – sickness – Seychelles – sugar – redundant – Toronto – orange – exercise – England – Delilah – homework – kismet – tavern – nuisance – emotional – laburnum – manager – Rommel – Lewis – snub – brew – William – moth – hall – lard – dye
The two materials are:
CAVALRY TWILL and DOUBLE DAMASK

## No 21

ACROSS: 1 Gumbo 4 Can 6 Washed out 7 Well-to-do 9 Margarita 10 Took 12 Help 14 Bewilder 17 Inactive 19 Inky 21 Glue 23 Inner city 25 Arsonist 27 Inventory 28 Nil 29 Where
DOWN: 1 Gown 2 Masseur 3 Overleaf 4 Crocodile 5 National park 8 Smuts 11 Opera 13 Firth 15 Devil 16 Civilisation 18 Beryl 20 King's evil 22 Brand new 24 In-store 26 Byte

## No 22

| A | S | K | E | W |   |   |   |   |   | S |   | C |
|---|---|---|---|---|---|---|---|---|---|---|---|---|
| R |   |   | O | O | Z | E |   | S | E | E | R |   |
| R | U | G |   | R |   | N |   |   | N |   | U |   |
| E |   | O | G | L | E |   | L | I | F | T | E | D |
| S |   | R |   | D |   | A |   | I |   |   | E |   |
| T | A | I | L |   | D |   | R | E |   | A |   |   |
|   |   | L |   | L | A | R | G | E | N | E | S | S |
| A |   | L |   | R |   | E | D |   | H |   |   |   |
| S | H | A | T | T | E | R |   | V |   | E |   |   |
| P |   | H |   | A | G | O |   | V |   | I |   |   |
| E | A | G | E | R |   | G |   | T | H | A | W | S |
| C |   | E |   | H | E | R | E |   | D |   | L |   |
| T | A | L | O | N |   | D |   | M | E | T | E |   |

## No 23

The girl bought apron g

## No 24

ACROSS: 1 Bestride 5 Scot 9 Daystar 10 Panel 11 Eft 12 Debris 15 Idiot 17 Oslo 19 Redden 22 Instal 24 Yawn 26 Cycle 27 Remark 30 Lea 32 Bambi 33 Parable 34 Toll 35 Splatter

# SOLUTIONS

DOWN: 1 Body 2 Style 3 Rotor
4 Duress 6 Consist 7 Tell-tale 8 Option
13 Bud 14 Iona 16 Brickbat 18 Line
20 Decimal 21 Eyelid 23 Spa 25 Wrap
up 28 Maria 29 Rebut 31 Beer

## No 25
ACROSS: 1 Blacksmith 6 Acid 9 Rub
down 10 Inwards 12 Take advantage
14 Harlow 15 Asbestos 17 Mackerel
19 Soccer 22 Southern Ocean
24 Reserve 25 Sawbill 26 Warm
27 Prepayment
DOWN: 1 Barn 2 Arbiter 3 Knock
together 4 Manual 5 Thievish 7 Currant
8 Dispensary 11 Winged one's way
13 Thumbscrew 16 Hear hear
18 Cruiser 20 Confine 21 Gossip
23 Blot

## No 26

## No 27
Goalkeeper – Touchline – Crossbar
– Referee – Centre circle – Sweeper –
Ball – Goalpost – Substitute – Penalty
spot – Striker – Goal line – Midfielder
– Corner flag

## No 28

## No 29
Discovering he had no cheese,
Jo baited his mousetrap with a
photograph of stilton. The next day, the
picture of cheese had gone, and in its
place was a picture of a mouse!

## No 30
Keeping Up Appearances, One Foot
in the Grave, Steptoe and Son, Vicar
of Dibley, Last of the Summer Wine,
Rising Damp

## No 31
ACROSS: 1 Practice 6 Misgovern 7 Old
8 Testy 9 Mountain 12 Oast 13 Scar
16 Salt marsh 18 Spectator 19 Inns
20 Acme 23 Narcotic 26 Bagel 27 Bit
28 Integrate 29 Rainy day
DOWN: 1 Pompom 2 Assiduous
3 Trotting 4 Chelsea 5 Only
10 Northerner 11 Possession 14 Carat
15 Amity 17 Lie in 21 Chipboard
22 Hooligan 24 Regatta 25 Steely
26 Bail

## No 32

## No 33
ACROSS: 1 Plea 5 Arch 8 Float
10 Shoot 11 Enrol 12 Rob 14 Ream
17 Able 19 Aligned 20 Star 21 Dame
22 Compile 23 Mash 25 Rent 28 Nor
30 Devil 32 Groin 33 Arson 34 Drop
35 Used
DOWN: 2 Loofa 3 Aft 4 Polo 5 Ate
6 Carob 7 Tsar 9 Flue 12 Railman
13 Bendier 15 Extra 16 March 17 Adder
18 Lemon 23 Mode 24 Sever 26 Erode
27 Tang 29 Oast 31 Lap 32 Gnu

# SOLUTIONS

## No 34

1 Basement 2 Ahead, fret 3 Salary, sty 4 Infer, rife 5 Lethargic 6 Hound, rude 7 Upshot, bid 8 Minor, work 9 Envisage Human love is rewarding for it brightens up the day and makes the burdens of life easier to carry.
Basil Hume

## No 35

TO AND FRO: Pressing, glowers, shares, skipper, ream, mittens, scares, score, emir, remit, tea, appal, lean, newt, tress, sale, erst, towed, dacha, algae, end, deep, pain, nicer, rent, tail, Lisa, about, terns, slept, triads, Sao, our, root, toy, yes, sec, caller, Romeo
DOWN AND UP: Permit, tor, read, does, sinews, steep, prepare, erect, tram, moot, Tai, idea, aim, miss, skimp, plan, nip, purer, relic, cap, pets, sin, net, trash, hail, loll, loss, spas, sloe, erg, glance, eel, leant, taco, orb, beg, grass, shows, scent, tad, doe, eyes, set, tun, newer, rare

## No 36

The unscrambled words in their correct order are: Tall, gaRden, bEech, Elm, chainSaw, cUt, expeRt, Grows, nEat, Oak, braNches
The occupation is: TREE SURGEON

## No 37

Mass, cape, fork, tare. The phrase is: AS A MARK OF RESPECT

## No 38

The identical vases are: middle vase, top row – middle vase, third row – end vase, bottom row

## No 39

1 (3) Trout 2 (1) Orion 3 (2) Tense

## No 40

## No 41

ACROSS: 1 Isles 4 Majestic 11 Transfuse 12 Bower 13 Iced 14 Hooded 16 Ski 18 Pay 19 Pastry 22 Marl 24 Kendo 26 Greatcoat 27 Repartee 28 Swift
DOWN: 2 Stately 3 East 5 Amend 6 Embody 7 Tow 8 Cordiality 9 Strip poker 10 Ludo 15 Opt 16 Seal off 17 Uproar 20 Segue 21 Reef 23 Stow 25 Nip

## No 42

ACROSS: 1 Rock 3 Cabin 6 Bell 8 Victoria 10 Tennis 11 Flakes 12 Super 13 Satin 15 Instant 18 Stud 19 Acid 20 Admiral 23 Party 25 Lunch 26 Trials 28 Letter 29 Interest 31 Cube 32 Welsh 33 Wire
DOWN: 1 Reverse 2 Kit 3 Carol 4 Blanket 5 Notes 6 Banana 7 Lesson 9 Computer 11 Friday 13 Stalls 14 Triangle 16 Sum 17 Air 21 Initial 22 Whistle 23 Public 24 Turtle 26 Throw 27 Latch 30 Raw

## No 43

Leopard, Lion, Giraffe, Elephant, Gazelle, Antelope, Jaguar, Hippopotamus, Rhinoceros, Chimpanzee, Gorilla, Porcupine, Tiger, Kangaroo, Beaver, Wallaby

# SOLUTIONS

**No 44**

Pedal, 1 and 4; hat, 1 and 6; shell, 2 and 5; mask, 3 and 4; pelican, 3 and 6

**No 45**

**No 46**

Silhouette 1 is artefact f, and silhouette 2 is artefact d

**No 47**

**No 48**

RADIAL: 1 Prong 2 Gulag 3 Gable 4 Adder 5 Gouda 6 Admit 7 Addle 8 Ayres 9 Seine 10 Sepal 11 Moses 12 Drily 13 Drone 14 Salad 15 Bread 16 Agree 17 Cooee 18 Cadge 19 Image 20 Resin 21 Ready 22 Cedar 23 Radar 24 Along
CIRCULAR: 1 Par 5 Greg 6 Tea 9 Elm 12 Yes 17 Cab 22 Cynic 25 Rule 26 Oily 27 Loan 28 Gran 29 Mao 30 Ideal 31 Blood 32 Mud 33 Drip 34 Lois 35 Adore 36 Sad 37 Add 38 E'er 39 Aegean 40 Sag 41 Red

**No 49**

**No 50**

| | | | | | | | |
|---|---|---|---|---|---|---|---|
| 5 0 1 0 4 | | 1 | 3 | | 2 0 6 0 9 | | |
| 1 8 | 3 | | 8 1 0 1 1 | | 0 | | 2 |
| 0 8 | 7 | 2 | 1 | 4 | 8 | | 2 |
| 0 9 | 3 0 5 | | 9 | 2 | 9 | | 0 |
| 9 3 1 2 6 | | 6 4 9 | | 4 8 1 3 2 | | | |
| 9 | | 8 | | 3 | 8 | | |
| 8 0 0 1 7 | | 5 9 2 1 6 | | 0 | | | |
| 0 | 6 1 2 0 0 | | 3 | | 5 1 0 | | |
| 3 9 1 1 3 6 | | 5 | | 2 8 6 | | | |
| 2 | 4 2 5 9 9 1 | | 8 | | | | |
| 2 0 5 0 4 | | 9 1 7 | | 6 3 4 8 1 | | | |
| 1 | 4 | 3 6 2 | 3 | | | 7 | |
| 8 6 6 1 2 | 0 | 1 | | 9 0 8 3 9 | | | |
| 3 | 3 9 9 | | 4 6 8 | | | 0 | |
| 7 3 0 3 3 | | 9 8 1 | | 2 8 3 0 4 | | | |

**No 51**

ACROSS: 6 Truncated 7 Elver 8 Din 9 Mode 10 Joss 12 Naturism 15 Biannual 17 Dispose of 18 Mitigate 20 Vibrancy 23 Chew 24 Chip 27 Ail 28 Annal 29 Piggy-bank
DOWN: 1 Streaming 2 Curved 3 Scorn 4 Studious 5 Oddness 11 Ironmongery 13 Twinset 14 Clef 16 Uneaten 17 Dams 19 Sylph-like 21 Ideology 22 Scrappy 25 Hangar 26 Satyr

# SOLUTIONS

**No 52**
ACROSS: 3 Sales 7 French 8 Over
9 Often 11 Baron 12 Critics 13 Only
15 Cup 16 Held 18 Trained 20 Appal
22 Noted 23 Made 24 Opened
DOWN: 1 Britain 2 Anybody 3 Shot
4 Later 5 Son 6 Pressed 10 Time
12 Could 13 Outcome 14 Lead
16 Happier 17 Learned 19 Enter
21 Idol 22 New
The character described is:
FRED PERRY

**No 53**

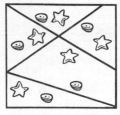

**No 54**
Artist 1 has an extra band on his
sleeve. Artist 2 has an extra paint
splash on his palette. Artist 3 has an
extra button on his tunic pocket. Artist
4 has a tuft on his beret

**No 55**
1 (3) Grain 2 (1) Anger 3 (2) North

**No 56**
Picture 1 is missing a brick in the wall.
Picture 2 is missing a carrot. Picture 3
is missing a potato in the top left box.
Picture 4 is missing a banana. Picture
5 is missing part of the stall-holder's
collar. Picture 6 is missing a wheel hub.
Picture 7 is missing one of the doors
on the van behind the stall. Picture 8 is
missing a mark on the coconut in the
bottom right box.

**No 57**
ACROSS: 6 Well-matched 8 Low 9 Wee
10 Wagtail 12 Idiot 13 David 14 Ply
16 Wonder 17 Archer 18 Oak 20 Awful
22 Moral 23 Typhoon 24 Ark 26 Ace
27 Dinner-dance
DOWN: 1 Pew 2 Float 3 Pastel 4 Acrid
5 Sew 6 Word for word 7 Deliverance
10 Woodcut 11 Latch on 14 Pro
15 Yak 19 Adhere 21 Lying 22 Molar
25 Kip 26 Act

**No 58**

| C | O | S | T | L | Y |   | S | L | A | L | O | M |
| O |   | H |   | A |   | A |   | A |   | A |   | A |
| W | H | A | C | K | E | D |   | W | A | I | S | T |
| L |   | R |   | E |   | O |   | L |   | R |   | U |
|   | O | P | U | S |   | B | L | E | N | D | E | R |
| F |   | L |   | E |   | S |   |   |   |   |   | I |
| L | A | Y | M | A | N |   | A | S | S | I | S | T |
| U |   |   |   | I |   | T |   | M |   |   |   | Y |
| E | N | D | O | R | S | E |   | M | O | P | E |   |
| N |   | R |   | M |   | R |   | E |   | L |   | L |
| T | I | A | R | A |   | S | U | C | R | O | S | E |
| L |   | M |   | I |   | E |   | C |   | R |   | V |
| Y | E | A | R | L | Y |   | F | A | K | E | R | Y |

**No 59**

| O |   | G |   | A | I | R |   |   | P |   | H |   |
| P |   | O | D | D |   | E | L | I | C | I | T |   |
| A | L | B |   | O | K | R | A |   | E |   | L |   |
| L |   | L |   |   |   | S | T | R | O | L | L |   |
|   | R | E | P | A | R | T | E | E |   |   | O |   |
|   |   | T |   | J |   | A |   | R | E | D |   | U | D |
|   |   |   | A | P | R | O | N |   |   |   | D |   |
| E |   | C |   | R |   | T |   |   | P |   |   |   |
| S | T | U | D |   | P | A | T | E |   | E | V | E |
| C |   | R |   | P | I | N |   | L |   | S |   | V |
| A |   | A | L | O | E |   | M | A | N | T | L | E |
| P |   | T |   | S |   |   | T |   |   |   |   | N |
| E | Y | E |   | T | W | I | N | E |   | P | E | T |

**No 60**
ACROSS: 1: 258; 3: 213; 5: 112;
7: 32; 8: 199; 9: 361; 11: 345;
13: 815; 14: 56980; 16: 159162;
21: 110880; 22: 41760; 25: 211;
27: 110; 28: 221; 30: 270; 31: 51;
32: 900; 33: 441; 34: 295

# SOLUTIONS

DOWN: 1: 2268; 2: 834512; 4: 156;
5: 1939; 6: 1948; 9: 3791102;
10: 1568871; 12: 5040; 15: 6258;
17: 5916; 18: 110; 19: 1241;
20: 602112; 23: 1120; 24: 7070;
26: 1305; 29: 264
The date is: 29/1/1856 – the Victoria
Cross was instituted

**No 61**

**No 62**

| S |   | A | D | D | E | N | D | A |   | L |
|---|---|---|---|---|---|---|---|---|---|---|
| A | L | T | A | R |   | O | U | I | J | A |
| T |   | O | M | I | T | T | E | D |   | D |
| A | L | L |   | P | R | E |   | E | W | E |
| Y | A | L | E |   | I |   | A | D | E | N |
|   | Y |   | L | I | N | E | R |   | A |   |
| S | E | E | K |   | K |   | T | E | L | L |
| E | R | A |   | G | E | L |   | A | D | O |
| N |   | S | O | R | T | I | N | G |   | U |
| O | P | E | R | A |   | N | E | E | D | S |
| R |   | D | E | B | A | T | E | R |   | E |

**No 63**

ACROSS: 1 Emit 5 Ogre 8 Aster
10 Manor 11 Brute 12 Ewe 14 Trot
17 Seat 19 Recital 20 Plea 21 Acre
22 Dialect 23 Lyre 25 Ever 28 Eat
30 Organ 32 Purse 33 Olive 34 Flow
35 Amen.
DOWN:  2 Mango 3 Tar 4 Stew 5 Orb
6 Route 7 Smut 9 Newt 12 Enclave
13 Entreat 15 Relay 16 Trade 17 Slate
18 Agree 23 Loop 24 Regal 26 Verse
27 Reef 29 Arid 31 Now 32 Pea

**No 64**

ACROSS: 1 Tripper 5 Halfwit 9 Refuse
collector 10 Worth 11 Elaborate
12 Reassured 14 Moist 15 Serve
16 Stressful 18 Nightgown 21 Merit
22 Ploughman's lunch 23 Test run
24 Tangent
DOWN: 1 Thrower 2 Infernal regions
3 Posthaste 4 Ruche 5 Hollander
6 Lie to 7 With a difference 8 Torrent
13 Roscommon 14 Musk melon
15 Sandpit 17 Latchet 19 Tiger
20 Nonet

**No 65**

Absalom, aBel, isRael, isAac, estHer,
noAh, ephraiM.
The staircase character is: ABRAHAM

**No 66**

**No 67**

ACROSS: 4 Ash 8 Full stop 9 Equate
10 Aplomb 11 Lead time 13 Edam
15 Moped 16 Debt 18 Black eye
20 Demons 22 Bureau 23 Encircle
24 Pod
DOWN: 1 Humped 2 Alto 3 Stub
4 Apple-pie bed 5 Herald 6 Rutted
7 Stem 12 Eat 13 Ebb 14 Mickey
15 Meet up 17 Bangle 19 Lout
20 Duck 21 Mark

**No 68**

2, 6 and 9

# SOLUTIONS

## No 69
Pall, noon, hurt, dive.
The answer is: Rudolph Valentino

## No 70

## No 71
Cream, grOan, leaRn, riNse, spinE,
sTate: CORNET

## No 72
The four objects appear in squares 3C,
6B, 7D and 6F

## No 73
Beloved, deckchair, Roundhead,
difficult, tamper, rubber, rascal, lever,
raincoat, tantrum, muffler, ratio,
over, retina, aloof, flab, bus, Shrove,
eels, sea. The two diagonals are:
BUFFLEHEAD and CANVASBACK

## No 74
1 Squ 2 Int 3 App 4 Eal 5 End 6 Ear
7 Les 8 Son 9 Pla 10 Ned 11 Net
12 Ted

## No 75

## No 76

## No 77

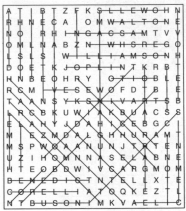

## No 78
ACROSS: 1 Share 4 Teacher 8 Dreaded
9 Strap 10 Later 11 Untried
12 Remedy 14 Obeyed 18 Central
20 Allow 22 Rated 23 Medical
24 Destroy 25 Ruled
DOWN: 1 Saddler 2 Alert 3 Endured
4 Tedium 5 Asset 6 Horrify 7 Rapid
13 Minutes 15 Boarder 16 Dawdled
17 Clumsy 18 Cured 19 Rider 21 Local
The person is: LOUIS BRAILLE

## No 79
3, 5, 8 and 12

# SOLUTIONS

## No 80

He WORKS with BOOKS and
PAMPHLETS, too, INTERPRETS
MEANINGS so that you
Can READ and UNDERSTAND what's
SAID
In LANGUAGES ALIVE and dead.
The person is a TRANSLATOR

## No 81

## No 82

ACROSS: 1 Information 7 Polar
8 Amidships 10 Rotting 11 Machete
12 Plain 13 Ancestral 16 Thermidor
18 Magog 19 Transit 22 Rat-a-tat
23 Committed 24 Adorn
25 Defenceless
DOWN: 1 Ill at ease 2 Foreign
3 Rearguard 4 Axiom 5 Insects
6 Naive 7 Peripatetic 9 Shed light on
14 Cartridge 15 Righteous 17 Mastiff
18 Methane 20 Aimed 21 Titan

## No 83

ACROSS: 1 Potato 5 Beadle 9 Often
10 Scruff 11 Glower 12 Reeled
15 Asleep 17 Yet 18 Erect 19 Die
20 Sip 22 Topic 24 Bee 26 Teacup
27 Donors 28 Pursue 30 Fringe
31 Lyric 32 Rotate 33 Redeem
DOWN: 1 Pastry 2 Turret 3 Toffee 4 Off
5 Beg 6 Enlist 7 Dawned 8 Europe
13 Eerie 14 Droop 15 Acrid 16 Eider
20 Stupor 21 Parrot 22 Tumult
23 Coerce 24 Bounce 25 Esteem
29 Eye 30 Fir

## No 84

ACROSS: 1 Clutch 5 Assail 9 Heart
10 Vermin 11 Talent 12 Rasher
15 Scouts 17 Tut 18 Larch 19 Eat
20 Set 22 Fever 24 Old 26 Prison
27 Waiter 28 Rascal 30 Pigeon
31 Given 32 Tilted 33 Teased
DOWN: 1 Covert 2 Unrest 3 Chisel
4 Hen 5 Art 6 Starch 7 Avenue
8 Latest 13 Auger 14 Raven 15 Screw
16 Table 20 Spirit 21 Tinsel 22 Forage
23 Ravine 24 Others 25 Droned 29 Lid
30 Pet

## No 84

| 1 | 2 | 3 | 4 | | 5 | 6 | 7 | 8 | 9 | | 8 | 6 | 4 | 9 |
|---|---|---|---|---|---|---|---|---|---|---|---|---|---|---|
| 3 | | 5 | | 7 | | | | 3 | 7 | | | | | 8 |
| 5 | | 6 | 2 | 1 | 2 | 7 | | 6 | 2 | 6 | 2 | 1 | 6 | |
| 7 | 0 | 2 | 7 | | | | 7 | 8 | 2 | | | | 3 | |
| | 9 | 8 | 7 | 1 | | 7 | | | | 2 | 7 | 5 | 7 | |
| 4 | 0 | 2 | | | 8 | 1 | 5 | 2 | 4 | | 1 | | | 1 |
| | 4 | 5 | 6 | 7 | | | 5 | 0 | 4 | 3 | | | 1 | |
| 3 | 2 | 2 | | | 9 | 0 | 0 | 0 | 9 | | | 4 | | 4 |
| 9 | 4 | 6 | 8 | 5 | | | | 5 | 5 | 1 | 1 | 0 | 2 | |
| 2 | | | 7 | 0 | 1 | 4 | 0 | 2 | | | 6 | | | |
| 2 | | 1 | | 0 | | | | | | 5 | 8 | 7 | 1 | |
| 2 | 0 | 6 | 1 | 7 | | | 3 | 2 | 2 | 2 | 0 | | | 1 |
| 8 | | 7 | 4 | 7 | 4 | 8 | | 1 | | 6 | 1 | 2 | 0 | |
| 8 | | 0 | | | 0 | | 9 | | 1 | | | | 7 | |
| 1 | 2 | 1 | 1 | | 6 | 0 | 4 | 0 | 8 | | 3 | 4 | 7 | 7 |

## No 85

| J | U | D | O | | S | C | R | I | B | B | L | E |
|---|---|---|---|---|---|---|---|---|---|---|---|---|
| A | | U | | V | | A | | N | | E | | E |
| U | N | K | N | O | W | N | | S | I | S | A | L |
| N | | E | | L | | D | | U | | E | | S |
| D | I | S | Q | U | A | L | I | F | I | E | D | |
| I | | | P | | E | | F | | C | | O | |
| C | O | M | E | T | S | | Z | E | P | H | Y | R |
| E | | O | | U | | W | | R | | | D | |
| | I | N | T | O | X | I | C | A | T | I | O | N |
| I | | G | | U | | T | | B | | D | | A |
| B | A | R | K | S | | H | A | L | C | Y | O | N |
| I | | E | | L | | I | | E | | L | | C |
| S | P | L | A | Y | I | N | G | | G | L | U | E |

## No 86

BeaSt, bAred, fLake, shOut, nOose,
sNail
The word is SALOON

# SOLUTIONS

**No 87**
No 7

**No 88**
ACROSS: 1 Insomniac 9 Obesity
10 Ion 11 Run in 12 On ice 14 Chute
16 Baton 18 Yap 19 Sot 21 Payer
22 Ovate 23 Vowel 25 Built 26 Hip
27 Article 28 Tormentor
DOWN: 1 Idiocy 2 Send up
3 Marketplace 4 Ignobly 5 Con
6 Reconnoitre 7 Midi 8 Type 13 Coot
15 Halo 17 Terrier 19 Sachet
20 Temper 23 Veal 24 With 25 Bet

**No 89**
ACROSS: 1 Quaint 5 Trance 9 Eerie
10 Ironed 11 Epping 12 Edible
15 Unseen 17 Roc 18 Exert 19 Die
20 Sow 22 Sleep 24 Shy 26 Prompt
27 Dilute 28 Rudder 30 Jackal
31 Rabat 32 Tandem 33 Meadow
DOWN: 1 Quiver 2 Atomic 3 Needle
4 Ted 5 Tie 6 Repent 7 Nailed 8 Engine
13 Donor 14 Exalt 15 Urged 16 Eight
20 Spirit 21 Wooden 22 Sphere
23 Pirate 24 Sucked 25 Yellow 29 Ram
30 Jam

**No 90**

**No 91**
Weights A and C will rise, and weights B
and D will fall

**No 92**
THATCH

**No 93**
Sovereign, general, chieftain,
chancellor, chairman, dictator,
monarch, president, supremo, viceroy,
governor, captain, commander,
conductor, emperor

**No 94**
Pancake, yOghurt, taPioca, bisCuit,
rissOle, custaRd, chickeN
The other food is: POPCORN

**No 95**

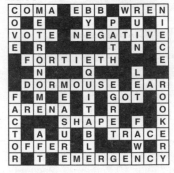

**No 96**
ACROSS: 1 Truncate 6 Musketeer 7 Lot
8 Cabal 9 Clueless 12 Undo 13 Beau
16 Self-worth 18 Car dealer 19 Iron
20 Acre 23 Neurotic 26 Visor 27 Bra
28 Nursemaid 29 Secluded
DOWN: 1 Timely 2 Unsettled
3 Clenched 4 Tremble 5 Oral
10 Southerner 11 Subsection 14 Enrol
15 Tweet 17 Largo 21 Chipboard
22 Doorbell 24 Upsurge 25 Banded
26 Vane

**No 97**
ACROSS: 4 Later 9 Achieve 10 Evict
11 Nan 12 Ram 13 Fad 14 Cremate
15 Department store 19 Linctus
20 Rug 21 Mac 22 See 23 Photo
24 Leak out 25 Nappy
DOWN: 1 Hatred 2 Sham 3 Perforation
4 Lend 5 Tin can 6 Reverse gear
7 Mikado 8 Stye 16 Pinion 17 Mess up
18 Excite 19 Lope 20 Rely 21 Moot

# SOLUTIONS

## No 98

| T | E | N | | G | R | A | P | H |
|---|---|---|---|---|---|---|---|---|
| A | R | O | S | E | | S | E | A |
| P | A | T | | O | | I | N | N |
| S | | E | N | G | L | A | N | D |
| | T | | O | R | E | | Y | |
| V | I | B | R | A | T | E | | H |
| A | R | E | | P | | A | T | E |
| S | E | E | | H | O | T | E | L |
| E | S | S | A | Y | | S | A | D |

## No 99

| | U | | B | | T | | |
|---|---|---|---|---|---|---|---|
| A | S | P | | U | T | A | H |
| | I | S | I | S | | T | |
| | T | I | C | K | E | T | S |
| I | S | L | E | | D | O | H |
| | O | | | I | O | U | |
| Z | I | N | G | | N | N | |
| N | | O | P | A | R | T | |
| S | H | U | S | H | | I | |
| A | | L | I | L | L | E | |
| O | N | T | O | | E | E | L |
| | D | | W | E | N | D | Y |

## No 100

ACROSS: 1 Orchestra 6 Weakened
10 Ski 11 Tease 12 Deposits
13 Disease 15 Band 17 Shoulder
19 Interest 21 Ring 23 Victory
24 Ignorant 27 Examined 30 Smashed
33 Hum 34 Era 35 Pressure
36 Enables 37 Clearly 39 Acid
40 Restore 44 Texture 47 Limb
48 Attempt 50 Exactly 51 Discover
52 Tar 53 Ire 54 Suspect 58 Resource
60 Sprinkle 62 Mermaid 63 Lend
65 Envelope 66 Ice-cream 68 Drug
70 Pulling 74 Doorbell 75 Ounce
76 Own 77 Recently 78 Greatness
DOWN: 1 October 2 Chain 3 Eyed
4 Taps 5 Asia 6 Widest 7 Approximately
8 Easel 9 Destroyed 14 Intense
16 Digits 18 Drown 20 Sun 22 Item
25 Ashamed 26 Temper 28 Instant
29 Earlier 30 Spear 31 Arabs
32 Descent 38 Letters 41 Edifice
42 Tobacco 43 Amateur 45 Untie
46 Egypt 48 Advertisement 49 Tories
55 Unknown 56 Peeled 57 Cain
58 Remainder 59 Serve 61 Pin
64 Degrees 65 Employ 67 Curve
69 Range 71 Long 72 Idle 73 Goat

## No 101

ACROSS: 1 Walrus 5 Lamprey 8 Hyena
9 Pamper 10 Moth 12 Turf 13 Wasp
15 Goat 19 Flea 20 Caribou 23 Koala
24 Sty 25 Oxen 27 Cygnet 28 Armadillo
31 Bear 33 Owl 35 Eland 39 Gnat
40 Pig 41 Rat 42 Ewe 43 Polecat
DOWN: 1 Wapiti 2 Lemur 3 Shrew 4 Vet
5 Lamb 6 Met 7 Yacht 11 Hog 14 Seal
16 Aunt 17 Yak 18 Hound 20 Cattle
21 Raccoon 22 Polar bear 24 Steer
26 Elm 29 Amen 30 Slug 32 Rabbit
34 Hare 36 Apt 37 Doe 38 Ape

## No 102

| S | I | L | K | | O | S | C | U | L | A | T | E |
|---|---|---|---|---|---|---|---|---|---|---|---|---|
| A | | A | | M | | E | | N | | L | | V |
| P | E | R | V | A | D | E | | F | A | L | S | E |
| P | | V | | S | | S | | A | | E | | R |
| H | E | A | D | Q | U | A | R | T | E | R | S | |
| I | | | | U | | W | | H | | G | | G |
| R | E | E | K | E | D | | B | O | W | Y | E | R |
| E | | J | | R | | Z | | M | | | | A |
| | S | E | X | A | G | E | N | A | R | I | A | N |
| C | | C | | D | | P | | B | | M | | D |
| L | I | T | R | E | | H | E | L | I | P | A | D |
| E | | O | | R | | Y | | E | | E | | A |
| F | O | R | E | S | T | R | Y | | S | L | I | D |

## No 103

3, 4, 5 and 7

## No 104

F

## No 105

RADIAL: 1 Resin 2 Ashen 3 Woden
4 Chews 5 Chant 6 Ceres 7 Cello
8 Plaza 9 Azure 10 Adder 11 Adler
12 Spear 13 Raise 14 Recap 15 Osier
16 Taper 17 Taste 18 Coast 19 Avast
20 Recto 21 Otter 22 Orate 23 Orbit
24 Drain
CIRCULAR: 4 Sward 8 Post 9 Err
16 Ropes 23 Terrace 25 Sow 26 Nell
27 Peer 28 SAS 29 Vote 30 Tee 31 Ire
32 Dear 33 Dual 34 Lei 35 Aspic
36 Act 37 Abash 38 Heir 39 Adze
40 East 41 Carton

# SOLUTIONS

## No 106

ACROSS: 6 Sun 8 Environment 9 Rag 10 Direct 11 Semi 13 Pot 14 Doll 15 Final 18 Force 19 Love 20 Pop 23 Rate 24 Corner 26 Ski 28 Combination 29 Lie DOWN: 1 Head 2 Overall 3 Brick 4 One 5 General 6 Strip 7 Negative 12 Pitch 14 Disposal 16 Costume 17 Council 21 Price 22 Royal 25 Ring 27 Oil

## No 107

ACROSS: 1 Coffee 5 Amused 9 Ivory 10 Carafe 11 Errand 12 Uneven 15 Façade 17 Sir 18 Lazed 19 Bed 20 *She* 22 Easel 24 Sip 26 Attend 27 Rascal 28 Knives 30 Oddity 31 Aisle 32 Desert 33 Draper DOWN: 1 Cactus 2 Farmer 3 Eiffel 4 Eve 5 Are 6 Myriad 7 Scarab 8 Dodged 13 Night 14 Naiad 15 Fever 16 Delia 20 Sacked 21 Ethics 22 Endear 23 Ladder 24 Scrimp 25 Player 29 Sit 30 Old ACROSS: 1 Scream 5 Yapped 9 Baker 10 Affray 11 Scales 12 Cherub 15 Benign 17 Her 18 Sugar 19 Dig 20 Boa 22 Sleep 24 TNT 26 Addict 27 Laxity 28 Mailed 30 Banana 31 Magic 32 Needed 33 Defeat DOWN: 1 Starch 2 Rafter 3 Abacus 4 May 5 Yes 6 Archer 7 Pallid 8 Dosing 13 Herod 14 Built 15 Bagel 16 Giant 20 Batman 21 Admire 22 Scheme 23 Palace 24 Tirade 25 Tyrant 29 Dad 30 Bid

## No 108

ACROSS: 1 Biopic 5 Catchy 9 One 11 Legroom 12 Rangers 13 Matt 15 Stamp 16 Garb 17 Nice 19 Downy 20 Lido 24 Surreal 25 Old hand 26 Emu 27 Hopper 28 See red DOWN: 2 Ingot 3 Poop 4 Comptroller 5 Ceremonious 6 Tiny 7 Hyena 8 Plumpness 10 Ash blonde 14 Toe 16 Gel 18 Curio 21 Irate 22 Peep 23 Edge

## No 109

ACROSS: 1 T-bone 5 Toot 6 Valuer 7 Arch 8 Bunion 9 Bath cube 12 Aeroplane 15 Nag 16 On air 17 Ovule 18 Can 19 Every time 21 Man-eater 24 Untidy 25 Bran 26 Crayon 27 Once 28 State DOWN: 2 Bravura 3 Nourish 4 Concise 5 Tranquil 9 Brainpower 10 Tyre gauge 11 Year-on-year 13 Progeny 14 Anarchist 20 Renounce 21 Migrant 22 Attract 23 Endmost

## No 110

```
.  B  B  O  L  I  V  I  A  .  R  .
F  L  U  T  E  .  A  .  I  .  P  R  E  S  S
O  .  C  H  E  S  T  .  S  K  E  I  N  .  A
R  A  K  E  .  P  E  C  A  N  .  V  A  S  T
U  .  L  A  I  R  .  R  .  E  D  A  M  .  Y
M  E  E  T  .  A  R  O  M  A  .  L  E  E  R
.  A  .  R  .  T  E  P  I  D  .  R  .  M  .
C  R  E  E  P  .  I  .  L  .  S  Y  R  U  P
O  .  Q  .  R  I  N  G  L  E  T  .  U  .  R
B  R  U  T  E  .  T  .  I  .  A  I  S  L  E
B  .  E  .  P  E  R  F  O  R  M  .  H  .  T
L  A  R  V  A  .  O  .  N  .  M  A  I  Z  E
E  .  R  .  R  A  D  I  A  T  E  .  N  .  N
R  H  Y  M  E  .  U  .  I  .  R  I  G  I  D
.  O  .  A  .  S  C  A  R  F  .  N  .  C  .
H  E  R  D  .  T  E  P  E  E  .  F  R  E  E
A  .  I  O  T  A  .  S  .  I  D  L  E  .  V
B  O  N  N  .  C  L  E  A  N  .  A  L  T  O
I  .  S  N  A  K  E  .  S  T  A  T  E  .  K
T  R  E  A  D  .  S  .  T  .  S  E  N  S  E
.  D  .  D  I  S  M  I  S  S  .  T  .
```

## No 111

```
D  .  .  .  R  E  G  A  L  .  B  A  G
A  R  E  N  A  .  .  .  A  .  E  .  .
U  .  L  .  T  .  W  A  R  M  L  Y  .
B  A  L  D  E  R  .  .  G  .  I  .  O
.  F  .  A  .  E  C  T  O  D  E  R  M
.  A  .  S  .  D  .  E  .  O  .  .  E
A  R  C  H  .  D  I  A  T  O  M  .  N
D  .  A  .  E  .  S  .  R  .  .  .  .
V  .  B  L  E  N  D  E  R  .  T  E  A
E  E  L  .  A  .  .  R  O  S  E  .  B
R  .  E  .  S  .  U  .  T  .  N  I  L
S  .  .  D  E  C  R  Y  .  .  S  .  E
E  G  G  .  L  .  N  .  C  R  E  W  .
```

# SOLUTIONS

**No 112**
Banana – 30p; Orange – 40p; Apple – 50p; Pear – 60p

**No 113**
Pots, some, holt, gave
The phrase is: MOVE THE GOALPOSTS

**No 114**
ACROSS: 1 Gregorian calendar
2 Remove; near; Nile; Aga 3 Ageless; giant; fairy 4 Vend; rote; awe; rat; sew 5 Ended; read; lees; épée 6 Stone; tan; scrap; raid 7 Osprey; dither; point 8 Attune; moral; orange 9 Preliminary; mortal 10 Serene; send; raw; loll 11 Percentage; eclipse 12 Italic; erect; orator 13 Tine; northern; Irish 14 Endanger; omen; stray 15 Fawn; bedaub; bike; arm 16 Unison; gin; elver; din 17 Leg; extend; reed; mess
DOWN: 1 Grave; soap; spiteful 2 Regent Street; inane 3 Emend; opt; errand; wig 4 Golden rule; cleanse 5 Over; Dee; nine; inn; box 6 Resort; Yemen; cogent 7 Instead; mister; edge 8 Aegean; ion; ear; train 9 Naiad; strange; hound 10 Crawl; char; December 11 Anne; ere; lyre; treble 12 Litre; aroma; connive 13 Elf; asp; prowl; risked 14 Neater; oar; liar; term 15 Dais; pain; top; tirade 16 Agreeing; also; saris 17 Ray; wed; teller; hymns

**No 115**
SIBERIA

**No 116**
ACROSS: 1 Howard 6 Ideal 7 Skilled 8 Event 10 One 12 Son 13 Next 14 Three 15 Court 16 Lord 17 Use 18 Man 19 Later 22 Domingo 23 Sales 24 Lovers.
DOWN: 1 Historical 2 Write 3 Died 4 Adventure 5 Plan 9 Tremendous 11 Centuries 12 Style 18 Monte 20 Also 21 Pool
The person described is:
ALEXANDRE DUMAS

**No 117**
1 Gos 2 Sip 3 Pro 4 Pel 5 Hon 6 Est 7 Per 8 Mit 9 Sen 10 Ate 11 Ten 12 Der

**No 118**

| U | N | R | E | S | T |   | M | Y | S | E | L | F |
|---|---|---|---|---|---|---|---|---|---|---|---|---|
| N |   | E |   | P | I | Q | U | E |   | C |   | O |
| R | E | P | A | I | D |   | S | A | I | L | O | R |
| O |   | O |   | N | A | D | I | R |   | A |   | M |
| B | A | R | N |   | L | A | C |   | D | I | V | A |
| E | X | T | O | L |   | M |   | P | E | R | I | L |
|   | I |   | T | I | G |   | Z | A | P |   |   | C |
| M | O | P | E | D |   | J |   | T | O | N | A | L |
| A | M | I | D |   | S | A | C |   | T | O | R | E |
| D |   | E |   | T | H | R | O | W |   | V |   | N |
| C | O | R | N | E | A |   | B | O | X | I | N | G |
| A |   | C |   | S | K | I | R | L |   | C |   | T |
| P | L | E | N | T | Y |   | A | F | R | E | S | H |

**No 119**
ACROSS: 1 Disrepair 9 Academy 10 Tip 11 Giant 12 Ridge 14 Corgi 16 Gusto 18 Hub 19 Arm 21 Humid 22 Igloo 23 Utter 25 Relet 26 Ass 27 Impasse 28 Directive
DOWN: 1 Detach 2 Superb 3 English rose 4 Amalgam 5 Rat 6 Macrobiotic 7 Fend 8 Tyre 13 Giro 15 Oust 17 Saddler 19 Alkali 20 Mousse 23 Unit 24 Tops 25 Red

**No 120**
The words, in their correct order, are:
wHitelaw, Office, williaM, blunkEtt, Straw, michaEl, jaCk, howaRd, hEld, prioriTy, dAvid, oRder, countrY
The occupation is: HOME SECRETARY

**No 121**

# SOLUTIONS

### No 122

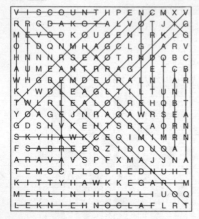

### No 123

```
 9 7 2 9 2 6    4 3 1 6 2 9 9
 9   6   0   5     2   3     5
 2 3 3 6 5 4 0   1 3 6 2 3   3
 5   0   7   2     1   5 4 6 0
 7 3 4 0   3 7 6 4 1 8   1   3
 1   1   2 0 9     8 4 2 0 7 7
 7   6   5   8 0 3 3   6   3
   2 9 9 1 6 3       2   0
   5   6   2   5 4 0 1 0 1 2
 4 3 1 7 0 1   7     9     9
 1   6     4 1 8   9 3 2 8 4
 9 1 1   6   2   3   5   0
 3   1 4 6 6 4 0   3 9 2   1
 8 7 3   3   2 6 5 0   2 5 7 5
 2   2 0 2 2 3     8   1
```

### No 124

1 Maiden, mined, dine 2 Signal, gains,
sing 3 Admire, dream, mead 4 Garlic,
Grail, liar 5 Orient, toner, rent
6 Repeat, Peter, peer 7 Formal, flora,
oral 8 Anorak, Koran, rank 9 Rental,
leant, late 10 Knight, night, nigh
11 Stereo, steer, rest 12 Convey, concy,
cone 13 Seaman, manse, seam
The dancers are: ALICIA MARKOVA and
MARGOT FONTEYN

### No 125

Mickey Mouse, earth, Holland,
dormouse, empress, Scotland, dentist,
tarantula, Atlantic, Cenotaph, harangue,
elementary, yellow, Wales, stiletto,
orchard, duenna, aria, appear, recess,
sangria, Arts, swig, garb, baa, alp
The two drinks are:
MINERAL WATER and SARSAPARILLA

### No 126

ACROSS: 1 Go off 5 Tour 6 Gemini
7 Rows 8 Mature 9 Forelock
12 Limestone 15 Ear 16 Arena 17 Laird
18 Ash 19 Ridge tile 21 Sentence
24 Callow 25 Mini 26 Divide 27 Vile
28 Inert
DOWN: 2 Oregano 3 Failure 4 Bulwark
5 Tired out 9 False alarm 10 Remarried
11 Decathlete 13 Swaddle
14 Operation 20 Genocide 21 Solicit
22 Enliven 23 Chowder

### No 127

### No 128

The antique dealer chose vase e

### No 129

Squirrel, Rat, Otter, Boar, Rabbit, Fox,
Wildcat, Bat, Dormouse, Toad, Stoat,
Hare, Badger, Pony, Fieldmouse, Shrew,
Weasel, Mole, Hedgehog, Stag, Ferret,
Water rat

# SOLUTIONS

## No 130

## No 131

A cat was lying in a patch of sunlight and getting very hot. 'Why don't you move out of the sun if you're too hot?' asked his friend. 'Why should I?' replied the cat, 'I was here first.'

## No 132

The Grand Old Duke of York, Humpty Dumpty, Old King Cole, Little Miss Muffet, Old Mother Hubbard, Georgie Porgie

## No 133

ACROSS: 6 Temperament 8 Bow 9 Yam 10 Sidearm 12 Scent 13 Taper 14 Wee 16 Stroke 17 Breath 18 Bob 20 Upper 22 Pouch 23 Rampart 24 Asp 26 Pub 27 Taxidermist
DOWN: 1 Yew 2 Split 3 Frieze 4 Smart 5 Any 6 Touch-typist 7 Talent scout 10 Snooker 11 Matelot 14 Web 15 Ebb 19 Osprey 21 Rabid 22 Prime 25 Pat 26 Psi

## No 134

## No 135

| B | | L | | U | | W | |
|H|A|C|I|E|N|D|A|
| |K| |M| |D| |R|
|S|U|P|P|L|I|E|D|
| |A| |O|D|D|S| |
| |E|V|I|L| |G| |
|O|N|E| |A|B|E|T|
| |O| | |U|S|A| |
| |L|O|P|E|S| |N|
|B|A|C|H| |T|A|T|
| |H|E|L|L|E|R| |
|J|E|W| |E|R|A| |

## No 136

ACROSS: 1 Dark glasses 7 Demon bowler 8 Pas 10 Sermon 12 Answered 13 Belief 14 Alarmist 17 Dreadful 18 Optima 19 Entr'acte 21 Gdansk 23 Ton 24 Hard-hearted 26 Omnipresent
DOWN: 1 Dam 2 Run to seed 3 Glow 4 All in all 5 Shrew 6 Supervision 7 Disobedient 9 Sidetracked 11 Rallentando 15 Repudiate 16 Butter up 20 Ashen 22 Shoe 25 Tilt

## No 137

## No 138

ACROSS: 5 Athletic 7 Lie 8 Medal 9 Escapade 11 Exam 12 Anti 14 Cakes 15 Sit 16 Heiress 20 Off 21 Basis 23 Tosh 24 Floe 26 Advocacy 28 Annoy 29 Lap 30 Aspirant
DOWN: 1 Falls 2 Sheepshank 3 Red meat 4 Misdiagnosis 6 Alleviate 10 De-ice 13 Ascribe 17 Effusiveness 18 Root-canal 19 Ashes 22 Salt cellar 25 Acrylic 27 Spate

# SOLUTIONS

## No 139

|   |   |   |   |   |   |   |   |   |   |   |
|---|---|---|---|---|---|---|---|---|---|---|
| C | H | I | R | O | P | O | D | I | S | T |
| O |   | A |   | A |   | U |   |   |   | E |
| N |   | S | N | I | G | G | E | R |   | L |
| T | O | O |   | N | E | E |   | O | W | E |
| E |   | F | E | N |   | M | U | M |   | P |
| N | O | T | E |   |   |   | S | A | S | H |
| T |   | E | L | F |   | W | A | N |   | O |
| M | R | S |   | A | S | H |   | C | A | N |
| E |   | T | A | D | P | O | L | E |   | I |
| N |   | M |   | U |   | A |   |   |   | S |
| T | E | M | P | E | R | A | M | E | N | T |

## No 140

ACROSS: 1 Recipe 4 Virgin 9 Tar
10 Sonic 11 Sit 12 Near 14 Ogre
16 Era 18 Dozen 19 Lager 21 Doe
24 Abed 25 Ante 28 Tip 30 Amend
31 Hod 32 Nursed 33 Censor
DOWN: 1 Retune 2 Car 3 Posh 5 Inch
6 Gas 7 Netted 8 Incur 13 Atone
15 Glean 16 End 17 Ale 20 Tartan
22 Owned 23 Feeder 26 Mace 27 Idle
29 Par 31 Has

## No 141

1 Boundary 2 After, heat 3 Sword, rash
4 Invent, lot 5 Loose, oath 6 Heaven,
toe 7 Under, soft 8 Merge, show
9 Evidence.
We need another, or others, to satisfy
the cravings of our human hearts. We
need to love and be loved.
Basil Hume

## No 142

TO AND FRO: Initial, lever, rebel, lid,
damsel, laces, say, yarn, Nile, emirs,
Seine, eon, net, tubes, sirens, self,
fibre, eaten, nape, energy, yot, tepid,
dreg, gag, gel, leaps, sent, toast, trod,
dwarf, fern, noon, nob, brae, emu,
USA, all, lei, inst, tapas, strop, pin, now,
wear, rot
DOWN AND UP: Iceberg, gas, salt,
Tolstoy, yes, Susan, nil, Latin, not, true,
era, aim, Monterey, yetis, sane, épée,
Eden, news, saws, span, normal, lanes,
snip, part, ton, nab, brad, Dee, Enid,
devil, lilt, tref, fop, pip, panel, leaf,
feeler, rems, siege, Eros, sort, tong,
garb, bribe

## No 143

John - No 3 - June, Jack - No 2 - Joan,
Ian - No 1 - Kay, Richard - No 4 - Mia

## No 144

Teak, Tang, Hose, Week
The phrase spelt out is:
GO WEAK AT THE KNEES

## No 145

Pictures C and D are identical
(Picture A has a crack in the pot on the
ground, and picture B has a black band
on the spade handle)

## No 146

1 (3) Prate 2 (1) Allot 3 (2) Extol

## No 147

|   |   |   |   |   |   |   |   |   |   |   |   |
|---|---|---|---|---|---|---|---|---|---|---|---|
| P | I | C | K | L | E | D |   | W | A | F | E | R |
| U |   | H |   | I |   | E |   | E |   | A |   | Y |
| B | R | A | W | N |   | C | H | A | L | I | C | E |
| L |   | I |   | G |   | A |   | K |   | R |   |   |
| I | N | N | U | E | N | D | O |   | S | E | A | M |
| S |   |   | R |   | E |   | C |   | S |   |   | A |
| H | Y | B | R | I | D |   | V | O | R | T | E | X |
| E |   | R |   | E |   | C |   | N |   |   |   | I |
| R | O | U | T |   | M | A | R | J | O | R | A | M |
|   |   | S |   | J |   | M |   | U |   | A |   | I |
| E | S | Q | U | I | R | E |   | G | A | Z | E | S |
| W |   | U |   | L |   | R |   | A |   | O |   | E |
| E | V | E | N | T |   | A | L | L | U | R | E | D |

## No 148

ACROSS: 1 Wig 8 Labyrinthine 9 Tea
11 Drawn 12 Engross 14 Dare
15 Packet 18 Welder 20 Acid 23 Leave
go 25 Unite 27 Two 28 Non-alcoholic
29 Hay
DOWN: 1 Water polo 2 Glad 3 Abrade
4 Grind 5 Sneer 6 Thug 7 Untold
10 Astronomy 13 New 16 Crayon
17 Tag 19 Edible 21 Couch 22 Duchy
24 Exam 26 Etch

# SOLUTIONS

**No 149**

ACROSS: 3 Thread 6 Ladder 7 Special
8 Transit 9 Arm 12 Art 13 Drug
14 Date 16 High 18 Star 19 Mud
20 Ear 22 Regular 23 Anemone
25 Leader 26 Spirit
DOWN: 1 Advantage 2 Bedside
3 Top 4 Record 5 Away 7 Structure
10 Marmalade 11 Seed 12 Ache
15 Trigger 17 Hammer 21 Snap 24 Nut

**No 150**
Nos 5 and 10

**No 151**
Plug 3

**No 152**

**No 153**

**No 154**

**No 155**

ACROSS: 1: 271, 3: 127, 5: 144, 7: 82,
8: 618, 9: 721, 11: 401, 13: 168,
14: 72328, 16: 623427, 21: 292005,
22: 24256, 25: 929, 27: 328, 28: 120,
30: 312, 31: 64, 32: 790, 33: 103,
34: 441
DOWN: 1: 2781, 2: 189861, 4: 222,
5: 1143, 6: 4802, 9: 7733961,
10: 1728000, 12: 1872, 15: 2770,
17: 2525, 18: 412, 19: 8423,
20: 759444, 23: 4239, 24: 2810,
26: 9041, 29: 290
The date is: 15/3/1877 – the first
cricket Test Match between England
and Australia

**No 156**    Each column contains all
four symbols and point in
the opposite direction to
the second row

**No 157**
ACROSS: 1 Transform 5 Backdrop 9 Ear
10 Ozone 11 Embalmer 12 Scapula
14 Golf 16 Salvager 18 Unionist 20 Skin
22 Estuary 23 Nonsense 26 Fossil
29 Mislaid 32 Egg 33 Teaching
34 Sheriff 35 Enthral 37 Oath
38 Nonagon 42 Subside 45 Kept
46 Ceramic 48 Obeying 49 Fabulous
50 Eon 51 Dreamer 55 Golden
57 Enraging 59 Scuffle 61 Ekes
63 Memorial 64 Resettle 66 Sofa
67 Message 71 Time bomb 72 Total
73 End 74 Strainer 75 Abstained
DOWN: 1 Troughs 2 Sees 3 Okra
4 Menu 5 Breast 6 Cobbles 7 Delia
8 Portrayal 13 Chianti 15 Funnel
17 Glass 19 SOS 21 Kiwi 24 Naughty
25 Exeter 26 Frail 27 Schools
28 Ignited 29 Mason 30 Stern
31 Defence 36 Abscond 39 Oregano
40 Astound 41 Emperor 43 Idiom
44 Eager 46 Clown 47 Rescue
52 Raising 53 Angels 54 Ease
55 Gastritis 56 Louts 58 Née 60 Let-
down 62 Stapled 63 Member
65 Enema 68 Soda 69 Alas 70 Etna

# SOLUTIONS

## No 158

```
S K E T C H ▪ M ▪ T U B A
E ▪ R ▪ O A F I S H ▪ A
Q U A R T Z ▪ L ▪ A S P S
U ▪ A ▪ Y ▪ D E N T ▪ A
E L O P E ▪ E ▪ N ▪ R ▪ K
L ▪ R ▪ J U X T A P O S E
▪ I ▪ E ▪ P ▪ C ▪ K ▪ ▪
E F F I C I E N T ▪ E ▪ Z
D ▪ I ▪ T ▪ L ▪ S E D G E
G ▪ C A S T ▪ B ▪ A ▪ A
E V E N ▪ R ▪ A E R I A L
▪ O ▪ T R U S T Y ▪ C ▪ O
T W E E ▪ E ▪ S E L E C T
```

## No 159

ACROSS: 1 Countess 6 Musketeer 7 Lot
8 Soppy 9 Clarinet 12 Nude 13 Echo
16 Homeopath 18 Navigator 19 Idea
20 Ohms 23 Granular 26 Top-up
27 Boo 28 Scrubland 29 Engender
DOWN: 1 Comely 2 Unsettled
3 Treasury 4 Steepen 5 Prey
10 Toothbrush 11 Unthinking 14 Coast
15 Bough 17 Movie 21 Headboard
22 Culpable 24 Aspirin 25 Holder
26 Tusk

## No 160

ACROSS: 1 Years 6 All 8 Escaped 9 Age
10 Men 12 Son 13 Panama 15 Sea
16 Add 18 Death 20 Lad 22 Era
24 Plight 26 His 28 Rue 30 Let
31 Running 32 Was 33 Owner
DOWN: 2 England 3 Set 4 Acts
5 Spanish 6 Admiral 7 Long 11 Had
14 Awe 17 Dealers 18 Dashing 19 Top
21 Achieve 23 Him 25 Crew 27 Sail
29 Ago
The person described is:
HENRY MORGAN

## No 161

Tangles 1 and 3 will form a knot

## No 162

The mirror image pairs are: a and f, b
and i, c and h, d and e. The odd one
out is g

## No 163

Address, mIssive, aeRial, meMo,
postAge, radIo, channeL
The staircase word is: AIRMAIL

## No 164

The missing details are: 1) a bird in the
background 2) a patch on the umbrella
3) the large pebble next to the duck 4)
the right-hand cloud 5) the window of
the left-hand house 6) the chimney pot
on the centre house 7) the puddle to
the right of the duck 8) the top of the
umbrella

## No 165

ACROSS: 1 Over the Moon 9 Bolt
10 Inclination 11 Left 14 Fibre
17 Manse 18 Totem 19 Vouch
20 Nurse 21 Eaten 22 Rotor 25 Mead
29 Toffee-apple 30 Noel 31 Deerstalker
DOWN: 2 Vine 3 Rule 4 Hindi 5 Motor
6 Obol 7 Nonentity 8 Statement
12 Amendment 13 Entreated 14 Fever
15 Blunt 16 Ether 23 Offer 24 Overt
26 Dole 27 Opal 28 Blue

## No 166

```
B U D D H A ▪ P R O B E D
O ▪ A ▪ O ▪ ▪ O ▪ A ▪ E
M O N R O E ▪ O U T R U N
B ▪ N ▪ K N A V E ▪ I ▪ I
A R I A ▪ T ▪ E ▪ A N T S
Y ▪ I M P A I R I N G ▪ E
▪ ▪ O ▪ N ▪ U ▪ G ▪ ▪
C ▪ S U G G E S T E D ▪ A
R U H R ▪ L ▪ I ▪ R U N G
I ▪ O ▪ L E A N T ▪ S ▪ A
S C R E E D ▪ G R A T E D
I ▪ E ▪ G ▪ ▪ I ▪ E ▪ I
S A D I S T ▪ S P I D E R
```

## No 167

```
▪ C L E A N S E R ▪ T O W E R
M O A ▪ U ▪ X ▪ A ▪ ▪ I
A R M P I T ▪ T O L L ▪ R ▪ P
O G E E ▪ ▪ O ▪ ▪ C R E E P
▪ I ▪ T ▪ P ▪ R ▪ E ▪ L ▪ L
C ▪ A R T I S T I C ▪ B Y R E
A ▪ L O R E ▪ ▪ H ▪ L ▪ D
C E L L A R ▪ A P O L O G Y
T ▪ U ▪ D ▪ F L O ▪ O B O E S
U ▪ R ▪ E R A T O ▪ A ▪ A S H
S H E A R ▪ T O R ▪ F I T ▪ Y
```

# SOLUTIONS

## No 168

| S | T | A | R | T | | S | A | B | R | E |
|---|---|---|---|---|---|---|---|---|---|---|
| A | | S | U | I | C | I | D | E | | N |
| U | P | P | E | R | | T | O | A | S | T |
| C | U | E | | E | R | E | | S | E | E |
| E | R | N | E | | H | | S | T | A | R |
| | S | | W | H | I | T | E | | S | |
| P | U | C | E | | N | | T | H | I | N |
| O | I | L | | F | O | B | | O | D | E |
| S | T | A | L | E | | R | U | L | E | R |
| E | | S | I | A | M | E | S | E | | V |
| R | I | S | E | R | | W | A | S | T | E |

## No 169

ACROSS: 7 Panted 8 Earner 9 End
10 Atom 11 Dote 12 Tar 14 Delta
17 Gable 19 Credo 20 Sheet 22 Death
24 Add 26 Tier 28 Dome 29 Gun
30 Chaste 31 Girdle
DOWN: 1 Battle 2 Item 3 Adept
4 Cedar 5 Arid 6 Lentil 13 Amend
15 Lee 16 Act 17 God 18 Bra
21 Height 23 Temple 24 Angel
25 Dingo 27 Rose 28 Dare

## No 170

| 3 | 2 | | | 4 | | 2 | | | 1 | 6 |
|---|---|---|---|---|---|---|---|---|---|---|
| 3 | 2 | 9 | 6 | 4 | | 6 | 2 | 1 | 1 | 8 |
| | 2 | | 4 | 8 | 4 | | | 1 | | |
| 2 | 2 | 2 | | | 4 | | | 1 | 1 | 1 |
| 2 | | 4 | 9 | 3 | 7 | 2 | 8 | 4 | | 1 |
| 8 | | 1 | 6 | 4 | 1 | 9 | 1 | 8 | | 3 |
| 0 | | 2 | 4 | 6 | 8 | 6 | 4 | 2 | | 2 |
| 1 | 2 | 1 | | | 2 | | | 5 | 1 | 2 |
| | 6 | | 1 | 3 | 2 | | | 9 | | |
| 1 | 6 | 0 | 0 | 0 | | 5 | 6 | 1 | 3 | 2 |
| 2 | 2 | | | 1 | | 6 | | | 6 | 6 |

The date in the shaded line is
16/4/1918 – the birth date of Spike
Milligan

## No 171

Deck, Buoyage, Anchor, Funnel,
Freight, Ensign, Galley, Mainsail,
Riptide, Undertow, Lifebelt, Tiller,
Watermark, Marina, Gangway, Ballast,
Crow's nest, Helm

## No 172

ACROSS: 1 Back-number 8 Elaine
9 Shanty town 10 Detach 11 Last in
line 12 Retain 13 Cape 15 Agitato
19 Adamant 21 Owen 22 Piping
25 Earthquake 27 Aslant 28 Humidifier
29 Tirade 30 Referendum
DOWN: 1 Basilica 2 Classy 3 Nutria
4 Metal 5 Rendered 6 Factotum
7 Inaction 13 Cow 14 Pan 16 Gainsaid
17 Trimaran 18 Together 20 Telegram
23 Squire 24 Varied 26 Thine

## No 173

1 Charles 2 Edward 3 Bernard 4 Daniel
5 Arthur

## No 174

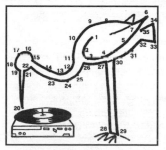

## No 175

ACROSS: 4 Logic 9 Agilely 10 Overt
11 Run 12 Oaf 13 Foe 14 Implied
15 French polishing 19 Capital 20 Cot
21 Pal 22 Ago 23 Panto 24 Knocker
25 Niece
DOWN: 1 Lay off 2 Riff 3 Deification
4 Lyre 5 Genial 6 Composition
7 Gemini 8 Stud 16 Expand 17 Palace
18 Galore 19 Cope 20 Coke 21 Pike

## No 176

1B, 2C and 3A

## No 177

Bend, Noel, seal, dart
The answer is: ABSENTEE LANDLORD

# SOLUTIONS

## No 178

|   |   |   |   |   |   |   |   |   |   |   |   |
|---|---|---|---|---|---|---|---|---|---|---|---|
| P | L | A | S | T | E | R | E | R |   | B | Y | E |
| I |   | F |   | R |   | E |   | A |   | L |   | T |
| Q | U | O | T | A |   | A | Z | I | M | U | T | H |
| U |   | O |   | N |   | P |   | L |   | S |   | E |
| A | N | T | I | Q | U | E | S |   | C | H | A | R |
| N |   |   |   | U |   | D |   | G |   | E |   |   |
| T | U | R | N | I | P |   | B | O | A | R | D | S |
|   |   | E |   | L |   | B |   | L |   |   |   | Y |
| J | I | L | T |   | W | O | N | D | R | O | U | S |
| E |   | A |   | W |   | W |   | F |   | V |   | T |
| A | N | X | I | E | T | Y |   | I | M | A | G | E |
| N |   | E |   | A |   | E |   | S |   | T |   | M |
| S | A | D |   | K | E | R | C | H | I | E | F | S |

## No 179
Plush, spaln, Squid, hearT, cOast, Lover
The word is: PISTOL

## No 180
No 6

## No 181
Christmas, sedentary, yield, diagram, Martina, awash, happening, goddess, stride, exquisite, easier, rigid, double, elusive, error, ruler, roar, rota, arm
The two colours are:
CHARTREUSE and AQUAMARINE

## No 182
1 Ban 2 Tam 3 Cor 4 Ner 5 Per 6 Son
7 Set 8 Tee 9 Hor 10 Net 11 Ter 12 Ror

## No 183
No 3 with side b at the top

## No 184

## No 185

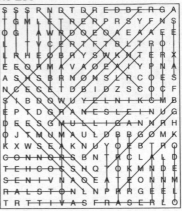

## No 186
ACROSS: 7 Interest 8 Aged 9 Refuse
10 Astute 11 Star 12 Tendency
14 Academic 18 Also 20 Proved
22 Upturn 23 Year 24 Splendid
DOWN: 1 Intent 2 Required 3 Repeat
4 Attain 5 Wait 6 Hectic 13 Exacting
15 Career 16 Modest 17 Couple
19 Strain 21 Very
The famous person described is:
TREVOR HOWARD

## No 187
The one in the lower right-hand corner

## No 188
The unscrambled words are: arTist's, pArlour, painTing, Types, wOrd, dOlphin, skIn, deSign and selecT
The occupation is: TATTOOIST

## No 189

# SOLUTIONS

## No 190

**1 (4)  2 (3)  3 (1)  4 (2)**

## No 191

ACROSS: 1 Hide 6 Clap 9 Invisible
10 Opal 12 Afar 14 Polite 16 Cartel
18 Sincere 20 Scott 21 Stool
22 Agree 23 Clean 25 Neill 27 Similar
30 Fiasco 32 Almond 35 Inca 36 Idea
37 Milestone 38 Heel 39 Erie
DOWN: 1 Hoop 2 Dial 3 Enlist 4 Linen
5 Piece 6 Claret 7 Left 8 Purl
11 Porcelain 13 Aeroplane 15 Titanic
17 Arsenal 19 Corgi 24 Assail
26 Ermine 28 Money 29 Laity 30 Fish
31 Acme 33 Oder 34 Dare
ACROSS: 1 Boss 6 Alps 9 Liquorice
10 Wren 12 Cart 14 Ledger 16 Teepee
18 Endless 20 Heart 21 Psalm
22 Rumba 23 Close 25 Reach
27 Cantata 30 Tomato 32 Cosmos
35 Anon 36 Tart 37 Stationer 38 Easy
39 Rear
DOWN: 1 Bowl 2 Sled 3 Singer 4 Guard
5 Crate 6 Access 7 Leap 8 Site
11 Rebellion 13 Reflector 15 Entreat
17 Esparto 19 Limit 24 Scanty
26 Easter 28 North 29 Actor 30 Tale
31 Moss 33 Mare 34 Stir

## No 192

```
8 1 2 9   7 9 9 4 3   3 7 4 5
0   3   9       3 3     9
3   4 1 1 7 3   3 7 1 9 7 2
7 8 3 0       9 0 5       8
    7 0 8 4   2     5 6 2 3
3 7 8     7 7 8 0 6   1     5
    2 3 6 3     1 1 1 2   6
7 3 2     2 8 3 5 5     8   7
  8 4 7 3 1     5 9 7 8 2 6
  3   7 1 7 7 7 5     1
  8   3   2     6 4 4 2
4 0 2 9 8   4 2 7 9 8     3
7   3 9 0 0 5   1   9 8 9 3
8   2     2   1 1       3
8 3 8 7   8 9 0 3 3   7 7 2 3
```

## No 193

```
P A R O D Y I N G ■ S E W
E E E ■ N ■ A O ■ A
R E L A X ■ S I Z Z L E S
K ■ I T T ■ E V ■ T
I N C U R R E D ■ K I T E
N ■ O ■ P F N ■ ■
G Y P S U M ■ J I N G L E
■ A ■ S B ■ E ■ ■ L
L U R K ■ L A C R O S S E
U ■ Q ■ H T ■ C L ■ C
N O U R I S H ■ E N A C T
G ■ E ■ S ■ E S S ■ E
E F T ■ S C R A T C H E D
```

## No 194

2D and 4B

## No 195

No 6

## No 196

ACROSS: 4 Web 8 Splutter 9 Evince
10 Crop up 11 Navigate 13 Tsar
15 Other 16 Dome 18 Maharaja
20 Caving 22 Lineal 23 Enfeeble
24 End
DOWN: 1 Spires 2 Gulp 3 Stop
4 Wrong-headed 5 Beaver 6 Hinged
7 Scut 12 Ewe 13 Tom 14 Roamer
15 Oracle 17 Mantle 19 Arid 20 Café
21 Veer

## No 197

ACROSS: 1 Joker 4 Cabaret 8 Clipper
9 Apple 10 Piece 11 Freesia 13 Tree
15 Toffee 17 Shield 20 Note
22 Penalty 24 Ridge 26 Actor
27 Tetanus 28 Nuclear 29 Cheer
DOWN: 1 Jackpot 2 Knife 3 Replete
4 Carafe 5 Brave 6 Riposte 7 Theta
12 Rest 14 Rent 16 Fanatic 18 Heretic
19 Dresser 21 Oyster 22 Plain
23 Large 25 Dance

# SOLUTIONS

## No 198

## No 199
No 2

## No 200
SPREAD

## No 201
ACROSS: 1 Swinish 7 Easel 8 Pit
9 Last 10 Grog 12 Spectate
14 Outfitter 15 Asteroid 18 Calabash
21 Tradename 23 Operable 25 Ibis
26 Crag 28 Hot 29 Koran 30 Adipose
DOWN: 2 Wasps nest 3 Null
4 Superstitious 5 Seclusion 6 Stagy
11 Strive 13 Erode 16 Self-appointed
17 Acute 19 Bleary 20 Jet engine
22 Ambergris 24 Pithy 27 Skip

## No 202
ACROSS: 1 Prevarication 9 Smarmy
10 Black ice 11 Maxi 12 Bingo
13 Pawn 14 Oil 15 Sue 16 Wren
18 Imply 20 Nick 22 Subtitle
24 Plasma 25 Introspection
DOWN: 2 Rumba 3 Version 4 Ray
5 Cabin 6 Tea cosy 7 Oak 8 Scow
12 Blister 13 Pennant 17 Roue
19 Press 21 Cameo 23 Tan 24 Pie

## No 203
This person MEASURES you with a
TAPE.
ADJUSTS the DUMMY to your SHAPE
And WORKS away with PLEAT and DART
To make a FASHION GARMENT smart.
The occupation is: DRESSMAKER

## No 204
1(3) Mouse; 2 (1) Under; 3 (2) Error

## No 205

## No 206
Francis, seldom, *Mayflower*, risotto,
oasis, stretch, Homburg, gander,
repentant, trouble, Excalibur, radiator,
rotunda, alike, enlist, toad, diverse
The two English ports are:
FOLKESTONE and SUNDERLAND

## No 207

## No 208
ACROSS: 1 Blackjack 6 Deposits 10 Eve
11 Exact 12 Producer 13 Scarlet
15 Zinc 17 Heritage 19 Analysis
21 Says 23 Assumed 24 Umbrella
27 Brighter 30 Sailors 33 Was 34 Toe
35 Examples 36 America 37 Theatre
39 Eats 40 Passage 44 Outside
47 Eggs 48 Pyjamas 50 Testing
51 Firewood 52 Use 53 Gin
54 Reached 58 Pressure 60 Deserted
62 Scratch 63 Dust 65 Material

# SOLUTIONS

66 Persuade 68 Echo 70 Release
74 Relative 75 Prowl 76 Lid
77 Solemnly 78 Yesterday
DOWN: 1 Breezes 2 Again 3 Kits 4 Asia
5 Keel 6 Depths 7 Procrastinate
8 Stunt 9 Surrender 14 Chamber
16 Casual 18 Admit 20 Ill 22 Area
25 Lowered 26 Absent 28 Happens
29 Elected 30 Stamp 31 Items
32 Stately 38 Rooster 41 Angrier
42 Sisters 43 Amounts 45 Irish
46 Edged 48 Pronunciation 49 Judged
55 Entries 56 Cuddle 57 Eros
58 Passports 59 Error 61 Era
64 Trolley 65 Merely 67 Scare
69 Chord 71 Lady 72 Asks 73 Epée

## No 209
ACROSS: 3 Scruff 6 Tendon 7 Bladder
8 Patella 9 Ear 12 Gum 13 Pate
14 Limb 16 Bust 18 Iris 19 Gut 20 Toe
22 Eyelash 23 Humerus 25 Middle
26 Tissue
DOWN: 1 Anatomist 2 Dollops 3 Sol
4 Radial 5 Flea 7 Batteries 10 Rio
Grande 11 Abet 12 Gibe 15 Ascetic
17 Towers 21 Judi 24 Use

## No 210

| | | | | | | | | | | | |
|---|---|---|---|---|---|---|---|---|---|---|---|
| E | X | C | A | V | A | T | E | | K | E | E | P |
| T | | O | O | | U | | S | | L | | A |
| C | A | N | A | L | | G | R | U | F | F | L | Y |
| H | | J | | U | | G | | B | I | | M |
| | Q | U | I | N | T | E | S | S | E | N | C | E |
| A | | R | | T | | D | | E | | | N |
| C | H | E | W | E | D | | S | Q | U | I | R | T |
| R | | | E | | R | | U | | N | | S |
| I | N | T | E | R | F | E | R | E | N | C | E |
| M | | I | | P | | N | | E | | | M |
| O | R | G | A | N | Z | A | | T | A | N | G | O |
| N | | E | | G | | I | | L | | S | | S |
| Y | A | R | N | | G | R | E | Y | N | E | S | S |

## No 211
Nos 4, 5 and 10

## No 212
1 Top leaf 2 Book-cover label 3 Window
4 Bottom droplet 5 Smoke 6 Watering-
can top 7 Puddle 8 Bush

## No 213
RADIAL: 1 Terse 2 Meant 3 Agent
4 Saint 5 Midas 6 Owers 7 Tsars
8 Harry 9 Diary 10 Abbey 11 Holey
12 Tress 13 Amass 14 Steep 15 Salts
16 Maple 17 Maker 18 Miser
19 Miami 20 Metre 21 Phare 22 Emits
23 Emmet 24 Sleet.
DOWN: 4 Tamest 5 Moth 11 Had
15 Spat 16 Err 19 Imps 25 Wing
26 Bias 27 Orme 28 Ale 29 Theme
30 Else 31 Die 32 Ear 33 Able 34 Plea
35 Task 36 Aim 37 Era 38 Arrest
39 Airmen 40 System

## No 214

| | | | | | | | | | |
|---|---|---|---|---|---|---|---|---|---|
| G | | M | | F | L | A | T | | W | O | O | D |
| R | A | I | N | | I | | H | | H | | I |
| E | | S | | I | N | V | I | S | I | B | L | E |
| A | | S | A | L | E | | N | | S |
| S | K | I | | L | | S | K | E | T | C | H |
| E | | O | | F | | I | | L | | O |
| | E | N | V | I | R | O | N | M | E | N | T |
| A | | I | | I | | G | | O | | S |
| R | O | C | K | E | T | | F | | T | E | A |
| | T | | N | | A | R | C | H | | F |
| S | E | C | O | N | D | A | R | Y | | I | | E |
| G | | R | | L | | E | | K | N | O | T |
| P | O | N | Y | | Y | E | A | R | | G | | Y |

## No 215
ACROSS: 1 Broken 5 Silent 9 Lines
10 Skylab 11 Cotton 12 Eleven
15 Lawman 17 Run 18 Donor 19 Bet
20 Sag 22 Serum 24 Cot 26 Traced
27 Seraph 28 Bongos 30 *Bolero*
31 Utter 32 Entity 33 Gyrate
DOWN: 1 Busker 2 Oxygen 3 Elated
4 Nib 5 Sec 6 Isobar 7 Entomb
8 Tenant 13 Lunar 14 Noted 15 Lotus
16 Aesop 20 Stable 21 Garnet 22 Set
out 23 Memory 24 Camera 25 Throne
29 Sty 30 Beg
ACROSS: 1 Reason 5 Obtain 9 Cedar
10 Reject 11 Remind 12 Skimps
15 Scores 17 Tun 18 Youth 19 Yet
20 Poe 22 Sieve 24 Sip 26 Island
27 Enamel 28 Anchor 30 Warden
31 Zones 32 Entrée 33 Bereft

# SOLUTIONS

DOWN: 1 Rarest 2 Adjoin 3 Occupy 4 Net 5 Oar 6 Breach 7 Apiary 8 Nudist 13 Kudos 14 Solid 15 Stove 16 Eerie 20 Pirate 21 Elicit 22 Snooze 23 Encase 24 Smudge 25 Planet 29 Roe 30 Web

## No 216

| R | E | P | A | S | T |   | R |   | P | L | A | I | C | E |
| E |   | R |   | W | H | E | E | D | L | E |   | N |   | R |
| S | H | O | W | E | R |   | C |   | E | A | S | T | E | R |
| I |   | T |   | D | I | C | K | E | N | S |   | E |   | A |
| S | H | O | V | E | L |   | O |   | T | H | I | R | S | T |
| T |   | T |   | L | A | N | K | Y |   | F |   | A |   |   |
|   | M | Y | T | H |   | L |   | N |   | A | P | E | X |   |
| A |   | P | R | E | D | E | C | E | S | S | O | R |   | A |
| S | T | E | A | M |   | R |   | E |   | P | R | E | E | N |
| C |   | D |   | S | T | A | L | K |   | T |   |   |   | O |
| R | E | C | I | P | E |   | R |   | I | N | F | A | N | T |
| I |   | T |   | W | O | M | A | N |   | O |   |   |   | H |
| B | A | S | I | S |   | T |   | E |   | G | L | A | D | E |
| E |   | C | O | U | N | T | E | R | F | E | I | T |   | R |
|   | L | A | N | E |   | E |   | I |   | N | O | T | E |   |
| S |   | V |   | O | R | D | E | R |   |   | R |   | A |   |
| T | R | E | M | O | R |   | O |   | E | T | H | I | C | S |
| A |   | N |   | B | A | R | R | A | G | E |   | B |   | S |
| R | E | G | R | E | T |   | M |   | I | N | J | U | R | E |
| C |   | E |   | S | O | M | E | O | N | E |   | T |   | S |
| H | A | R | D | E | R |   | R |   | A | T | H | E | N | S |

## No 217

ACROSS: 1 Bib 8 Enlightening 9 Rue 11 Prawn 12 Rat race 14 Tang 15 Papaya 18 Auntie 20 Nave 23 Lay odds 25 Essay 27 Out 28 Inefficiency 29 Oar
DOWN: 1 Bargepole 2 Beep 3 Floaty 4 Agent 5 Stern 6 Knot 7 Infant 10 Hereafter 13 Aga 16 Prying 17 And 19 Unsung 21 Astir 22 Eerie 24 Deft 26 Yo-yo

## No 218

ACROSS: 5 Cohesion 7 Mac 8 Pasta 9 Reminder 11 Omit 12 Edit 14 Mug up 15 Err 16 Adverse 20 Arc 21 Tommy 23 Also 24 Anna 26 Envisage 28 Lance 29 Rum 30 Aspirant
DOWN: 1 Scamp 2 Thickening 3 Aseptic 4 Lopsidedness 6 Tax return 10 Worms 13 Aplenty 17 Decisiveness 18 Bagatelle 19 Byway 22 Managerial 25 Ascetic 27 Smith

## No 219

| S | O | F | T |   |   | L |   | D |   | P | O | T |
| U |   | L |   | T | R | A | D | E | R |   |   | O |
| N |   | E |   | R |   | M |   | L |   | S | A | Y |
|   | C | A | S | E | M | E | N | T |   |   | D |   |
| L |   | S |   | A |   | N |   | A |   |   | D |   |
| E |   |   | S | A | T | E |   | R | U | I | N |   |
| A | C | T |   | U |   |   |   | O |   | N |   |   |
| T |   | R |   | R | E | P | O | R | T | A | G | E |
| I | O | N |   | A | P | E |   | O |   | A |   | D |
| O | N |   | S |   | F |   | B |   | I |   |   |   |
| F |   | C |   | D | E | T | E | R | G | E | N | T |
| F | R | E | T |   | R |   | E |   | E |   |   |   |
| S |   | D |   | R | U | S | E |   | T | A | G |   |

## No 220

Envelope – 10p; pen – £2.00; stamp – £3.00; tape – £1.00

## No 221

Lath, goat, mine, rung. The phrase is: NO LAUGHING MATTER

## No 222

ACROSS: 1 French and Saunders 2 Lot; alive; earn; aural 3 Ascribe; ember; Maria 4 Seer; pergola; eel; asp 5 Hot air; sun; examinee 6 Fret; one-time; lender 7 Rare; tact; cancel; ban 8 In a lather; coot; Eire 9 Agree; eerie; nostrum 10 Reappear; nark; prone 11 Imprint; Isle; hauled 12 Detective; theme; Eve 13 Enact; anathema; peel 14 Such; angle; oath; Arne 15 Oscar; gale; Ural; gala 16 Rerun; lying; sleeper 17 Bran; seed; sheer; dean.
DOWN: 1 Flash; friar; Ides; orb 2 Rose; orange; men; user 3 Et cetera; rapt; Accra 4 Narrate; leprechaun 5 Clip; iota; epic; tarns 6 Hibernate; entangle 7 Averse; cheating; aye 8 Née; gutter; rival; lid 9 Demonic; rinse; teens 10 Sable; mace; although 11 Area; xenon; rehearse 12 Unreal; cook; hem; tale 13 Name; meet; spa; Mahler 14 Dual; inlet; rue; paged 15 Errand; biro; leer; ape 16 Raise; ear; uneven; lea 17 Slap; erne; Mede; learn.

# SOLUTIONS

## No 223
UNIFORM

## No 224

| T | I | G | E | R | S |   | F | O | R | C | E | S |
| A |   | O |   | A |   | D |   | B |   | L |   | A |
| B | R | I | E | F |   | I |   | E | Q | U | A | L |
| L |   | N |   | T | A | S | T | Y |   | N |   | U |
| E | D | G | E | S |   | C |   | S | I | G | H | T |
| T |   | L |   | J | O | B |   | G |   | E |   | E |
|   | Z | E | B | R | A |   | I | N | L | A | Y |   |
| A |   | O |   | M | U | G |   | O |   |   |   | P |
| F | L | O | W | N |   | N |   | S | O | B | E | R |
| F |   | U |   | E | X | I | S | T |   | R |   | I |
| A | N | G | E | R |   | T |   | R | O | O | M | S |
| I |   | H |   | V |   | Y |   | A |   | O |   | O |
| R | A | T | H | E | R |   | S | P | O | K | E | N |

## No 225
ACROSS: 1 Senior service 9 Riffle
10 Incident 11 Stun 12 Bhaji 13 Cubs
14 Cur 15 Two 16 Zany 18 Inlay
20 Muff 22 Sit tight 24 Plug in
25 Complementary
DOWN: 2 Exist 3 Infancy 4 Rye 5 Erica
6 Vacuity 7 Cod 8 Knob 12 Bring up
13 Combust 17 Avid 19 Litre 21 Friar
23 Too 24 Pie

## No 226
ACROSS: 5 His 7 Cambridge 8 India
9 Off 11 Serious 12 Late 13 Was
14 War 17 One 19 Else 21 Against
22 Two 23 Alone 27 Exploring 28 Not
DOWN: 1 School 2 OBE 3 Add 4 Beirut
5 Had 6 States 10 Grew 11 Set
15 Rank 16 Met 17 Obtain 18 Agreed
20 Enough 24 Out 25 Spy 26 Try
The person described is: KIM PHILBY

## No 227
1 Pal 2 Let 3 Sul 4 Try 5 Hal 6 Ves
7 Len 8 Til 9 Hun 10 Ted 11 Led
12 Ger

## No 228
The words are: Tim, bEcker, eNthral,
heNman, borIs, Steffi, davenPort,
wimbLedon, grAf, lindsaY, audiEnce,
couRt
The occupation is: TENNIS-PLAYER

## No 229

## No 230

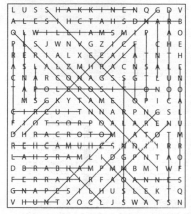

## No 231

| 1 | 3 | 5 | 0 | 2 | 8 |   | 3 | 4 | 2 | 1 | 0 | 0 |
| 0 |   |   | 4 | 0 | 1 | 2 | 2 |   | 5 |   |   | 5 |
| 6 | 2 | 3 | 8 | 8 | 1 |   | 8 | 1 | 3 | 0 | 9 | 1 |
| 3 |   | 1 | 3 |   | 1 | 2 | 4 |   | 2 |   | 4 | 9 |
| 9 |   | 0 | 3 |   |   | 1 | 3 |   | 4 | 0 | 6 |
| 4 | 1 | 6 | 2 | 9 | 4 |   | 3 | 9 | 7 | 1 | 6 | 2 | 3 |
|   | 6 |   |   | 8 |   | 9 |   |   |   | 7 | 5 | 9 |
|   | 5 |   | 2 |   | 4 |   | 4 | 7 | 2 | 8 | 5 | 1 |
|   | 5 |   | 8 | 3 | 0 | 1 | 3 | 6 |   | 0 |   | 4 |
| 2 | 3 | 0 | 5 | 1 |   |   | 2 |   |   | 2 | 1 | 7 | 2 |
|   | 1 |   | 2 |   | 6 | 8 | 3 | 1 | 4 | 8 |   | 4 |
| 1 | 5 | 2 | 8 | 4 |   | 5 |   | 0 |   | 3 | 1 | 6 | 9 |
| 8 |   | 3 |   | 1 |   | 5 | 2 | 2 | 1 |   |   | 2 |
| 8 | 5 | 0 | 5 |   | 6 | 1 | 3 |   | 0 |   | 7 | 3 | 7 |
| 6 |   | 6 |   | 9 |   | 6 | 3 | 8 | 6 |   |   | 8 |

## No 232
1 Sailed, slide, lied 2 Falter, alter, tear
3 Priest, spite, pest 4 Paired, pared,
dear 5 Priced, pride, ride 6 Eating,

# SOLUTIONS

tinge, ting 7 Garden, grade, aged
8 Strove, store, rest 9 Eclair, Clare,
lace 10 Cornea, crane, near 11 Halter,
Earth, rate 12 Praise, Paris, spar
13 Dither, hired, heir
The two plants are:
AFRICAN VIOLET and SLIPPER ORCHID

## No 233
Exclusion, newspaper, religion, narrow,
wood, dejected, dressing-gown,
Newcastle, enthusiast, traitor, redcoat,
tarantula, arrogant, tumbler, respected,
discreet, tutoring, Greenwich, hire car,
rococo, orca
The two singers are:
ENRICO CARUSO and JOSE CARRERAS

## No 234
ACROSS: 1 Asset 4 Calendar
11 Flexitime 12 Topaz 13 Arty
14 Powder 16 Sir 18 End 19 Put off
22 Weal 24 Ennui 26 News-stand
27 Telltale 28 Erode
DOWN: 2 Sweated 3 Exit 5 Amend
6 Eatery 7 Dip 8 Razor blade
9 Effacement 10 Kilo 15 Woo
16 Steward 17 Splint 20 Tonal 21 Fawn
23 Tsar 25 Nil

## No 235

## No 236
The conductor took sheet music b

## No 237
ACROSS: 1 Overhearing 9 Eels
10 Draughtsman 11 Tear 14 Wrath
17 Opera 18 Award 19 Toper
20 Tense 21 Swell 22 Reach 25 Reef
29 Archaeology 30 Case 31 Territorial
DOWN: 2 Very 3 Roué 4 Ether 5 Reset
6 Neat 7 Generated 8 Astraddle
12 Costa Rica 13 Beanfeast 14 Water
15 Alpha 16 Harsh 23 Esher 24 Crest
26 Free 27 Slur 28 Agra

## No 238

## No 239

## No 240
Hats 4 and 9 are identical

# SOLUTIONS

## No 241
RADIAL: 1 Trade 2 Eider 3 Eerie
4 Clear 5 Rayon 6 Order 7 Caper
8 Spell 9 Shell 10 Appal 11 Papal
12 Drama 13 Amigo 14 Arrow
15 Arson 16 Tatty 17 Stoat 18 Tenet
19 Inset 20 Stern 21 Bairn 22 Aspen
23 Sheen 24 Horde.
CIRCULAR: 7 Concert 11 Pass
12 Downy 20 Sits 21 Bash 25 Parole
26 Graph 27 Too 28 Tent 29 Ashore
30 Dare 31 Dyer 32 Peep 33 Pairs
34 Ton 35 Pies 36 Aide 37 Male
38 Rear 39 Rental.

## No 242
Oaf, own, fan; scenic, snazzy, celery;
versatile, turquoise, violinist.
The hidden word is: INFLUENZA.

## No 243

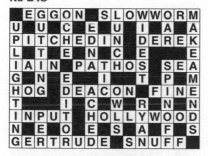

## No 244

## No 245

## No 246

## No 247

# SOLUTIONS

## No 248
CANDLES.

## No 249
Cork, cues, here, loft.
The phrase is: CLERK OF THE
COURSE.

## No 250

## No 251
Bowl – £2; tin of cat food – 70p; toy
mouse – £1.50; rubber ball – £1.

## No 252

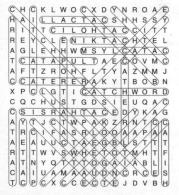

## No 253

| 2 | 3 | 5 | 9 | 6 | 7 | 1 | 4 | 8 |
|---|---|---|---|---|---|---|---|---|
| 4 | 6 | 1 | 5 | 8 | 2 | 9 | 3 | 7 |
| 8 | 9 | 7 | 1 | 4 | 3 | 6 | 2 | 5 |
| 6 | 1 | 9 | 3 | 5 | 8 | 4 | 7 | 2 |
| 7 | 5 | 2 | 4 | 1 | 9 | 8 | 6 | 3 |
| 3 | 8 | 4 | 2 | 7 | 6 | 5 | 1 | 9 |
| 1 | 4 | 3 | 7 | 9 | 5 | 2 | 8 | 6 |
| 9 | 2 | 8 | 6 | 3 | 4 | 7 | 5 | 1 |
| 5 | 7 | 6 | 8 | 2 | 1 | 3 | 9 | 4 |

## No 254
The words in their correct order
are: Professional, Ivories, bAby,
harmoNious, sOund, Tickling, mUsical,
tiNkle, resEmbles, gRand.
The occupation is: PIANO TUNER.

## No 255

## No 256

| W | A | S | P | S |   | S | Q | U | A | L | L | S |
| I |   | I |   | O |   | I |   | N |   | O |   | V |
| P | I | L | L | B | O | X |   | E | L | O | P | E |
| E |   | K |   | E |   |   |   | A |   |   |   | L |
| R | E | W | A | R | D | S |   | T | A | C | I | T |
| S |   | O |   |   | I |   | E |   | A |   | E |
|   | A | R | R | E | S | T | I | N | G | L | Y |   |
| Z |   | M |   | J |   | E |   |   | E |   | B |
| E | N | S | U | E |   | S | P | A | N | N | E | R |
| A |   |   | C |   |   | M |   | D |   |   | I |
| L | I | M | I | T |   | C | H | A | R | A | D | E |
| O |   | A |   | E |   | O |   | Z |   | R |   | F |
| T | I | R | A | D | E | S |   | E | A | S | E | S |

# SOLUTIONS

## No 257

1 Sli 2 Ver 3 Nou 4 Ght 5 Min 6 Cer 7 Gat 8 Her 9 Rev 10 Eal 11 Der 12 Ive.

## No 258

## No 259

## No 260

## No 261

Andrea, E14, two of clubs, in hand.
Gavin, A7, jack of clubs, up right sleeve.
Kenneth, D12, ace of diamonds, under hatband.

Maxine, C9, king of hearts, under lapel.
Susan, B6, queen of spades, up left sleeve.

## No 262

## No 263

## No 264

1 Falter, flare, real 2 Banish, basin, bins 3 Mister, strim, stir 4 Winter, nitre, tern 5 Single, sling, sing 6 Mislay, slimy, slim 7 Flakes, false, sale 8 Crusoe, scour, curs 9 Answer, Warne, wane 10 Bitter, tribe, bier 11 Couple, coupé, cope 12 Heroin, heron, hero 13 Prunes, super, spur 14 Shriek, shire, hire.

The programmes are (A) *THE WEAKEST LINK* and (B) *FAMILY FORTUNES*.

# SOLUTIONS

## No 265

| H | I | D | E | | P | O | R | O | U | S | | C |
| O | | O | | | L | | U | | U | | | O |
| C | O | G | | D | I | G | I | T | A | L | | V |
| O | | M | | | E | | N | | | K | | E |
| S | O | A | R | E | D | | | | | I | | R |
| | R | | E | | | F | I | S | H | N | E | T |
| A | D | V | I | S | E | | N | | | G | | |
| | E | | G | | L | I | K | E | D | | | C |
| B | R | A | N | | U | | T | | P | R | O | |
| | E | | | | D | | C | | | | | R |
| I | D | Y | L | L | I | C | | H | O | P | E | D |
| | E | | | | N | | | E | | | | R |
| C | A | N | I | N | G | | E | D | G | Y | | |

## No 266

Erratic – crumb – bypass – survive
– espadrille – emissary – year
– ramblings – scenario – overhead
– den – Neapolitan – Neptune – Easter
– rearguard – dandruff – flexitime
– espalier – radiance – expose – extra
– apt – tube – ethos – since.
The invention and inventor is: ELASTIC
BANDS and STEPHEN PERRY.

## No 267

| | S | H | R | I | M | P | S | | B | L | E | W |
| W | | Y | | M | | A | | E | | I | | E |
| A | G | E | | M | I | S | Q | U | O | T | E | D |
| L | | N | | E | | T | | P | | U | | S |
| T | I | A | R | A | | E | X | H | O | R | T | |
| Z | | S | | | | O | | O | | G | | A |
| E | Y | E | F | U | L | | F | R | A | Y | E | D |
| S | | A | | R | | I | | | | | | V |
| | C | R | E | A | M | S | | C | A | B | L | E |
| J | | S | | B | | A | | A | | R | | R |
| U | N | H | E | L | P | F | U | L | | A | P | T |
| N | | O | | Y | | E | | L | | I | | S |
| K | I | T | S | | C | R | A | Y | O | N | S | |

## No 268

Plain, intend, tendon, onset, settee,
teeth, throb, robot, other, herring,
ringlet, letter, terrain, rained, edit,
itches, chesty, typed, pedals.

## No 269

| | G | R | A | N | D | E | U | R | | D | E | A | T | H |
| | | A | | A | | A | | O | | A | | M | | A |
| C | O | C | K | I | E | R | | O | R | I | G | A | M | I |
| O | | O | | L | | L | | S | | N | | T | | R |
| R | U | N | S | | | O | U | T | S | T | R | I | P | S |
| R | | T | | M | | B | | S | | I | | | | P |
| E | Y | E | L | I | N | E | R | | I | N | S | T | I | L |
| S | | U | | S | | S | | P | | E | | R | | I |
| P | U | R | E | S | T | | C | O | N | S | T | A | N | T |
| O | | | I | | G | | R | | S | | D | | T | |
| N | A | R | R | O | W | E | S | T | | P | E | R | I | |
| D | | I | | N | | N | | R | | C | | W | | N |
| I | N | G | R | A | T | E | | A | M | U | S | I | N | G |
| N | | H | | R | | V | | I | | R | | N | | |
| G | E | T | B | Y | | A | T | T | I | T | U | D | E | |

## No 270

The man buys polo shirt d.

## No 271

| D | I | S | T | U | R | B | | F | R | O | N | T |
| O | | E | | G | | A | G | A | | R | | U |
| P | O | P | U | L | A | R | | U | P | P | E | R |
| E | | T | | Y | | N | I | L | | H | | N |
| D | A | I | S | | S | | | T | E | A | | I |
| | C | H | I | E | F | L | Y | | N | U | N | |
| T | | Y | | M | | A | | O | | G | | |
| I | M | P | | V | I | C | T | O | R | Y | | |
| T | | L | I | E | | E | | B | E | A | T | |
| A | | A | | N | O | W | | C | | O | | I |
| N | O | T | E | D | | I | N | H | U | M | A | N |
| I | | E | | O | I | L | | I | | E | | N |
| C | I | D | E | R | | D | E | C | E | N | C | Y |

## No 272

Ballet shoes, riding-boots,
wellingtons, football boots, tennis
shoes, flip-flops, golf shoes.

## No 273

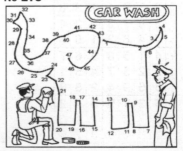

# SOLUTIONS

## No 274
Pug, lurcher, beagle, saluki, great dane, collie, spaniel, corgi, rottweiler, bulldog, afghan, boxer, dalmatian, labrador, airedale, poodle, whippet, huskey

## No 275
ACROSS: 1 Amidst 4 Elapse 9 Gas 10 Weird 11 Tip 12 Race 14 Polo 16 Tea 18 Stale 19 Phase 21 Nit 24 Earl 25 Atom 28 Now 30 Adept 31 Gnu 32 Sprite 33 Credit.

DOWN: 1 Angora 2 Its 3 Sewn 5 Lido 6 Pot 7 Employ 8 Ridge 13 Cater 15 Onset 16 Ten 17 Apt 20 Tennis 22 Inset 23 Amount 26 Salt 27 Star 29 War 31 God.

## No 276

## No 277

## No 278

## No 279

## No 280

## No 281
David – 3, Alison; Phil – 4, Jane; Chris – 1, Carla; Nick – 2, Gillian.

# SOLUTIONS

## No 282

## No 283

RADIAL: 1 Obese 2 Taste 3 Haste
4 Bacon 5 Apron 6 Stern 7 Sworn
8 Oiled 9 Steed 10 Chord 11 Award
12 Tarot 13 Pilot 14 Elect 15 Erect
16 Liege 17 Stage 18 Eerie 19 Ernie
20 Belle 21 Exile 22 Ladle 23 Addle
24 Morse.
CIRCULAR: 4 Basso 9 Scat 13 Peel
17 See 20 Bela 24 Moth 25 Apt
26 With 27 Wail 28 Rite 29 Rex
30 Ado 31 Baa 32 Creole 33 Oar
34 Lee 35 Earn 36 Lid 37 Dress
38 Roc 39 Gill 40 Store 41 Tee 42 End.

## No 284

## No 285

## No 286

1 will close and 2 will open.

## No 287

CR/AV/AT.

## No 288

1 (1) Chaos 2 (3) Ample 3 (2) Sheen.

## No 289

## No 290

1 SUR 2 FER 3 CON 4 VEY 5 RET
6 ARD 7 SUL 8 LEN 9 PAR 10 ENT
11 TIL 12 TED.

## No 291

# SOLUTIONS

## No 292
DOME, DONE, LONE, LANE, LANK, RANK, RANT, RENT, TENT.

## No 293

```
P . P E . I
A L A R M E D
R . W . M . O
J O B . D A H L
. L U R E . I
P E G . A R T S
. L . F I S H .
Y E S . G . A
. E . U S H E R
M A X I . T I P
. R . T H E R E
U S E S . D E N
```

## No 294
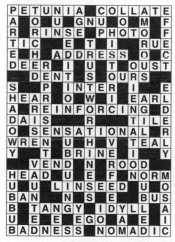
```
P E T U N I A . C O L L A T E
A . O . U . G N U . O . M . F
R . R I N S E . P H O T O . F
T I C . . E . T . I . R U E .
E . H . A D D R E S S . O . C
D E E R . I . U . T . O U S T
. . D E N T . S . O U R S .
S . P . I N T E R . I . . E
H E A R . O . W . I . E A R L
A . R E I N F O R C I N G . D
D A I S . . R . . T I L E . E
O . S E N S A T I O N A L . R
W R E N . U . H . V . T E A L
Y . T . B R I N E . I . . Y
. V E N D . N . R O O D .
H E A D . U . E . F . N O R M
U . U . L I N S E E D . U . O
B A N . N . S . E . . B U S
B . T A N G Y . I D Y L L . A
U . E . E . E G O . A . E . I
B A D N E S S . N O M A D I C
```

## No 295
ACROSS: 1 Depress 5 Shrew 8 Evade 9 Novices 10 Meditate 11 Mule 13 Rookie 15 Rioted 18 Stud 19 Harmless 22 Brigand 23 Noise 24 Tutor 25 Respect.
DOWN: 1 Dreamer 2 Plaid 3 Electric 4 Sonata 5 Save 6 Recount 7 Waste 12 Diamonds 14 Oculist 16 Descent 17 Gander 18 Sabot 20 Exile 21 Fair.

## No 296
```
I V A N . P A W N B R O K E R
M . P . S . P . O . A . N . E
A L E R T . P L A I N T I F F
G . R . O . R . H . S . F . U
I N T E R N A L . R A K E I N
N . U . M . I . T . C . . D
E A R L Y . S T R I K E R S .
S . E . . I . E . . E . E
. A S T O U N D S . D U M P S
T . . V . G . P . I . . C
I R O N E D . S A R D I N I A
N . C . R . G . S . C . D . P
P R E S S U R E S . O M E G A
O . A . E . A . E . T . R . D
T E N D E R N E S S . I S L E
```

## No 297
```
4 7 3 8 9 6 1 5 2
9 6 5 1 7 2 3 4 8
8 1 2 4 5 3 9 6 7
5 3 8 7 1 4 2 9 6
6 2 7 3 8 9 5 1 4
1 4 9 2 6 5 8 7 3
7 9 4 5 3 8 6 2 1
2 8 6 9 4 1 7 3 5
3 5 1 6 2 7 4 8 9
```

## No 298

```
A . I . C . . J . F . M
C O N S U L S . A Z U R E
Q . N . S . E . V . E . N
U S U R P . N E E D L E D
I . E . . S . L . . . S
T I N . E Y E P I E C E .
S . D . G . L . N . A . R
. M O N G R E L S . L I E
E . . S . S . . F . V
B U N C H E S . W A S T E
B . A . E . L . I . K . N
E X P E L . Y A P P I N G
D . S . L . . E . N . E
```

## No 299

```
F O R T N I G H T . S W E P T
. V . R . O . A . O . R . A
J E S U I T . N E W W O R L D
. R . T . A . G . N . T
A L P H A . O G L E . E N V Y
. A . . R U L E D . . O
S P A M . O T I S . S C A L E
. I . U . D . S . R . C
H E L S I N K I . P A Y D A Y
. G . T . D . N . I . P . N
T O K Y O . A G I T A T I O N
```

# SOLUTIONS

## No 300
LIFE, BACK, BONE, ROOM, FOOL, FIRE,
DROP, MIND, DAMP, BALL.
The novel is: *ANIMAL FARM*.

## No 301

## No 302

## No 303

## No 304
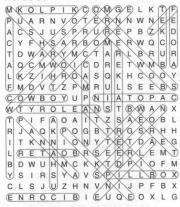

The date in the shaded line is:
31/5/1859 – the date Big Ben's
clock started recording time.

## No 305
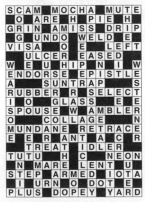

## No 306

| S C A M | M O C H A | M U T E |
|---|---|---|
| O | A R E | H | P I E | H |
| G R I N | A M I S S | D R I P |
| G | U N D O | W E L D | E |
| V I S A | O | E | L E F T |
| U L C E R | E A S E D |
| W | E | U | H I P | N | I | W |
| E N D O R S E | E P I S T L E |
| A | S U N T R A P | S |
| R U B B E R | R | S E L E C T |
| I | O | G L A S S | E | E |
| S P O U S E | W | A M B L E R |
| O | C O L L A G E | N |
| M U N D A N E | R E T R A C E |
| E | E | R A N T | A | C | R |
| T R E A T | I D L E R |
| T U T U | H | C | N E O N |
| N | M A R E | L E N T | U |
| S T E P | A R M E D | I O T A |
| I | U R N | O | D O T | E |
| P L U S | D O P E Y | Y A R D |

## No 307
Fishes 3 and 10 are identical.

# SOLUTIONS

## No 308

| | A | S | I | A | N | | C | A | S | H | F | L | O | W |
|---|---|---|---|---|---|---|---|---|---|---|---|---|---|---|
| C | | K | | R | | E | R | | A | | O | | A | |
| H | A | Y | S | T | A | C | K | S | | I | N | G | O | T |
| A | | L | | Y | | H | O | R | | R | | | E | |
| S | W | I | G | | H | O | R | N | E | D | | T | O | R |
| T | | N | | S | | O | | O | | O | | S | | |
| E | Y | E | | T | A | C | T | I | C | | O | P | A | L |
| N | | | A | | O | R | U | S | | | S | | I | |
| I | V | O | R | Y | | B | O | O | K | S | T | A | N | D |
| N | | D | | I | | R | N | | E | | I | | E | |
| G | R | E | E | N | M | A | N | | O | D | D | L | Y | |

## No 309

Monocle.

## No 310

## No 311

| R | | R | | A | | P | | S | | T | | A | |
|---|---|---|---|---|---|---|---|---|---|---|---|---|---|
| A | V | A | I | L | | L | A | T | C | H | E | S | |
| Z | | D | | K | | Y | | R | | O | | T | |
| O | R | I | G | A | M | I | | E | X | U | D | E | |
| R | | A | | L | | N | | W | | | | R | |
| | S | T | R | I | N | G | E | N | T | L | Y | | |
| | | O | | | | | | O | | | | | |
| | G | R | O | T | E | S | Q | U | E | L | Y | | |
| E | | U | | O | | P | | L | | | P | | |
| M | A | J | O | R | | F | A | T | H | O | M | S | |
| P | | A | | B | | T | | A | | P | | A | |
| T | U | R | M | O | I | L | | K | N | E | E | L | |
| Y | | S | | T | | Y | | E | | D | | M | |

## No 312

Bigly, pale brown, artist, Sweden.
Cuthbert, yellow, jockey, Germany.
Jersey, cream, cowboy, USA.
Mayday, orange, soccer player, Italy.
Scramble, dark brown, pirate, Hong Kong.

## No 313

| C | | F | A | U | L | T | E | D | | S | | |
|---|---|---|---|---|---|---|---|---|---|---|---|---|
| A | | A | | O | | R | | | A | | | |
| M | O | U | N | D | | P | | C | I | N | C | H |
| P | | N | | J | I | G | | N | | K | | |
| | | E | | N | | | | K | N | E | W | |
| S | E | E | D | I | N | G | | E | | D | | |
| K | N | | I | | A | I | R | S | | H | | |
| A | L | M | S | | C | A | D | | T | I | | |
| T | E | | H | | D | E | V | O | I | D | | |
| E | N | S | U | R | E | D | | P | | M | | |
| | H | O | | D | I | P | P | E | D | | | |
| | | S | O | W | | C | | E | | | | |
| | F | E | Y | | | S | O | D | A | | | |

## No 314

| A | | L | | N | | L | | | | |
|---|---|---|---|---|---|---|---|---|---|---|
| G | L | O | V | E | B | O | X | | | |
| G | | N | | W | | O | | I | | |
| R | A | G | | B | A | K | E | S | | |
| O | | J | | O | | I | | O | | |
| | C | U | R | R | A | N | T | S | | |
| S | | M | | N | | G | | C | | |
| P | O | P | S | | O | G | R | E | | |
| E | | E | | C | | L | | L | | |
| C | A | R | E | R | | A | L | E | | |
| S | | | U | | S | | S | S | | |
| | C | O | R | N | I | S | H | | | |
| F | | P | | C | | | | L | | |
| O | R | E | | H | O | R | B | Y | | |
| B | | N | | Y | | I | | I | | |
| B | O | I | L | | S | T | U | N | | |
| E | | N | | T | | T | | G | | |
| D | E | G | R | A | D | E | D | | | |
| O | | N | | B | | R | | S | | |
| F | R | I | L | L | | N | I | P | | |
| F | | G | | O | | E | | A | | |
| | C | H | A | I | N | S | A | W | | |
| | | T | | D | | S | | N | | |

## No 315

Weights A and B will rise, and weights C and D will fall.

## No 316

sCent, Abode, bonCe, aTlas, loUse, Steal: CACTUS.

## No 317

*Wuthering Heights, Jane Eyre, Oliver Twist, Black Beauty, Kidnapped.*

## No 318

Sombrero, fiesta, galleon, bolero, armada, mustang, flamingo, corral, patio, iguana, bonanza, rodeo, cargo, vamoose, mosquito, alligator, albino, guerrilla.

# SOLUTIONS

## No 319
ACROSS: 1 Peacock 4 Snooker
8 Personality 11 Show 12 Safe
13 Latin 15 Nettle 16 Rider 17 Alley
18 Purse 20 Earth 22 Goods
23 Young 25 Witted 27 Stair 29 Iris
31 Alan 32 Temperature 33 Lantern
34 Crystal.
DOWN: 1 Poison 2 Crew 3 Castle
5 Nylon 6 Oats 7 Research 8 Poster
9 Nut 10 Yard 14 Isles 16 Rye
17 About 18 Physical 19 Egg
21 Rattle 24 Unit 25 Writer 26 Dental
27 Super 28 Air 30 Seat 31 Arms.

## No 320

| | C | | S | | D | | C | |
|---|---|---|---|---|---|---|---|---|
| G | H | E | T | T | O | | H | |
| | E | | I | | O | W | E | |
| | F | A | R | | R | O | E | |
| | L | | O | W | N | S | | |
| E | D | I | T | | A | | E | |
| | R | | A | B | Y | S | S | |
| Z | E | B | R | A | | O | | |
| | A | | A | N | G | L | E | |
| A | M | P | | T | I | D | E | |
| | U | | P | A | N | E | L | |
| O | P | T | | M | A | R | S | |

## No 321

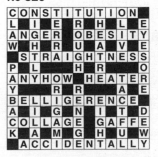

## No 322

| 7 | 3 | 6 | 1 | 4 | 5 | 9 | 8 | 2 |
|---|---|---|---|---|---|---|---|---|
| 2 | 5 | 1 | 8 | 3 | 9 | 6 | 4 | 7 |
| 9 | 4 | 8 | 2 | 6 | 7 | 1 | 3 | 5 |
| 4 | 6 | 5 | 3 | 2 | 8 | 7 | 9 | 1 |
| 1 | 9 | 3 | 4 | 7 | 6 | 5 | 2 | 8 |
| 8 | 2 | 7 | 9 | 5 | 1 | 4 | 6 | 3 |
| 5 | 8 | 4 | 6 | 1 | 3 | 2 | 7 | 9 |
| 6 | 7 | 9 | 5 | 8 | 2 | 3 | 1 | 4 |
| 3 | 1 | 2 | 7 | 9 | 4 | 8 | 5 | 6 |

## No 323
The pink ball swerved round the blue,
rebounded off the top cushion and
just missed a red before dropping into
a corner pocket. What a shame he
was aiming for the brown!

## No 324

| C | O | R | N | F | L | O | U | R | | S | | G | | I |
|---|---|---|---|---|---|---|---|---|---|---|---|---|---|---|
| H | | A | | E | | I | | A | L | T | E | R | E | D |
| O | L | D | | A | L | L | E | Y | | A | | I | | L |
| O | | I | | R | | S | | | B | O | N | N | Y | |
| S | T | U | F | F | | K | H | A | K | I | | | O | |
| Y | A | M | | U | | I | | I | | L | G | E | T | |
| | C | | L | O | N | E | R | | I | C | I | L | Y | |
| W | O | M | E | N | | M | | S | | R | | C | | |
| E | | I | | E | | A | L | I | B | I | | D | U | O |
| E | N | D | U | S | E | R | | L | | N | | L | | O |
| D | | I | | S | | E | V | E | R | G | R | E | E | N |

## No 325
Paste tube in F – 6; megaphone in E
– 4; hat in D – 1; mushroom in F – 2.

## No 326

| C | O | N | S | T | I | T | U | T | I | O | N | |
|---|---|---|---|---|---|---|---|---|---|---|---|---|
| L | | I | E | | R | | H | | L | | E | |
| A | N | G | E | R | | O | B | E | S | I | T | Y |
| W | | H | | R | | U | | A | | V | | E |
| | S | T | R | A | I | G | H | T | N | E | S | S |
| P | | L | | H | | R | | | O | | | O |
| A | N | Y | H | O | W | | H | E | A | T | E | R |
| Y | | | R | | R | | A | | E | | | |
| B | E | L | L | I | G | E | R | E | N | C | E | |
| A | | I | | G | | N | | I | | T | | D |
| C | O | L | L | A | G | E | | G | A | F | F | E |
| K | | A | M | | G | | H | | U | | | W |
| | A | C | C | I | D | E | N | T | A | L | L | Y |

# SOLUTIONS

## No 327
Clown 1 has an extra petal on his flower. Clown 2 has an extra button on his left sleeve. Clown 3 has an extra stripe on his left trouser leg and clown 4 has an extra piece of tie on show.

## No 328

## No 329

## No 330

## No 331

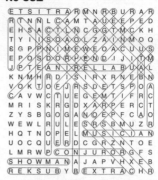

## No 332
Coracle, cHopper, whAler, feRry, sleIgh, tractOr, tugboaT. The staircase word is: CHARIOT.

## No 333
Squares d – 4; e – 5 and j – 3.

## No 334

## No 335

# SOLUTIONS

## No 336
Veil, soon, Yule, dale. The love song title is:
ALL YOU NEED IS LOVE.

## No 337

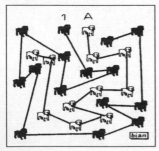

## No 338
Sapphire, moonstone, amethyst, peridot, emerald, quartz, pearl, opal, jade, citrine, jasper, diamond, agate, topaz, onyx, lapis lazuli, turquoise, amber, ruby.

## No 339

## No 340
RADIAL: 1 Baker 2 Spear 3 Ranee
4 Prawn 5 Pried 6 Perry 7 Pease
8 Senna 9 Antic 10 Arena 11 Aries
12 Motel 13 Ledge 14 Ariel 15 Level
16 Grass 17 Grain 18 Genre 19 Genie
20 Emend 21 Emery 22 Nurse
23 Arise 24 Rider.
CIRCULAR: 1 Bran 2 Send 6 Yes
11 Sac 12 Meals 17 Needy 25 Ewer
26 Seine 27 Ogre 28 Iris 29 Urn
30 Pair 31 Air 32 Ant 33 Tie 34 Avid
35 Anne 36 Dire 37 Ken 38 Erne
39 Mere 40 Sear 41 Reg 42 Lap.

## No 341

## No 342
1 Escape 2 Unripe 3 Endear 4 Caesar
5 Rialto 6 Tomato 7 Moment
8 Decant 9 Escort 10 Albert 11 Mantle
12 Impale 13 Madame 14 Cicada
15 Cicero 16 Beware 17 Newest
18 Panama 19 Madras 20 Dallas
21 Rename 22 Raceme 23 Secret
24 Magnet 25 Dearer 26 Laurel
27 Nausea 28 Coffee 29 Coffer
30 Govern 31 Eroded 32 Erased
33 Estate 34 Effete 35 Effort
36 Revert 37 Opened 38 Aramis
39 Trauma 40 Forage 41 Forego
42 Voyage 43 Enrobe 44 Imbibe
45 Mutely 46 Gamely 47 George
48 Garage 49 Bitter 50 Tether
51 Menage 52 Orange 53 Thrive
54 Native.

## No 343

# SOLUTIONS

## No 344

```
F O R C E F U L .
R . I . X . N . E
A B D I C A T E D
C . I . H . R . I
A R C . A D U L T
S . U . N . T . .
. F L A G S H I P
O . E . E . . . R
F A D E . J A N E
F . . S . R . . T
L I G H T S O U T
I . R . A . M . I
C H I E F T A I N
E . P . F . . . E
N E E D . R O S S
C . . D . V . . S
E X C E E D E D .
. A . N . R . . M
B L U N T . W E E
A . T . U . O . N
W H I P R O U N D
L . O . E . N . E
. O N E S I D E D
```

## No 345

The words, in the order in which they appear, are: plAn, cReate, funCtion, tHat, buIld, besT, pEople, Commission, strucTure.

The occupation is: ARCHITECT.

## No 346

| 6 | 9 | 3 | 4 | 2 | 8 | 5 | 7 | 1 |
| 7 | 4 | 2 | 9 | 5 | 1 | 3 | 8 | 6 |
| 5 | 1 | 8 | 6 | 7 | 3 | 9 | 4 | 2 |
| 8 | 3 | 5 | 2 | 1 | 6 | 7 | 9 | 4 |
| 1 | 6 | 4 | 3 | 9 | 7 | 8 | 2 | 5 |
| 9 | 2 | 7 | 8 | 4 | 5 | 6 | 1 | 3 |
| 3 | 8 | 9 | 1 | 6 | 2 | 4 | 5 | 7 |
| 4 | 5 | 1 | 7 | 3 | 9 | 2 | 6 | 8 |
| 2 | 7 | 6 | 5 | 8 | 4 | 1 | 3 | 9 |

## No 347

## No 348

Paintings 5, 7, 8, 11 and 12 are fakes.

## No 349

```
R O Y A L S . P E N P A L .
G . M . N E A R . O . R . A
I C E D T E A . E N D L E S S
V . G . S . R . A . E . N . H
E L A N . S C A R Y . L A M B
C . . I . . H . H . . I . . L
H E L P . G L O A T . P E S O
A . E . V . I . N . F . R . N
S O A R I N G . G O A H E A D
E . S . V . H O E . L . C . E
. R E P A S T . D E L E T E .
```

## No 350

```
G R A B . S E E K . P A D .
. U . E . O . I . A . A . A
S M U T T Y . S N A R E D .
. B . W . . . . T . . . . O
H A R E D . M U F T I . . .
I . E . . . A . U . N . . .
J O I N E R Y . S . G . . S
A . G . . . O A S T . . . A
C O N I F E R . E . . . . D
K . O . . . A L D E R . . D
. D R I V E L . . M . . . E
. E . E . . . . . E . I C O N
I N D E X . . T O T . . . .
```

## No 351

```
1 1 2 . 6 4 6 . 1 2 8
2 . 3 2 . 2 . 3 3 6 .
9 . 4 . 1 0 1 . 6 5 4
2 2 4 . 8 . 6 4 2 4 4
. . 2 5 5 1 6 4 . . 4
1 . 1 1 5 1 9 8 1 . 4
1 . . 1 0 4 2 4 1 . .
1 2 5 4 4 . 6 . 2 0 2
1 1 8 . 4 4 4 . 1 . 2
. 5 3 4 . 1 . 5 6 . 6
2 6 7 . 3 2 3 . 2 1 1
```

The date in the shaded line is: 11/5/1981 – the day the musical Cats was first produced in London.

## No 352

```
S C R E W S . B R O G U E
O . X . T . U . Z . N . .
I N V A D I N G . O A F S
T . M . F . L . N . L . .
D R O P . F R E N E T I C
A . L . E . . . . . N . .
S C R E E N . B R E A C H
T . . . . . E . Q . . . H
J U G G L E R S . U N I T
A . U . A . P . A . N . .
A L E S . S H O R T A G E
L . T . E . K . E . . . L
N Y L O N S . E S S A Y S
```

# SOLUTIONS

## No 353

| A | L | S | A | T | I | A | N |   | B | R | I | O |
| L | L |   | E |   | R |   | D |   | H |   | P |   |
| O | N | I | O | N |   | C | H | E | M | I | S | T |
| U |   | P |   | T |   | T |   | S |   | N |   | I |
| D | U | P | E |   | S | I | C | K | R | O | O | M |
|   | E |   | G |   | C |   | T |   |   | U |   |   |
| T | E | D | I | U | M |   | L | O | G | J | A | M |
| R |   | M |   | B |   | P |   | A |   |   |   |   |
| O | V | E | R | S | E | A | S |   | A | C | T | S |
| U |   | H |   | S |   | A |   | U |   | H |   |   |
| P | E | A | C | O | C | K |   | R | A | Z | O | R |
| E |   | I |   | E |   | I |   | Z |   | U |   |   |
| R | O | L | L |   | S | T | E | A | M | I | N | G |

## No 354
Plug a.

## No 355

## No 356

| | M | E | N | T | I | O | N | |
| W | | M | | A | | V | | Y |
| A | L | B | U | M | | E | G | O |
| T | | R | | E | | R | | U |
| E | N | Y | A | | W | E | L | T |
| R | | O | | H | | L | | H |
| H | A | N | D | Y | M | A | N | |
| O | | I | | P | | B | | U |
| L | E | C | H | E | R | O | U | S |
| E | | | U | | R | | | H |
| | T | R | I | P | L | A | N | E |
| S | | H | | | T | | R | |
| H | A | Y | F | E | V | E | R | |
| U | | T | | N | | | A | |
| S | C | H | E | D | U | L | E | D |
| H | | M | | E | | O | | V |
| | E | S | C | A | L | O | P | E |
| P | | E | | R | | K | | N |
| E | A | C | H | | H | A | R | T |
| A | | T | | E | | F | | U |
| K | O | I | | C | A | T | E | R |
| Y | | O | | R | | E | | E |
| | I | N | Q | U | I | R | Y | |

## No 357

| | | W | | | T | |
| N | O | G | O | O | D | |
| | P | | K | N | E | A | D |
| P | E | W | | S | A | G | A |
| | R | | S | P | L | A | Y |
| G | A | S | | E | | I | |
| | K | | C | A | N | E | |
| E | P | I | C | | R | | A |
| | A | | O | P | A | L | S |
| U | R | D | U | | B | U | T |
| K | | G | U | I | L | E | |
| C | A | S | H | | C | U | R |

## No 358
ACROSS: 1 British 4 Student
9 Secretary 10 Tent 11 Silk 12 Nurse
13 Record 16 Labels 19 Pep
21 Lounge 22 Empire 24 Art 27 Tunnel
29 Lethal 30 Extra 31 Trap 33 Keep
34 Afternoon 35 Nursery 36 Brother.
DOWN: 1 Battery 2 Test 3 Second
5 Travel 6 Days 7 Turkish 8 George
14 Crown 15 Range 17 Apple 18 Earth
19 Pea 20 Pet 23 Station 25 Return
26 Slipper 28 Letter 29 Labour
32 Pass 33 Knot.

## No 359
SHERPA.

## No 360
Gait, Mean, Wine, Lute: UNTIL WE
MEET AGAIN.

## No 361

| V | E | X | I | N | G | | A | K | I | M | B | O |
| | Q | | N | | E | | R | | N | | U | |
| J | U | T | E | | S | Y | M | M | E | T | R | Y |
| | A | | X | | T | | P | | | P | | N |
| A | L | P | A | C | A | | L | O | T | I | O | N |
| | | C | | T | | A | | | | O | | U |
| H | U | N | T | | I | O | N | | G | A | T | E |
| N | | O | | O | | D | | L | | | | |
| S | I | L | K | E | N | | S | H | A | R | E | D |
| | T | | N | | C | | | Z | | | X | |
| P | A | N | O | R | A | M | A | | I | O | T | A |
| R | | W | | F | | P | | E | | E | | O |
| C | Y | G | N | E | T | | E | E | R | I | L | Y |

## No 362
Model 7 is silhouette a and model 9 is
silhouette b.

# SOLUTIONS

## No 363

## No 364

## No 365

## No 366

## No 367
RADIAL: 1 Hoist 2 Harsh 3 Awash 4 Carat 5 Cairn 6 Cedar 7 Cello 8 Class 9 Swiss 10 Strop 11 Stabs 12 Annie 13 Genie 14 Pause 15 Erase 16 Melon 17 Totem 18 Steam 19 Manna 20 Crete 21 Motte 22 Atone 23 Enter 24 Hoots.
CIRCULAR: 1 That 9 Scorn 13 Gasp 14 Pen 20 Cast 21 Mars 25 Waste 26 Lara 27 Bowl 28 Near 29 Too 30 Torn 31 Tote 32 Rio 33 Arid 34 Lair 35 Annual 36 Net 37 Eat 38 Season 39 Sit 40 Scheme.

## No 368

## No 369

## No 370

| | | | | | | | | |
|---|---|---|---|---|---|---|---|---|
| 2 | 3 | 4 | 5 | 8 | 1 | 9 | 7 | 6 |
| 8 | 7 | 9 | 4 | 3 | 6 | 1 | 2 | 5 |
| 6 | 5 | 1 | 2 | 7 | 9 | 4 | 8 | 3 |
| 3 | 8 | 6 | 7 | 2 | 4 | 5 | 1 | 9 |
| 5 | 4 | 7 | 9 | 1 | 8 | 3 | 6 | 2 |
| 1 | 9 | 2 | 3 | 6 | 5 | 7 | 4 | 8 |
| 4 | 1 | 3 | 6 | 9 | 2 | 8 | 5 | 7 |
| 9 | 2 | 5 | 8 | 4 | 7 | 6 | 3 | 1 |
| 7 | 6 | 8 | 1 | 5 | 3 | 2 | 9 | 4 |

# SOLUTIONS

## No 371

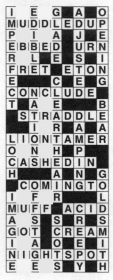

## No 372

Bet, rut, bar; Kirsch, speech, squawk; shambolic, convivial, spherical.
The occupation is: BARRISTER.

## No 373

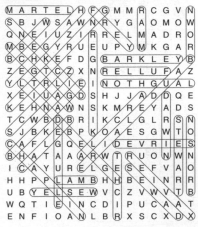

## No 374

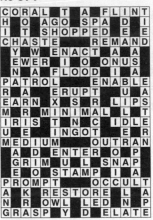

## No 375
MESSAGE.

## No 376
Mint, toes, lean, shin. The phrase is:
IN LESS THAN NO TIME.

## No 377

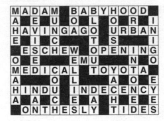

## No 378
Spool – £15; hook – £5; tin of shot – £10; box of worms – £2.50.

## No 379

# SOLUTIONS

## No 380

```
B E A M S   A B H O R
T Q   I S   L G   E
S P U R N   T R A W L E D
A A   I   I Z   E   I
R O T   M U F T I   D U B
  O     F   N     L
U N R I P E   I G N O R E
P     E T     V
K E N   R H Y M E   E L F
E   I   J P   X   R U
E X E C U T E   A L B U M
P   C   R D   C   I E
  B E R Y L   S T U D Y
```

## No 381

The words in their correct order, are:
subSidence, damp coUrse, bRicks,
serVices, tilEs, finallY, rOof, stRucture.
The occupation is: SURVEYOR.

## No 382

Sins, opus, brig, Eden: SUSPENSION
BRIDGE.

## No 383

```
C O P Y   S E M I   T
O   E   R   D R A W L
B A R B E D   L   U E
    F C   M Y O P I A
I R O N Y   A   E   R
N   R C   W E B     N
J U M B L E D   S I T
U   E   U N F I T
R     T   A   U
E L U D E   I   R D   B
  U   X   F U M E D   R
I L L   A   U   E E   I
  L   S M I L E D   D U G
```

## No 384

```
A D L I B   B E E
I   A   A   L   N
D A Y S C H O O L
E   E   K   W   I
  C R A S H I N G
W   E   E   N   H
O N D R A U G H T
U     T   U   E
N I C E   S P A N
D   H   S     I
  F I T T E D I N
F   N   O   I   G
E V A C U A T E
C   T     T   M
K I S S   T Y R E
L   E   C     R
E X P O R T I N G
S   T   A   N   E
S P E C T A T E
N   M   E   E   U
E M B A R R A S S
S   E   R   E
S I R   D O S E D
```

## No 385

1 Rec 2 Ant 3 Acc 4 Ord 5 Hem
6 Med 7 Use 8 Ful 9 Can 10 Dle
11 Fil 12 Ter.

## No 386

## No 387

1 Offend 2 Attend 3 Insane 4 Feline
5 Tested 6 Agreed 7 Formal 8 Sandal
9 Linnet 10 Street 11 Redeem
12 Anthem 13 Reform 14 Neared
15 Neaten 16 Revise 17 Devote
18 Thresh 19 Rotted 20 Erased
21 Etched 22 Singed 23 Tossed
24 Seated 25 Thrift 26 Aromas
27 Crouch 28 Naming 29 Sambas
30 Assert 31 Fitted 32 Ambled
33 Cuddly 34 Nicely 35 Absent
36 Recent 37 Thrust 38 Befall
39 Defend 40 Chrome 41 Shrine
42 Clause 43 Surely 44 Lately
45 Neuron 46 Motion 47 Nitwit
48 Submit 49 Tenant 50 Urgent
51 Tidies 52 Twines 53 Genius
54 Discus.

## No 388

Oregon, Louisiana, Minnesota,
Florida, Colorado, Vermont,
California, Wyoming, Montana,
Indiana, Ohio, Arizona, Delaware,
Alabama, Kansas, Nevada, Hawaii.

# SOLUTIONS

## No 389

| 5 | 2 | 4 | 7 | 1 | 8 | | | 9 | 2 | 6 | 3 | 3 | 1 |
|---|---|---|---|---|---|---|---|---|---|---|---|---|---|
| 3 | | | | 6 | 0 | 1 | 4 | 8 | | 8 | | | 1 |
| 5 | 0 | 3 | 9 | 2 | 2 | | | 3 | 0 | 3 | 1 | 5 | 6 |
| 1 | | 9 | | 5 | | 7 | 2 | 8 | | 0 | | 2 | 3 |
| 6 | | 1 | | 5 | | | 2 | | 0 | | 8 | 2 | 5 |
| 4 | 2 | 4 | 0 | 1 | 3 | | 3 | 8 | 1 | 8 | 1 | 4 | 5 |
| | 6 | | 1 | | 1 | | | | | 2 | 8 | 4 | |
| 3 | | 9 | | 0 | | 2 | 5 | 1 | 9 | 6 | 6 | | |
| 8 | | 9 | 1 | 4 | 2 | 8 | 3 | | | 2 | | 4 | |
| 3 | 1 | 3 | 0 | 5 | | | 4 | | | 1 | 5 | 9 | 2 |
| 4 | | | 8 | | 9 | 3 | 2 | 5 | 6 | 0 | | 5 | |
| 9 | 2 | 1 | 4 | 7 | | 1 | | 8 | | | 6 | 5 | 2 | 1 |
| 1 | | 3 | | | 2 | | 3 | 1 | 2 | 6 | | | 3 |
| 2 | 8 | 2 | 6 | | 3 | 3 | 8 | | 9 | | 5 | 5 | 6 |
| 3 | | 6 | | | 4 | | 4 | 9 | 2 | 3 | | | 2 |

## No 390

|   | P |   | G |   | O |   | P |
|---|---|---|---|---|---|---|---|
| A | B | Y | S | M | A | L |   |
| I |   | M |   | I |   | A |   |
| A | N | T |   | S | T | A | Y |
|   | T | H | I | N |   | U |   |
| U | S | E |   | A | C | R | E |
|   | M |   | G | L | A | M |   |
| W | E | B |   | A |   | P |   |
| H |   | L | A | U | R | A |   |
| M | E | N | U |   | S | E | T |
| E |   | F | R | E | S | H |   |
| C | L | E | F |   | S | T | Y |

## No 391

## No 392

Bertram's, stationery, Patter Street, 1997.

Colin's, confectionery, Commercial Lane, 2002.

Get Fleeced, wool, Stock Road, 1985.

Robinson's, cheese, Hawking Way, 1994.

Webster's, paint, Pitch Place, 1988.

## No 393

1 Wander, wader, dare 2 Demean, named, damn 3 Dawdle, addle, dead 4 Faster, aster, rate 5 Shoals, slash, lass 6 Duties, sited, side 7 Garden, grade, drag 8 Spider, pries, pies 9 Caller, clear, lace 10 Failed, filed, fled 11 Reason, arose, soar 12 Dearth, heart, heat.

The two dogs are: (A) NEWFOUNDLAND and (B) WELSH TERRIER.

## No 394

| C | O | S |   | A |   | S |   | C |   | A |   | E |   |
|---|---|---|---|---|---|---|---|---|---|---|---|---|---|
| R |   | C | O | N | S | T | R | U | C | T | I | N | G |
| A | P | U |   | O |   | I |   | R |   | O |   | R | R |
| B |   | T | H | I | E | F |   | V | A | M | P | I | R | E |
| S |   | N |   | I |   | F | E | E | T |   | C |   | A |
| T | H | I | R | T | Y |   |   | E | I | T | H | E | R |
| I |   | N |   | O | A | S | T |   | G |   |   | R |
| C | E | L | S | I | U | S |   | R | A | N | C | H | A |
| K |   | I |   | P |   | C |   | A |   | I |   | Y | E | N |
|   | U | N | A | S | S | O | C | I | A | T | E | D | G |
|   | E |   | O |   | T |   | T | E |   | E | X | E |   |

## No 395

| 5 | 1 | 9 | 7 | 4 | 3 | 6 | 2 | 8 |
|---|---|---|---|---|---|---|---|---|
| 7 | 8 | 6 | 9 | 1 | 2 | 5 | 4 | 3 |
| 2 | 4 | 3 | 8 | 5 | 6 | 1 | 7 | 9 |
| 4 | 5 | 8 | 6 | 9 | 7 | 3 | 1 | 2 |
| 3 | 6 | 2 | 1 | 8 | 5 | 4 | 9 | 7 |
| 1 | 9 | 7 | 2 | 3 | 4 | 8 | 6 | 5 |
| 9 | 2 | 1 | 3 | 6 | 8 | 7 | 5 | 4 |
| 8 | 7 | 4 | 5 | 2 | 1 | 9 | 3 | 6 |
| 6 | 3 | 5 | 4 | 7 | 9 | 2 | 8 | 1 |

## No 396

| Q |   | K |   | G |   | R |   | L |   | P |   |
|---|---|---|---|---|---|---|---|---|---|---|---|
| B | U | R | N | E | R |   | U | N | I | S | E | X |
| I |   | O |   | O |   | N |   | C |   | N |   |
| G | N | A | W |   | C | A | N | O | E | I | N | G |
| T |   | E |   | E |   | N |   | Y |   |
| F | E | A | T | U | R | E | L | E | S | S |
| T |   | R |   |   |   | E |   | S |
| | C | O | M | P | L | A | C | E | N | C | Y |
| B |   | T |   | L |   | N |   | R |
| S | L | I | T | H | E | R | Y |   | B | O | O | K |
| O |   | E |   | A |   | W |   | E | O |
| M | O | R | R | I | S |   | A | V | E | N | G | E |
| D |   | S |   | E |   | Y |   | S |   | E |

# SOLUTIONS

## No 397

Census – strayed – Denmark
– kangaroo – outcast – telescope
– eggplant – temerity – yacht – thimble
– Ernest – tennis – satchel – laird
– disc – content – turret – toad.
The two wines are: CONSTANTIA and
CHARDONNAY.

## No 398

## No 399

## No 400

## No 401

## No 402

Jack Sprat, Willie Winkie, Georgie
Porgie, Mother Hubbard, Simple Simon,
Duke of York, Miss Muffet.

## No 403

## No 404

Plaque, quest, strum, rumba, baton,
tonsil, silent, entrap, rapport, portray,
rayon, onward, warden, ensign, signal,
also, soak, akin, inlay.

## No 405

# SOLUTIONS

**No 406**
The rocker takes boot n.

**No 407**
Samosa, biryani, pilau rice, vindaloo, balti, jalfrezi, naan, pasanda, bhuna, chapati, bhaji, tikka masala, tandoori, rogan josh, dopiaza, dhansak, chat aloo.

**No 408**

**No 409**

**No 410**

**No 411**
ACROSS: 1 Bistro 4 Almond 9 Dew 10 Psalm 11 Elm 12 East 14 Dare 16 Lea 18 Delta 19 Caper 21 Pot 24 Arty 25 Idle 28 Gas 30 Overt 31 Rat 32 Nature 33 Adhere.

DOWN: 1 Badger 2 Saw 3 Ripe 5 Lame 6 Ode 7 Damper 8 Lance 13 Sheet 15 Amend 16 Lap 17 Act 20 Margin 22 Onset 23 Centre 26 Tour 27 Stud 29 Sit 31 Roe.

**No 412**

**No 413**

**No 414**
Gary – A, Frank; Paul – D, Jack; Jim – C, Fred; Tom – B, Mick.

**No 415**
Dips, pity, curl, bile.
The phrase is: PUBLIC-SPIRITEDLY.

**No 416**
ST/OD/GE.

# SOLUTIONS

## No 417

## No 418

| 5 | 6 | 4 | 7 | 9 | 2 | 8 | 3 | 1 |
|---|---|---|---|---|---|---|---|---|
| 9 | 3 | 7 | 6 | 8 | 1 | 2 | 4 | 5 |
| 2 | 1 | 8 | 3 | 4 | 5 | 6 | 9 | 7 |
| 6 | 4 | 1 | 8 | 5 | 9 | 3 | 7 | 2 |
| 3 | 8 | 9 | 2 | 1 | 7 | 4 | 5 | 6 |
| 7 | 2 | 5 | 4 | 6 | 3 | 1 | 8 | 9 |
| 1 | 9 | 6 | 5 | 3 | 4 | 7 | 2 | 8 |
| 8 | 7 | 3 | 9 | 2 | 6 | 5 | 1 | 4 |
| 4 | 5 | 2 | 1 | 7 | 8 | 9 | 6 | 3 |

## No 419

## No 420

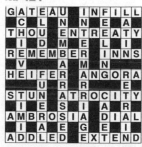

## No 421
Vases 5, 9 and 11 are identical.

## No 422
TRIPLET.

## No 423
BACK, RACK, ROCK, ROOK, BOOK, BOOR, DOOR.

## No 424

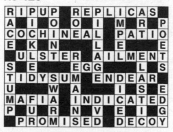

## No 425
Squares I – 1, K – 2 and D – 3 are identical.

## No 426

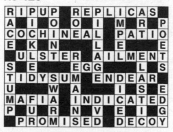

# SOLUTIONS

## No 427

## No 428

TO THE RIGHT: 1 Display 2 Tor
3 Runaway 5 Bar 6 Carol 7 Cat 9 Melon
10 Ramadan 12 Sun 14 VAT 16 Dab
18 Seminar 20 Rob 22 Beneath 23 Bee
24 Steroid 25 Strop 26 Sat 28 Blood
30 Err 32 Ten 33 Ate.
TO THE LEFT: 2 Tim 3 Roses 4 Surplus
6 Caravan 7 Caraway 8 Far 11 Today
13 Loner 15 Mat 17 Lad 19 Baste
21 Mob 22 Bible 23 Ben 24 Senator
25 Steered 27 Narrate 29 Tooth 31 Ore
34 Pie.

## No 429

The bottom right print was created by
the stamp.

## No 430

Fluke, clalm, aloNe, spinE, gRaze,
Yearn: FINERY.

## No 431

## No 432

RADIAL: 1 Osier 2 Timer 3 Taper
4 Adore 5 Litre 6 Sabre 7 Erode
8 Lorna 9 Loner 10 Swirl 11 Pearl
12 Emcee 13 Tepee 14 Plane
15 Ensue 16 Arson 17 Elton 18 Learn
19 Adorn 20 Debit 21 Orbit 22 Roast
23 Beast 24 Elder.
CIRCULAR: 2 Toe 6 Slat 7 Ears 11 Pet
14 Pea 20 Dale 21 Orb 25 Aisle
26 Aid 27 End 28 Mew 29 Rule
30 Led 31 Ore 32 Boat 33 Baa
34 Dim 35 Pot 36 Rob 37 Cain
38 Pass 39 Error 40 One 41 Rise
42 Relent.

## No 433

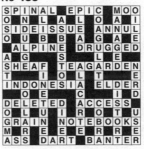

## No 434

ACROSS: 1 Breeze 4 Effect 7 Sin
8 Star 10 Rain 12 Thought 13 Lash
15 Heed 18 Atlas 21 Grass
22 Hedge 23 Happy 26 Land 29 Grim
31 Emperor 32 Idea 33 Asks 35 End
36 Nights 37 Energy.
DOWN: 1 Bus 2 Earth 3 Escort
4 Enigma 5 Forth 6 Tin 9 Tea 11 Ice
13 Legal 14 Stain 16 Elder 17 Dream
18 Ash 19 Lip 20 Shy 24 Apples
25 Parade 27 Aid 28 Death 29 Grace
30 Ink 32 Inn 34 Sky.

## No 435

# SOLUTIONS

## No 436

## No 437

1 Absent 2 Vacant 3 Throne 4 Serene
5 Career 6 Fester 7 Unbent 8 Rodent
9 Recent 10 Relent 11 Street 12 Septet
13 Become 14 Deride 15 Cense
16 Legate 17 Regime 18 Potent
19 Modest 20 Digest 21 Sitter
22 Taster 23 Mister 24 Neater
25 Demote 26 Galore 27 Talent
28 Sublet 29 Submit 30 Albert
31 Toasts 32 Roasts 33 Needed
34 Elated 35 Impede 36 Recede
37 Access 38 Arrows 39 Errand
40 Ararat 41 Praise 42 Canape
43 Seemly 44 Woolly 45 Namely
46 Aridly 47 Sister 48 Patter 49 *Oliver!*
50 Meaner 51 Ideals 52 Steals
53 Answer 54 Easter.

## No 438

The mirror images
are 1 and 8, 2 and
9, 3 and 4, 5 and 6.
The odd one out is 7.

## No 439

## No 440

Plug d is connected to the guitar.

## No 441

sWank, sHore, vOice, drOop, sPilt,
Ships.
The word is: WHOOPS.

## No 442

## No 443

| 3 | 6 | 9 | 8 | 1 | 4 | 7 | 2 | 5 |
|---|---|---|---|---|---|---|---|---|
| 2 | 5 | 8 | 9 | 7 | 3 | 1 | 4 | 6 |
| 1 | 7 | 4 | 5 | 2 | 6 | 3 | 9 | 8 |
| 4 | 9 | 2 | 7 | 5 | 8 | 6 | 3 | 1 |
| 8 | 1 | 6 | 2 | 3 | 9 | 5 | 7 | 4 |
| 7 | 3 | 5 | 6 | 4 | 1 | 2 | 8 | 9 |
| 5 | 4 | 3 | 1 | 8 | 7 | 9 | 6 | 2 |
| 6 | 8 | 1 | 3 | 9 | 2 | 4 | 5 | 7 |
| 9 | 2 | 7 | 4 | 6 | 5 | 8 | 1 | 3 |

## No 444

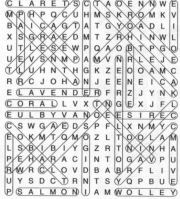

# SOLUTIONS

## No 445

| D | E | F | U | S | E | D | | B | A | B | Y | S | I | T |
|---|---|---|---|---|---|---|---|---|---|---|---|---|---|---|
| E | | A | | U | | I | C | E | | U | | U | | A |
| A | | S | E | R | U | M | | T | U | N | I | C | | U |
| R | A | T | | E | | F | | N | | | K | E | G | |
| T | | E | | R | A | P | I | D | L | Y | | I | | H |
| H | U | S | H | | L | | X | | A | | K | N | O | T |
| | | T | A | M | P | | E | | R | I | N | G | | |
| A | | | V | | A | I | D | E | D | | O | | | E |
| C | A | P | E | | C | | | E | | W | I | N | D | |
| T | | E | N | D | A | N | G | E | R | I | N | G | | I |
| R | E | D | | | A | | | | | | | L | E | T |
| E | | A | R | C | H | I | P | E | L | A | G | O | | I |
| S | O | L | O | | A | | O | | L | O | A | N | | |
| S | | | B | | R | U | M | B | A | | A | | G | |
| | F | O | R | M | | A | | T | E | R | M | | | |
| F | O | O | T | | E | | X | | H | | E | U | R | O |
| U | | R | | A | D | M | I | R | E | R | | M | | P |
| R | U | G | | L | | M | | A | | | B | E | E | |
| R | | | I | D | L | E | D | | R | E | B | E | L | N |
| O | | V | | O | | A | D | O | | B | | E | L | L |
| W | H | E | T | T | E | D | | T | H | I | R | S | T | Y |

## No 446

Pictures a and d are identical. Picture b has an extra ring on the bottom right pan and picture c has a button on the chef's shirt.

## No 447

| | I | C | E | P | A | C | K | |
|---|---|---|---|---|---|---|---|---|
| J | A | | A | | O | | A | |
| A | C | T | O | R | | M | I | D |
| C | | A | | T | | P | | A |
| K | I | L | L | | G | A | N | G |
| K | | Y | | B | | S | | E |
| N | U | T | T | I | E | S | T | |
| I | | | S | | I | | A | |
| F | A | C | E | T | I | O | U | S |
| E | | | R | | N | | S | |
| | I | M | M | O | L | A | T | E |
| E | | O | | T | | T | | |
| D | O | D | D | E | R | E | R | |
| I | | E | | V | | | S | |
| C | A | R | R | I | E | D | O | N |
| T | | N | | N | | I | | A |
| T | H | I | C | K | S | E | T | |
| F | | I | | E | | S | | C |
| R | I | S | K | | R | I | C | H |
| O | | T | | F | | D | | I |
| W | H | O | | L | I | E | I | N |
| N | | R | | E | | N | | G |
| | D | Y | N | A | S | T | Y | |

## No 448

| 1 | 1 | 2 | 9 | | 4 | 4 | 3 | 6 | 8 | | 2 | 5 | 1 | 5 |
|---|---|---|---|---|---|---|---|---|---|---|---|---|---|---|
| 0 | | | 2 | | 5 | | | 2 | | 0 | | | | 2 |
| 7 | | | 7 | 2 | 5 | 6 | 1 | | 8 | 0 | 1 | 5 | 8 | 9 |
| 4 | 6 | 9 | 1 | | | 3 | 1 | 0 | | | 9 | | | |
| | 5 | 0 | 1 | 4 | | 0 | | | | 6 | 5 | 0 | 6 | |
| 1 | 8 | 7 | | | 9 | 0 | 0 | 1 | 7 | | 9 | | | 4 |
| | 7 | 8 | 9 | 0 | | | 8 | 9 | 1 | 8 | | | 5 | |
| 7 | 2 | 6 | | | 3 | 1 | 5 | 2 | 9 | | | 9 | 9 | |
| | 1 | 4 | 5 | 1 | 1 | | | 5 | 2 | 4 | 5 | 1 | 5 | |
| 3 | | | 6 | 5 | 2 | 6 | 6 | 1 | | | 9 | | | |
| 2 | | | 5 | | 8 | | | | | 5 | 2 | 2 | 4 | |
| 2 | 1 | 1 | 9 | 2 | | 4 | 4 | 4 | 0 | 1 | | | 3 | |
| 0 | | | 5 | 9 | 0 | 9 | 4 | | 8 | | 6 | 1 | 5 | 2 |
| 1 | | | 9 | | | 8 | | 9 | | 8 | | | | 4 |
| 3 | 2 | 9 | 1 | | 8 | 0 | 0 | 9 | 7 | | 7 | 6 | 0 | 1 |

## No 449

| J | E | W | E | L | L | E | R | Y | | S | | E | |
|---|---|---|---|---|---|---|---|---|---|---|---|---|---|
| X | | D | | U | | H | | | W | H | O | M | |
| F | I | N | G | E | R | T | I | P | | O | | B | |
| | T | | Y | | E | | N | | A | R | I | A | |
| Q | | A | | D | O | O | M | | T | | T | | |
| U | N | F | I | T | | C | | I | N | L | E | T | |
| I | | F | | O | V | E | R | T | | I | | L | |
| C | U | R | I | O | | A | | T | A | S | T | E | |
| K | | O | | L | I | N | K | | T | | D | | |
| S | I | N | K | | G | | N | | O | | S | | |
| T | | T | | F | L | O | O | D | G | A | T | E | |
| E | Y | E | D | | O | | C | | L | | Y | | |
| P | | D | | Z | O | O | K | E | E | P | E | R | |

## No 450

1 CLE 2 VER 3 TRE 4 NCH 5 MIN
6 DER 7 MOR 8 SEL 9 STR 10 IDE
11 DOM 12 AIN.

## No 451

| D | E | M | O | | H | | | A | F | A | R |
|---|---|---|---|---|---|---|---|---|---|---|---|
| O | | | | F | O | U | G | H | T | | E |
| U | | | T | | N | | O | G | L | E | D |
| R | | | E | S | C | H | E | W | | L | |
| | F | I | N | | H | | | P | R | E | P |
| | | | A | | | | | A | | D | |
| L | I | V | I | D | | S | E | T | | | H |
| O | | A | | J | U | T | | H | O | G | U |
| G | | U | | O | | A | | | R | | S |
| J | O | L | T | I | N | G | | P | O | U | C | H |
| A | | T | | N | | I | | U | | B | |
| M | E | E | K | | | N | | N | U | B | |
| | | D | | M | U | G | G | Y | | Y | A | M |

504

# SOLUTIONS

## No 452

## No 458

## No 453

## No 454

Concave, cRanny, opEning, raVine, mortIse, trenCh, fissurE. The hole is a CREVICE.

## No 459

## No 460

Plug A.

## No 461

## No 455

ACROSS: 1 Spirits 4 Fellow 8 Artificial 9 Mobile 10 Deep 12 Heels 14 Licence 17 Hog 19 Peter 20 Ant 21 Apple 23 Far 24 Trouble 26 Trail 28 Slow 31 Guinea 33 Revolution 34 Morris 35 Chinese.
DOWN: 1 Search 2 Interest 3 Third 4 Film 5 Lotion 6 Wage 7 Time 11 Plate 13 Shrub 15 Chart 16 Eye 18 Gates 19 Pot 22 Practice 25 Oliver 27 Lounge 29 Love 30 Welsh 31 Germ 32 Arts.

## No 456

Jelly beans, black jacks, wine gums, love hearts, bonbons, aniseed balls, dip dabs, pear drops, fudge, gobstopper, liquorice, cola cubes, sugar mice, flumps.

## No 457

Benjamin Harcourt, missionary, embezzler.
Jonathan Bracegirdle, philanthropist, moneylender.
Lucy Rowlandson, headmistress, thief.
Millicent Horsley-Jones, poetess, opium addict.
Sebastian Somerfield, naval officer, bigamist.

## No 462

The date in the shaded line is: 13/4/1828 – the date *Webster's Dictionary* was first published.

# SOLUTIONS

## No 463

```
S   C   S   A   S
CHOPPEDUP
A U A   L   E
LUPIN   ILL
L O K   B L
YANK ABLE
W     FED
ANACONDA
G M O       G
 CABLECAR
 S I R     I
DUSTSHEET
A E H A
TIDINESS
E     E E P
 CONSIDER
A V S       O
TWEE ATOM
T R   P E E
AGA LEARN
C L O P   A
HOLLYWOOD
E S S   T E
```

## No 464

Front, Loose, Poker, Hitch, Chair, Heart, Block, Drift, Alley, Fever: HOVERCRAFT.

## No 465

```
STEPS DISGUST
  H R I   L A P
DEFERRAL   UPON
  S D R   E   N N
GEMINI   GATES
  C   T I     O
SPAT ART JURY
I     B I   O
 CORGI   MOUSSE
 C I   L A R W
GONG INTENDED
 L   I T E E E
GOODBYE NYMPH
```

## No 466

| 7 | 2 | 6 | 1 | 8 | 3 | 9 | 5 | 4 |
|---|---|---|---|---|---|---|---|---|
| 3 | 4 | 1 | 5 | 7 | 9 | 6 | 8 | 2 |
| 9 | 8 | 5 | 2 | 6 | 4 | 7 | 1 | 3 |
| 5 | 6 | 4 | 9 | 2 | 8 | 3 | 7 | 1 |
| 8 | 9 | 7 | 6 | 3 | 1 | 4 | 2 | 5 |
| 1 | 3 | 2 | 4 | 5 | 7 | 8 | 9 | 6 |
| 4 | 7 | 3 | 8 | 1 | 2 | 5 | 6 | 9 |
| 6 | 1 | 9 | 7 | 4 | 5 | 2 | 3 | 8 |
| 2 | 5 | 8 | 3 | 9 | 6 | 1 | 4 | 7 |

## No 467

```
SPORT CASANOVA
A   I   I E R   C R   I
FACEFACTS   CABER
F   T   E H O   E   R
ABUT JOINUP   IOU
B   R M   C   T N   A
IRE ASSERT ORAL
L   D   P E A O   I
INFER OVERDRAFT
T   L A O   D A D   Y
YOURSELF SMASH
```

## No 468

```
 SAXOPHONE
H F F A Y K
REBOOT ZOMBIE
R O E E P L
COATING THROW
A N R R A R
PUG EQUAL BOO
E E N I B N
DOLLY TATTING
V I L S A O
JAUNTY TILING
L E R E O E
 ENDEARING
```

## No 469

```
CRUSH   ARREST
R   E LOP   E E
EARN E TAPER
P   T S   R I
TIGRESS   I E
 O Y AMONGST
 T FAB T   IN
FABLE LAG O N
A E EYE BUT
C L B     L
TRIPLE SLOSH
 E E A N E
 FORCING GYM
```

## No 470

# SOLUTIONS

## No 471

Brian Fangio, White Renault.
Colin Schumacher, Red BMW.
Frank Hunt, Green Vauxhall.
Fred Mansell, Silver Jaguar.
George Senna, Black Ford.

## No 472

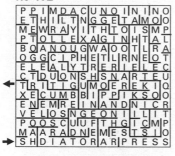

## No 473

## No 474

AP/PE/AL.

## No 475

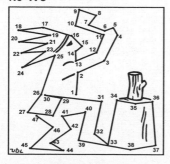

## No 476

CORONATION STREET, DOCTORS,
CROSSROADS, BROOKSIDE,
EASTENDERS, HOLBY CITY,
CASUALTY, THE SULLIVANS,
EMMERDALE, ELDORADO,
NEIGHBOURS, FAMILY AFFAIRS.

## No 477

## No 478

# Puzzle Notes

# Puzzle Notes

# Puzzle Notes